STEWARDS OF GOD'S GRACE

SIEGFRIED GROSSMANN

STEWARDS OF GOD'S GRACE

translated by

MICHAEL FREEMAN

Exeter
The Paternoster Press

ISBN: 0 85364 287 7

AUSTRALIA:
Bookhouse Australia Ltd.,
3-7 Richmond Road,
Homebush West, NSW 2140

SOUTH AFRICA:
Oxford University Press
P.O. Box 1141, Cape Town

British Library Cataloguing in Publication Data

Grossmann, Siegfried
Stewards of God's grace.
1. Pentecostalism
2. Church renewal
I. Title
270.8'2 BR1644

ISBN 0-85364-287-7

Typeset by Photoprint, Paignton, Devon
and Printed in Great Britain for The Paternoster Press,
Paternoster House, 3 Mount Radford Crescent, Exeter, Devon
by Butler & Tanner, Frome, Somerset

Contents

Introduction

For many Christians the word *charisma* has become almost a magic spell. Everything worth striving for in the realm of spiritual experience is adorned with the epithet "charismatic". The charismatic movement is, in their eyes, the greatest revival in the history of the church, a movement which in a few short years has crossed all the national and denominational frontiers. After a false trail followed for two thousand years, the true church, the church of the Spirit, is now in the process of being formed.

For others the word *charisma* is more like a term of abuse. A spirit of fanaticism has broken in: the church is facing her greatest crisis, a crisis of eschatological dimensions. The "spirit from below" who has found his way into the church is a master of disguise, and knows how to pass himself off as the Spirit of God. The deception began with the Pentecostal movement at the beginning of this century, and now the charismatic movement has leapt over the carefully constructed defences and established itself in the heart of the church.

Others, who are by no means opposed in principle to distinctively charismatic experiences, have heard enough of the word *charisma*. Too much has been said and too much written about it. Charismatic gifts are after all only one among the various ways in which the Holy Spirit works. Spontaneity is good, but it is not everything. Equally important are order and institutions, preaching of the word and mission, service and teaching. "We need the Spirit of God", they say, "but not this continual talk about charisms."

What this kaleidoscopic pattern of judgments and opinions seems to make clear is that exaggeration is possible on both sides. An unhealthy fear of charismatic gifts is just as wrong as an exaggerated enthusiasm for them. But one cannot say simply that the truth lies in the middle. The subject is too complex for that, both from the point of view of the biblical statements and from the actual expressions of charismatic experience as we meet it today. This book will therefore attempt to explore the various aspects of the subject as comprehensively as possible: in other words, to do justice to the many levels and kinds of experiences which confront us and to the questions which these raise. In order that the book should not be too lengthy, there will sometimes be areas which can be dealt with only in outline form. There is another reason, too, why this is unavoidable: the experiences of the *charismatic movement* are still very "young", so that too much is still in a state of flux.

Even a superficial look at the statistics makes it clear that there is a large and rapidly growing number of Christians who have had distinctively charismatic experiences. The classic *Pentecostal churches* have more than 20 million adherents; possibly the number is considerably higher than this, since there are many small groups for which no statistics are available. The *charismatic movement* within the larger churches presents a similar picture. In the Roman Catholic Church there are throughout the world probably more than half a million people who meet in charismatic prayer groups. Although the charismatic renewal movement in the Catholic Church may have the numerical advantage over similar movements in Protestantism, here too we can speak of a powerful movement. Nearly all the national Protestant churches contain charismatic groups, and the same is true for most of the Protestant free churches. There is so great a number of centres, publications and informal contacts, some confined to one denomination and others ecumenical, that one may justly speak of a world-wide, interdenominational movement.

The ground has been gone over by many theologians. Harding Meyer claims that by now it is so generally agreed as to be scarcely open to question that the era in which he and his contemporaries grew up was one in which the Spirit was forgotten. *Otto A. Dilschneider* maintains that, following the eras of the Fathers, the Schoolmen and the Reformers, the twentieth century has seen the commencement of a new era, in which the Church concerns herself particularly with the Holy Spirit.[1] *Heribert Mühlen*, the leading theologian of the Roman Catholic renewal movement in Germany, draws much more radical conclusions. He suggests that with the new awareness of the reality of the Holy Spirit, the *Constantinian era* of the church is coming to its end. In this connection he writes: "The new social form of the church will have to be that of the congregation-centred church. The focal point of this church is the congregation of believing, convinced, committed Christians who live scattered throughout secular society, more or less as individual believers among the indifferent, the non-believers and those of other faiths, and who meet to hear the word of God and to celebrate the Eucharist. The church of the future will not be so much an institution sanctioned by the state, into which people grow almost 'automatically', as a church of those who, definitely and personally converted on the basis of deep conviction, have received baptism and the Spirit of Christ (cf. Acts 2:38)."[2]

The church has great difficulty in admitting her lack of authority in the face of a world which appears to be hastening towards disaster. It is understandable therefore that people's hopes are being increasingly concentrated on a totally new beginning for the church — both from above, by the theologians, and from below, at the grass roots. The *Jesus People* as a movement has disturbed many Christians and made them ask questions about their own authority. *Cardinal Julius Döpfner* says about this:."For us it is becoming a question of conscience whether our Christianity has grown so tired that it is no longer attractive even to the seeker. Perhaps we have too often made compromises between the Christian and the well-fed citizen of a prosperous age, so that the illuminating power of the message of Jesus has become obscured. That should cause us to think afresh about our faith and its life-shaping power, so that our Christianity can become once again the 'salt of the earth'."[3]

Does the charismatic movement mark an authentic new beginning, or is it merely one of the swiftly changing fashions of the age? Is a new theology of the Holy Spirit just one more offering among the many modern theologies which appear so suddenly and are so quickly forgotten? Or can it become the vehicle for something which will help the church really to become again "salt" and "light"?

The various denominations which have been confronted suddenly, within their own ranks by charismatic prayer groups, prayer in other languages, healing of the sick or visions, have so far reacted positively on the whole. They see the possibilities of a charismatic renewal of their churches — even if there is an undertone of concern about the difficulty of controlling such free groups and the danger of extremism. Typical of this attitude was the response of the American Catholic bishops in 1969.[4] Other churches would surely have agreed when the Committee for Matters of Faith concluded that the movement should not at that time be suppressed, but rather should be allowed to develop. But it demanded that care be taken. The bishops must exercise their pastoral responsibility to oversee and guide the movement within the Church. The errors of classical Pentecostalism were to be avoided. Christians in North America tended to let religious experience supplant religious doctrine. Official recognition should be given to intelligent priests associated with the movement.

In the meantime the reaction of the Catholic Church became if anything more positive, not least because of a certain amount of papal encouragement. Speaking to members of charismatic groups at a general audience on 16th October 1974, Pope *Paul VI* said among other things: "We have a need for the miracle of Pentecost to continue in the history of the church and of the world, in the twofold form in which the gift of the Holy Spirit is bestowed on men: firstly, to sanctify them (that is the pre-eminent and indispensable form, by means of which man becomes an object of God's love . . .); and then, to equip them with especial privileges, the so-called charisms . . . for the benefit of their neighbours and above all for that of the fellowship of believers. There is much talk about this today. And when we consider how complex and delicate such a subject is, we can only wish that the Church of God may be granted today a new abundance not only of grace but of charisms."[5]

The Protestant Churches have produced very few statements of general validity. However, the department for parish work of the Lutheran Church of America accepted in 1974 certain guidelines for relations with the charismatic movement in their churches. Where the movement is authentic — i.e. where it produces good fruits — the charismatic experiences are to be understood as a part of the church's life. There is no reason for Lutheran pastors or church members either explicitly or implicitly to hold that one cannot at the same time be charismatic and a good Lutheran.[6]

The subject has also been intensively discussed in the free churches. The Theological Studies Commission of the Council of Methodist Central Conferences in Europe concluded that the charismatic groups were raising a fundamental issue. To outside observers they seemed to be filled with power and vitality, unencumbered by the burden of a lengthy history, not hemmed in by a rigid system. Under their influence, people were opening themselves to the working of the Holy Spirit and were being led to a new dedication to God and to missionary zeal for the world around them. Was it possible that the powers of the Holy Spirit seen in these groups might free Methodism from its stiffness? Indeed, the charismatic churches were pointing out the road to church renewal. However, renewal was not a human achievement but something bestowed by God as and when he chose. Yet he wants his people to pray for it.[7]

The Baptist churches seem to present a disunited front — perhaps just because in their local churches there is so much evidence of the influence of the charismatic movement. In the

Southern Baptist Convention in the U.S.A. there are, according to their own figures, some 100 charismatic churches with 10,000 members; and in addition just about as many Baptists with charismatic experience who belong to churches in which distinctly charismatic experiences form no part of the church life.[8] On the other hand it is known that two Baptist churches were excluded from the Union of Southern Baptists in Texas on account of their charismatic activities.[9] In the German churches belonging to the *Bund Evangelisch-Freikirchlicher Gemeinden*, which is largely made up of Baptist churches, we find a broad spectrum of experiences. This has come about through the agency of the *Ruferbewegung*, an evangelical movement which from the outset has had connections with the charismatic renewal. It has led in part to the strengthening of local churches, but also to tensions and controversy. Theological study conferences have attempted to encourage the various groups to share their experiences, and to integrate charismatic experiences into the life of the local church.

In contrast to the predominantly united and cautiously positive stance of these churches stands the unequivocal rejection of the charismatic movement by a portion of the official "Evangelical" (i.e. Lutheran and Reformed) Church in Germany. The clearest warning has come from the part of the evangelical movement which belongs to the national church, and which has been moulded by the *Gemeinschaftsbewegung*.[10] In the agonizing which followed the appearance of the Pentecostal movement at the beginning of this century, the *Gemeinschaftsbewegung* unequivocally repudiated charismatic tendencies, a rejection which culminated in the *Berlin Declaration*. Today, special concern is being expressed that in the emergence of new charismatic experiences *fanatical* counterfeits could find a place in the life of the churches. *Peter Beyerhaus* writes: "It must now be stated quite clearly that a fanatical spirit is not merely an unhealthy attitude on the part of men, but a spirit from the pit. It is one of the ways in which the ancient enemy of souls chooses to work. Ultimately it amounts to personal demon-possession."[11] This view is expanded by *Erich Lubahn*: "Have the charisms needed by the church been recognised sufficiently by the church's theologians, and awakened and nurtured by her pastors? In my opinion there has been a lack at this point, which has given the spirit of fanaticism the opportunity to produce and to practise charisms in an uncontrollable and unscriptural manner."[12]

Hand in hand with warnings against fanaticism there often goes the view that some of the New Testament charisms were given for a limited time only: "With the writing of the New Testament, and its availability to believers, God's revelation was closed. Three of the original gifts of the Spirit, namely the revelatory gifts of tongues, prophecy and charismatic knowledge, have now fulfilled their purpose. With the appearance of the New Testament they have, in accordance with 1 Cor. 13:8, been removed from the list of early Christian charisms and have ceased to be."[13]

Despite the deep rift between these differing judgments of the charismatic movement, there are also signs of integration, for example in the revival movement in Indonesia. This is clearly as strongly evangelical as it is charismatic. Thus *Volkhard Scheunemann*, teacher at the Batu Bible Institute, writes: "There are many pastors . . . who cry out for the Spirit and His gifts, and are very open, and the Lord can work — yet many people in the fellowships want to close themselves to it because of negative experiences. But we must not close ourselves, dear friends. Without the Spirit of God we cannot live. And there will never be a revival without the Spirit. The experience of the past surely teaches that when the rain comes, both grain and weeds sprout up; but that should not hinder us to such an extent that we stop praying for rain altogether. Rather it should make us pray for the spirit of discernment and for the courage to go into battle."[14]

Thus the question is raised which this book will try in part to answer. It is a matter of sound teaching, and of the healthy exercise of the gifts of the Holy Spirit. Our concern is not primarily to decide whether we are for the charismata or against them, but to decide how they may be constructively exercised. If any age needed spiritual authority, then it is ours. We must ask for rain, fully aware that the rain will help both grain and weeds to grow, but also aware that we need a sharpened discernment if we are to be able to tell the one from the other.

Part One

THE PHENOMENON OF A WORLDWIDE CHARISMATIC MOVEMENT

CHAPTER ONE

The Breakthrough

For several decades conscious and distinctive charismatic experience was confined to the churches of the classical Pentecostal movement. This set a limit to the area of activity, and the phenomena were regarded as features of a sect which no one need worry about. Thus there was no particular need to do any exegetical work on the subject. Early in the 1960's, however, distinctively charismatic experiences began to touch the roots of the mainstream churches. At first they did not attract wide publicity, but later they became the subject of sensational reports and embittered discussion. The *charismatic breakthrough* had arrived.

The various historical stages of the movement's development will be described later. To begin with we are concerned with the phenomenon itself. More important than what actually happened, it seems, was the personal effect on those undergoing the experiences. What did they feel? What expectations did they associate with the charismatic experience? What was it that fascinated them and, as it was passed on to others created the fascination of the movement? In order that we may deal with these questions on a basis of first-hand experience, let us listen to what various people involved have to say.

The earliest experiences outside the Pentecostal Churches were given to some of the recently formed Protestant religious communities. As an example I quote from the report of Mother *Basilea Schlink* of the Evangelical Sisters of Mary, on the charismatic experiences which accompanied the foundation of that community in 1945: "The judgment on our city taught us the way of daily penitence, which allows love for Jesus to be born, and from which in turn worship springs spontaneously. The Lord had blessed us richly with gifts, so that as the Apostle Paul puts it, 'you were not lacking in any spiritual gift'. The Lord gave us . . . not only the ability to worship, but other spiritual gifts . . . Grateful as we were for them, because they are 'for the common good' (1 Cor. 12:7), they never became the decisive factor in our spiritual life. The source of our spiritual life is to be found in our love for Jesus, which is born of penitence — this,

[af]ter long struggles, we had discovered at a deep level . . . In this [w]ay God preserved us from making what is called 'baptism in the Spirit' the foundation of our new life. It was an expression we never used . . ."[15]

One of the recognized spokesmen of the Protestant charismatic movement in the U.S.A. is *Dennis J. Bennett*, a priest of the Episcopal Church. His personal experience of *baptism in the Holy Spirit* in 1960 was taken as a signal, and to a large extent set the charismatic movement in motion. The nature of his experience partly accounts for the fact that this sector of the charismatic movement follows the theology of the Pentecostal churches more obviously than do others. Bennett writes:

" 'What do I do?' I asked them again. 'Ask Jesus to baptize you in the Holy Spirit', said John . . . I said: 'Now remember, I want this nearness to God you have, that's all; I'm not interested in speaking with tongues!' 'Well,' said they, 'all we can tell you about *that* is that it came with the package!' John came across the room and laid his hands first on my head, and then on my friend's. He began to pray, very quietly, and I recognised the same thing as when Bud had prayed with me a few days before: he was speaking a language that I did not understand, and speaking it very fluently. He wasn't a bit 'worked up' about it, either. Then he prayed in English, asking Jesus to baptize me in the Holy Spirit. I began to pray, as he told me, and I prayed very quietly, too. I was not about to get even a little bit excited! . . . I suppose I must have prayed aloud for about twenty minutes . . . and was just about to give up when a strange thing happened. My tongue tripped, just as it might when you are trying to recite a tongue twister, and I began to speak in a new language!"[16]

In 1962 a Lutheran pastor named *Arnold Bittlinger* went on a tour of the U.S.A. to study methods of evangelism. There he encountered the charismatic movement, particularly in connection with *Larry Christenson*. He describes the prayer meetings which he had the opportunity of observing:

"I had the chance to meet this newly awakened charismatic life in several churches, and was particularly impressed by the prayer meetings in which the gifts of the Spirit which Paul mentions in 1 Cor. 12-14 (e.g. prophecy, revelations, speaking in tongues and interpretation) were practised with great discipline, order and solemn, liturgical beauty. Nowhere did I find noisy or disorderly behaviour . . . As a rule these meetings took the following form: after an introduction in the form of some biblical teaching, opportunity was given for free charismatic contributions from the church members. Songs and prayers alternated with periods of complete silence, out of which now and then one member or another would speak words of prophecy, which were then tested by the congregation on the basis of scripture. Generally these prophecies consisted of simple instructions (spoken in the first person), relating to the present situation of the church. It was amazing how helpful such words of prophecy sometimes were in throwing light on a situation, or bringing comfort to people in particular difficulties. Glossolalia (speaking in tongues) was allowed only if there were interpreters present in the congregation who would be able to translate what was said."[17]

After he returned from this tour Arnold Bittlinger invited a selected group of leaders from the official church and from the free churches to a study conference with Larry Christenson. The conference took place in August 1963 at Enkenbach in the Palatinate, and about 80 took part. *Wilhard Becker* wrote describing the conference: "We went to Enkenbach with many expectations, but also with great scepticism. We had heard a certain amount already: a new tongues movement had appeared, the gifts of the Spirit had been experienced by Protestant pastors. The group which gathered consisted chiefly of critics and observers. The first surprise was the very sober atmosphere in which the meeting was convened. It was impossible for any kind of unhealthy emotionalism to develop; on the contrary, every participant was required to do some thorough Bible study . . . the discussion on the first evening once again provided an opportunity for strong criticisms to be expressed . . . All those present, whether theologians, psychologists, doctors, or businessmen, were however honest in their criticism. This was surely the reason why the majority not only listened, but were convinced . . . The experiences into which people entered in personal conversation and in prayer — in some cases with the laying on of hands — were taken away with them and passed on to the groups and movements from which they had come . . . So it was that the renewal began not somewhere on the fringe, among people attached to some sect, but in the centre of the churches. The new charisms were experienced not in exuberant enthusiasm nor in an ecstatic manner, but in a spirit of sobriety, control, evaluation, and above all great reverence. It was not speaking in tongues which stood out, but other gifts such as prophecy, the word of wisdom and the gift of discerning the spirits."[18]

There are many accounts of the beginning of the charismatic renewal movement in the Roman Catholic Church. Here I will quote from *Cardinal Suenens*, who was commissioned by Pope Paul VI to investigate the movement in the U.S.A. and who subsequently became the man who encouraged its growth and integration within the Roman Catholic Church. "This renewal first came into being in the Catholic Church among students in Duquesne University, Pittsburgh, Pennsylvania, during 1967. At a time of social and religious crises throughout their own country and the world at large, some of these young people, realizing the impossibility of finding a human solution, met for a weekend of prayer and fasting to ask the grace of the Holy Spirit . . . That weekend, for those who attended, proved to be in the true sense of the word a new Pentecost. Nor had they gone to it unprepared. Many had read David Wilkerson's *The Cross and the Switchblade* . . . The Spirit's response to them was an experience, over again, of what happened when the first disciples of the Lord were together in the upper-room in Jerusalem. An amazing spiritual transformation took place in them. They spoke of a new awareness of the love of God such as they had not experienced before: of a desire to pray and glorify God; of an insatiable thirst for Scripture. Moreover they felt power within them to bear witness to the risen Jesus. They talked of a 'baptism in the Holy Spirit' and of charisms given to them similar to those of which we read in the early Church . . . I have myself met many persons . . . who witnessed at first-hand what took place, and many of them have become my friends. Their witness makes a deep impression on me and their credibility seems beyond question."[19]

Cardinal Suenens includes in his report many personal experiences, and speaks candidly of how his own faith has been deepened. To quote him once again: "I still remember a session at Ann Arbor, attended by some fifty delegates. Many times during the meeting, the layman who presided interrupted our deliberations to suggest a few minutes of prayer and recollection before the Lord, to ask for the light of the Holy Spirit on the decisions we were about to make. This prayer in which we took part together — sometimes a murmur, sometimes for a moment 'in tongues' — plunged me deeply into an atmosphere of awareness of God. And I thought: how far we are from believing what we profess to believe! . . . Such as they are, in all their inadequacy, these words wish to say one thing: the Lord is near, God is not dead, Jesus is alive, the Spirit is faithful; in the heart of our twentieth century, Pentecost remains a reality."[20]

From a totally different background, that of the revival in Indonesia, comes the report of *Detmar Scheunemann*. In an address given at Adelshofen in the spring of 1969, he said: "The wonder of the revival in Timor is that illiterates have become witnesses of God . . . This has happened in two ways. Firstly, through direct *visions*. God has shown them spiritual truth in pictorial form. I have checked by the Bible all the visions which they have described to me, and found none which was not in harmony with it . . . The second way in which they have acquired their spiritual equipment is through the Spirit of God speaking to them audibly — they always mention this — not just by an inner voice. They hear a voice telling them a Bible verse, such as John 14:6 . . . Then they have to go to another village, to a brother or sister who has a Bible, and get them to look the verse up. They then learn it by heart."[21]

I regard the Jesus movement as at least in part belonging to the charismatic movement, especially in the American universities, where it was less spectacular. In the *Jesus People Report*, Frank Ashley used material from the Home Missions Board of the Southern Baptists. He quotes from the diary of Jeff Blake, a student at Asbury College. Blake found the scene on February 3, 1970, when the great Asbury awakening began, quite unbelievable. The marathon meeting had begun spontaneously on a cold Tuesday morning when the leader began by asking those who wanted to give a testimony or make any comments to come forward. There was a brief pause, then students began to get up from their seats and queue along the walls for their turn to give testimony at the microphone. Once this had begun it went on and on. It simply would not end. This revival meeting continued for 185 hours. Thousands of students and visitors knelt at the long altar. Many stood up to testify that they wanted to change their way of life and that they had found a new life. Walter L. Knight drew a number of conclusions. Emotion, he considered, was to be found everywhere in the Jesus movement, but speaking in tongues occurred only in a limited area and was not universally accepted. All, however, were affected by the high emotional temperature of the encounter, by the experience of intimate fellowship and of Christian love. He observed that the Jesus movement united people who had previously been separated. It was particularly successful in places where the young people themselves had taken on the leadership. Yet older church members, although they stood in the background, were frequently able to lead the newly converted on to greater maturity.

Perhaps these quotations will have served to clarify what is happening in the charismatic renewal, even if they do not make it any easier to evaluate. Various characteristics do emerge, which may even at this stage be tentatively summarized:

1. Despite totally different church backgrounds and diversity of social environment, there is a widespread similarity of experience in the *exercise of charisms*.

2. There are wide differences in the degree of *agreement with the Pentecostal movement*. In the U.S.A. there are some groups which are scarcely distinguishable from Pentecostals, whereas particularly in Germany there are areas of the charismatic movement which deliberately hold themelves aloof from the theology and practice of Pentecostalism. This attitude is also increasingly typical of the charismatic renewal in the Catholic Church.

3. Although there are frequently similarities in practice, theological assessment of charismatic phenomena varies very widely. This is most obvious when it comes to the problem of *baptism in the Holy Spirit*, a very complex issue which we shall have to study under a separate heading.

4. Although we have here brought together reports from various sources under the general heading of "charismatic movement", it is evident that in one situation church tradition will cause the movement to appear as charismatic, while in another it will take on more of the character of a revival — the latter is true especially of Indonesia and of the movement in the Catholic Church.

5. Among the evident effects of the charismatic movement, and responsible for the fascination it exerts, one can list the following: a closer personal walk with Jesus; more joy in the Bible, in prayer and in the fellowship of believers; more power; and finally, a greater motivation to evangelize. It is noticeably not the *charismata* which are given the greatest emphasis, but the *effects* they produce.

6. Almost all observers agree that the charismatic movement represents a genuine working of the Holy Spirit, but that it is also full of dangers. Therefore most churches are attempting to give the movement both *room for further development* and the opportunity of becoming *integrated* into existing church structures.

CHAPTER TWO

Charismatic Gifts over 2,000 Years

As yet, hardly anyone has written a history of charismatic revivals over the 2,000 years of the church's development. This could easily lead to the false conclusion that since the days of the earliest church there have been no consciously charismatic experiences, or at most only a very few here and there. In this chapter we shall be able to consider such charismatic revivals in outline only, not by any means in full. Nevertheless, if we wish to make a sound assessment of what is going on today, it is important that we should be aware that such experiences have accompanied the church throughout her entire history, and that they are one of the various forms of church order categorized by *Ed. Schweizer*[24] as the *Palestinian structure* (a church with official positions and a strong hierarchy), and *Johannine structure* (a Spirit-led church without such offices), and the *Pauline structure* (a church occupying the middle ground, having charismatic gifts and charismatic offices). What is happening today, in other words, is not something completely new, but a significant swing in the direction of a charismatic church structure.

A summary of the basic historical development in this area is given us by *Ernst Benz*: "In the earliest Christian communities the presence of the various gifts of the Spirit was such a dominant feature of church life that Paul, in describing the structure of the local church, mentions first the multiplicity of gifts and only secondly the various offices. He thus makes the offices actually dependent on the presence of spiritual gifts. A curious development then took place in the history of the church: the spiritual gifts were progressively subordinated to an institutional and legalistic concept of offices in the church. The result of this development was that the idea of a multiplicity of spiritual gifts was narrowed until only two were recognised, namely those which had to do with logical speech and reason: preaching, and the exposition of scripture . . . This development was opposed again and again by the outbreak of charismatic movements. These may be followed throughout the history of the church, but they were generally suppressed by the ruling state churches, declared heretical and persecuted until they disappeared."[25]

In addition to these, another repository of charismatic experiences existed in mysticism. Very little, of course, is known about this area. But we do know, from numerous allusions, that there was scarcely one of the New Testament charisms which ever completely died out. Further details about this are to be found in the volume *Kirche und Charisma*,[26] in the section dealing with charisms in the history of the Orthodox, Roman Catholic and Protestant Churches.

The short historical summary which follows is largely based on material from Arnold Bittlinger's book *Gemeinde ist anders*,[27] with many details taken also from the book *2000 Jahre Zungenreden*.[28]

From the second century onwards the offices in the church became dominant, and the development of free charismatic gifts progressively declined. It is true that many charismatic experiences were brought back into the church by the *Montanists*, but because of the theological errors of that movement they failed to survive. So, as has happened so often in the subsequent history of the church, "the baby was thrown out with the bath-water". "The church rejected ecstatic prophecy, but failed to give the charismatic gifts their rightful place in the church or in her theology. This was fatal, because it meant that from now on the impression was given that all free charismatics were at least close to being heretics."[29] It does not surprise us to find, therefore, that Augustine had no personal acquaintance with the phenomenon of glossolalia, and regarded it as a sign belonging to the period of primitive Christianity only.

The next few centuries are a period of silence as far as the charismatic gifts in the churches are concerned — at any rate those of an enthusiastic sort. It may, of course, be conjectured that charismatic phenomena appeared in the monasticism of the middle ages at their height, but they did not acquire any decisive influence. In the case of some individuals like St. John of the Cross or Hildegard of Bingen we hear of the gift of speaking in a foreign tongue.[30] Probably there were more charismatic experiences within the mediaeval Orthodox Church: contemporary Greek monks report that glossolalia lives on among them as an ancient tradition which has lasted to the present day. Joachim of Fiore, with his vision of a pure church of the Spirit, exercised a great influence on men of his own day, but this influence was unable to survive for long because of the extremes to which he went.

With the beginning of the pre-Reformation movements there

appears, after centuries of torpor, a new striving for the presence of charismatic gifts in the church. The *Waldensians* and the *Lollards* (followers of *John Wycliffe*) rejected the hierarchical structure of the official church, took the Holy Scriptures as their only standard, and formed small groups, mainly house churches, in which a rich charismatic life was the rule. Similar characteristics are seen among the Hussites, although in their case nationalistic elements soon outweighed the spiritual. Would the church find its way back again to that true balance between spiritual gifts and official structures?

For a time the *Reformation* fed such hopes, for instance in Luther's Introduction to the German Mass. But it soon became clear that only a very limited opportunity would be given for anything charismatic in the church. The nearest approach to a charismatic ordering of the church was developed by the *Anabaptists*, with their emphasis that every individual believer is filled with the Holy Spirit and their consequent rejection of any hierarchical structure. The extraordinary severity with which they were persecuted both by Catholic and Reformed Churches gives some indication of the fascination people found in the Anabaptist doctrines and church organization.

In the age of the Reformation only *Caspar von Schwenckfeld* seems to have found a balance between charismatic gifts and the official structure. He gives the gifts their proper place, as taught by St. Paul. He speaks of a *baptism with the Holy Spirit and with fire*. His concept of the charismatic church has been described by *Karl Ecke* — though not all will agree with this interpretation. Ecke writes: "Thus, through His agents who have been gifted by means of a spiritual calling, Jesus Himself rules in the Spirit both the whole ecclesia and each local congregation. In the local congregation the gifts of grace prove effective in the inward strengthening of all, 'since there are apostles, prophets, teachers, miracle workers, gifts of healing, helpers, judges and spiritual gifts of various kinds, which are distributed by the one Spirit for the good of all, for in each person gifts of the Spirit are manifested, as Paul says in 1 Cor. 12 . . .' The Spirit has unlimited freedom. When someone is moved by the Spirit to rise to his feet, the one who is speaking must stop. In addition to the gifts, the Spirit bestows for the service of the whole church the charismatic offices of apostle, prophet, evangelist, pastor and teacher. To the apostolate there belongs a special apostolic commission, which is evidenced by the signs of apostolic office."[31]

When the Edict of Nantes, which had guaranteed freedom of religion to Protestants in France, was revoked in 1685, there followed a general persecution of the *Huguenots*. The farmers in the hill country of the Cevennes offered the strongest resistance. Here ecstatic charismatic experiences developed, amazingly even among children and infants. A few small churches survived in the period which followed, and these manifested a rich charismatic life. At about the same time the *Quakers* began in England, and in the first phase of their development a similar abundance of charismatic gifts appears among them. The name "Quakers" originated in the shaking with which they were seized as a result of powerful religious emotions. At first glossolalia was also practised, though later the chief emphasis was placed on prophecy spoken in an intelligible language. Their doctrine of the inner light leaves plenty of scope for charismatic expression.

Pietism can certainly not be included directly among charismatic movements, since in the main it has remained faithful to the official structures of the church. However, because of its emphasis on the priesthood of all believers, and on the church as consisting of those "who are illumined with divine light and who have a true, simple and living faith",[32] Pietism may be seen as the ancestor of all the modern charismatic movements, including both Pentecostalism and the charismatic renewal of the present day. *Heribert Mühlen* has pointed out this connection. "With the Catholic charismatic renewal, impulses are returning from the U.S.A. to Germany which had their origin in German pietism, but which have since been enriched by free church elements."[33]

The first important charismatic movement to arise from Pietism was the spirituality of the *Moravian Brethren*. Günter Krüger describes their initial inspiration: "In addition to the various minor revivals since 1725, special mention must here be made of the great revival of 13th August 1727, which came upon practically the whole congregation and was experienced as a baptism of the Spirit, as the church's own Pentecost. Zinzendorf writes: 'At the communion that day, which was a true love-feast in fact as well as in name, the Saviour caused a spirit to come upon us of which we had previously known nothing.' Since that time the Brethren have provided a unique 'source of charismatic impulse', such as Protestantism had not hitherto experienced with that degree of intensity in such a tiny area."[34]

In the 18th and 19th centuries charismatic revivals became more frequent, until at the beginning of the 20th century the worldwide Pentecostal movement began. In early *Methodism* many charismatic phenomena may be observed, including ecstatic experiences and even glossolalia. These were not suppressed by Wesley. When someone objected that too much importance could be attached to extraordinary circumstances, Wesley replied: "Perhaps the danger is that we pay too little attention to them."[35] With the growth of the great revival movement in England and America, many evangelical groups both large and small began to flourish, and within them some people had consciously charismatic experiences. This in turn had a fertilizing effect on the rising Pentecostal movement when it came.

In 19th century England two utterly different movements appeared which had one thing in common: they developed very original structures of church organization. The first was *Darbyism*, which is still alive in England and Germany under the name of *Brethren* or *Christian Assemblies*. Erich Geldbach writes: "It is not the brethren themselves who lead the meeting, but the Holy Spirit, who works freely through whomever He will. The Spirit searches the hearts of the assembled company and chooses out as His instruments those who can express the feelings of the church towards God, and who can meet the spiritual needs of those who have gathered."[36] This corresponds exactly to the description of a free, charismatic service, such as may be found within the charismatic movement of today. True, there is scarcely any trace in Darbyism of the typical charismatic phenomena, but a form of service has developed there which is based upon that of the church at Corinth which Paul describes in 1 Cor. 14.

The second movement began in 1830, within circles influenced by Edward Irving. Here we have a charismatic movement in which the whole plenitude of New Testament gifts appeared, especially prophecy and glossolalia. From this Irvingite movement arose the Catholic Apostolic Church, in which Catholic and charismatic tendencies were combined in a unique way. An attempt was made to revive not only the New Testament charismata but also New Testament church organization. The Catholic Apostolic Church saw itself not as a denomination in its own right, but as the starting point for a new ecumenicalism like that of the early Christians. The influence it has exercised right up to the present day would be hard to over-estimate, and most recently this has extended to the charismatic movement.

Direct inspiration by the Holy Spirit, unaccompanied by the familiar charismatic phenomena, but still definitely charismatic in the New Testament sense, is to be found in abundance. To show that the history of charismatic experiences is not a unified picture with clear-cut edges, we may give an example from the history of the German Baptist Church. *Eduard Scheve* writes concerning a love-feast which was held on 25th December 1875 in Mülheim on the Ruhr: "The desire to pray became general, and so we sank down on our knees in order to talk with God in prayer and to enter into fellowship with Him. What happened next is hard to describe; I can only give some idea of what happened by referring to the words of Acts 4:31 — 'And when they had prayed, the place in which they were gathered together was shaken; and they were all filled with the Holy Spirit and spoke the word with boldness.' Nothing extreme or fanatical took place: there was complete self-control among all the people present. The prayers became simple, very short, childlike, sensible, and were uttered without any special sense of excitement — yet they were so overwhelming, so full of the Spirit, so heaven-inspired . . . A very worldly-minded girl was so powerfully gripped that she sank down and cried for mercy. Another girl came in intending to disturb the meeting, but as soon as she set foot among the assembled company, she was so mightily overcome by the Spirit of God that she cried out loud and sank to the floor . . . It was a remarkable scene. There was a general feeling that the place had been literally shaken. After this glorious prayer meeting had ended, six souls confessed that they had found peace with God."[37]

CHAPTER THREE

A New Pentecost?

The broad outline of events is well known. The growing frequency and intensity of charismatic outbreaks led to the appearance at the beginning of this century of a movement which became so strong that it developed into a new and independent denomination within Christianity, known as Pentecostalism. Various Pentecostal churches are members of the World Council of Churches; some co-operate in local Evangelical Alliance groups; and representatives of Pentecostal churches are taking part in the official Vatican dialogues between the Roman Catholic Church and the charismatic movement. On the other hand many churches write off the Pentecostals as a sect. It is understandable that attitudes vary in this way, for it is always difficult to make an accurate assessment of a highly emotional movement. What is universally agreed, however, is that the Pentecostals originally saw themselves as heading a movement for reform within the churches, and had no desire to have a denominational organization of their own — a pattern which has often recurred in the course of church history.

The most important forerunner of Pentecostalism was the holiness movement of the late nineteenth century. This movement owed a great deal to Methodism, and in particular to the teaching of John Wesley that there were differences between the ordinary Christian and the one who had been sanctified, or baptized in the Spirit. T. C. Upham, one of the leading theologians of the holiness movement, taught that the power of the Holy Spirit was not necessary in order for a person to get to heaven, but that it was needed for the undertaking of the specific tasks which were the responsibility of a Christian. The social and ethical motivation behind the holiness movement was however gradually forgotten, and its doctrine of regeneration and sanctification as the two key experiences in the life of the Christian remained, to become the most important factor in the emergence of Pentecostalism.[38]

Three outbreaks of charismatic gifts acted as a kind of signal for the Pentecostal movement to begin. In 1886, under the leadership of two Baptist preachers, a movement began called the Latter Rain Movement, which strove after the final outpouring of the Spirit as promised in Joel 2. In 1892 the first members of this movement received the "baptism in the Spirit", accompanied by the gift of speaking in tongues.[39]

The experiences of the holiness preacher Charles F. Parham in his Bible School at Topeka in the U.S.A. went further than this. The Catholic writer Francis A. Sullivan describes how as they read the account of Pentecost and other outpourings of the Holy Spirit in the book of Acts, Parham and his students concluded that the only certain scriptural mark of Holy Spirit baptism was the gift of speaking in tongues. So for several days and nights at the end of 1900 prayer was offered continually for the coming of the Holy Spirit in this way. On January 1, 1901, a student named Agnes Oznam asked Parham to lay his hands on her head while she was praying. As he did so she experienced the "baptism of the Spirit" and began to "speak in tongues". Within a few days, all the students and Parham himself had had a similar experience. The first 'Pentecostal' group had begun.[40]

The really decisive event took place five years later. Because of the disproportionately greater amount of publicity which it attracted, it became the most significant starting point for Pentecostalism. W. J. Seymour, a negro preacher who had been a student of Parham's, was invited to Los Angeles. The first "baptism in the Spirit" took place in a prayer meeting, and was quickly followed by others. In an old church in Azusa Street, in the most primitive surroundings, almost non-stop prayer meetings began to take place. Most Pentecostals see their real origin in this Azusa Street mission. Legendary reports surround this outbreak, which was evidently very much at the centre of public attention. "For three days and nights they shouted for joy. It was Eastertide. People came from all around. On the second day it was impossible to get near to the building. Anyone who did succeed in getting inside fell under the power of God. The whole city was excited. They shouted for joy until the foundations of the house shook, but no one was hurt."[41]

Was this a new Pentecost? The accounts make it clear that at least many frustrated church members regarded it as an event which could be compared with Pentecost. The outbreaks we have described and many other similar ones were highly emotional, and in some cases almost volcanic; and they affected people of various church backgrounds. Except for the emphasis on Spirit baptism and charismatic gifts, the theology was strongly influenced by Methodism. Everywhere the background of Methodist and Baptist experience showed through. The various outbreaks in every part of the world followed so rapidly on these events that it must be assumed that in many cases they were not derived from one another, but spontaneous.

In 1906, the same year as the events in Los Angeles, the Pentecostal movement crossed to Europe, reaching first Norway and then Sweden and Germany. Although there were tensions everywhere which led ultimately to splits between the Pentecostals and the established churches, nowhere did the events produce greater tension than in Germany. The effects of the outbreaks in Kassel and Grossalmerode are still noticeable today. For seldom has it been shown so rapidly and in such a restricted area, and one might say in such an exemplary fashion, how a charismatic movement ought not to proceed; nor has such a clear illustration been given of how the church for her part (in this case in particular the Fellowship Movement) ought not to react. Perhaps however it is still possible, even if 70 years too late, for a mutual learning process to begin.[42]

Firstly it is obvious that at the beginning of this century there existed in the Fellowship Movement an atmosphere of expectancy which acted on the "pentecostal bacillus" like a culture medium. Here, for example, is an account of R. A. Torrey's meetings at the Evangelical Alliance Conference in Blankenburg in 1905, taken from the *Allianzblatt*: "After Dr. Torrey . . . had set out . . . the conditions laid down in scripture for baptism in the Holy Spirit . . . he asked those who were willing to give up everything, even the best things and what was dearest to them, in order to receive everything from God, to stand up. Many hundreds of children of God stood up in the hall. Torrey then prayed that the Holy Spirit might fall on all those who asked for Him . . . For myself I can only say that a wonderful, gentle stream of fire came over me from above, and it seemed to me that if I had opened my closed eyes I should have seen a flame of fire throughout the room."[43]

It is not surprising, therefore, that the first direct contacts of the Fellowship Movement with the new Pentecostal experience resulted in an overflow of emotions. Of the spectacular events which took place in 1907 in Kassel under the leadership of Heinrich Dallmeyer, an evangelist who had his background in the Fellowships, Kurt Hutten writes: "In both places people spoke in tongues. All manner of unhealthy expressions of unbridled ecstasy broke out, resulting in a great deal of controversy. Men and women writhed about on the floor, groaning, twitching, having convulsions and shouting, 'Hallelujah!' When the excitement reached its climax people started speaking in tongues . . . The leader of one Fellowship leaped in the air. A pastor wove his way like a snake between the chairs. These events naturally provided plenty of material for sensational press reports. In Kassel there was a street riot, and the meetings were brought to an end at the urgent request of the police."[44]

Tension between those for and those against the events in Kassel mounted visibly. Although at first many followers of the Fellowship Movement were positive in their attitude, opinions began to change as a result of the abuses. In addition the events were rejected by the public at large, which regarded the meetings with derision or total incomprehension. Leading members of the Fellowship Movement condemned the new movement; after some hesitation, at the end of 1907, Dallmeyer himself concurred with this verdict and declared that the spirit behind it was not the Spirit of God but a lying spirit. Pastor Jonathan Paul, on the other hand, stuck to his positive assessment and became one of the leaders of the young German Pentecostal Church.

In the next two years various attempts at reconciliation failed. The final parting of the ways came when leaders of the Fellowship Movement produced the *Berlin Declaration* of 1909, in which Pentecostalism was strongly condemned. It is true that the Berlin Declaration contains a number of thoroughly acceptable theological statements, which would have served well as a warning against certain harmful tendencies in the Pentecostal movement. Its basic proposition, however, that Pentecostalism is a movement inspired by the devil, can only have the effect of stifling any dialogue before it begins. The decisive paragraph of the Declaration reads: "The so-called Pentecostal movement is not from above, but from below; many of its manifestations it has in common with spiritism. In it demons are at work which, cunningly guided by Satan, mingle truth with falsehood in order to lead astray the children of God. In many cases those who have so-called 'gifts of Spirit' have later shown themselves to have been demon-possessed."

It is a deep tragedy that this undiscriminating judgment on the young Pentecostal movement by the signatories of the Berlin Declaration succeeded only in achieving exactly the opposite of what was needed. Instead of corrective dialogue, it resulted in uncompromising separation. Even an open reply to the Declaration by the Mülheim Conference, couched in objective terms, was unable to restore the situation. The last chance had gone.

Many Pentecostal groups gradually took up an extreme position and separated themselves from the state church and from the free evangelical churches. The Mülheim movement was able, after a long struggle, to avoid that mistake, but it too suffered because of its separation from the Fellowship Movement. The revival which had been beginning in Fellowship circles at the beginning of the century seems generally to have been halted as a result of this controversy. Thus there remained a great deal of damage which to this day has not fully been repaired. E. von Eicken is right when he says: "The Berlin Declaration soon proved itself to be a protective dam against further floods of fanaticism. It certainly cemented the cracks in the Fellowship Movement. The age of the revival and holiness movements was over."[45]

Because there is not just one single Pentecostal Church, but many groups large and small, often with important differences between them, it is impossible to set out a Pentecostal theology on which all would agree. Their central concern has been set out accurately and concisely by Sullivan. Pentecostals believe that the experience of the first disciples on the day of Pentecost was the normal experience of all believers in the early Christian church, and that therefore today all believers can and should earnestly expect a similar experience of Baptism in the Spirit. Moreover they believe that this outpouring of the Holy Spirit is indicated as it was at Pentecost by the sign of glossolalia. They draw a distinction between glossolalia as the initial sign of baptism in the Spirit and the subsequent and lasting gift of speaking and praying in tongues, which is not given to all. Most classical Pentecosals will not recognize a "baptism in the Spirit" as genuine if it is not accompanied by this sign.[46]

The term "baptism in the Spirit" appears as early as John Wesley, the founder of Methodism, and also in the holiness movement. Here it refers to an experience of faith which can be described and dated; not something necessary for *salvation* like regeneration, but fundamental for the *service* of Christ. In the Pentecostal movement the experience of sanctification, also known as the "second blessing", becomes an experience of the total reception of the Spirit, with speaking in tongues as its sign.

Charles G. Finney describes his experience of sanctification as understood by the early holiness movement:[47] He was about to get a chair and sit down by the fire when suddenly he was overwhelmed, "spirit, soul and body", by the Spirit of God. He had never heard of the baptism of the Spirit let alone prayed for it. Finney compares the experience to an electric current pulsating through him, to successive waves of love rushing over him. It was like a breath of life from above. He felt himself stirred by invisible wings.

By the end of the 19th century Reuben Archer Torrey had already developed a thoroughgoing doctrine of the baptism in the Spirit, although this had no direct connection with speaking in tongues.[48] For Torrey it is a definite and distinct work of the Holy Spirit; a Christian may know whether he has received it or not (Luke 24:49, Acts 1:8). It is a work of the Holy Spirit in those who have been born again as may be seen by comparing Acts 1:5 with John 15:3 and 13:10 which show that the disciples were born again before they were baptized in the Spirit.

It was only a short step from this for Parham to see in the reception of the gift of tongues the objective evidence of Spirit baptism. He based this view on Acts 2:4; 10:44-46; 19:6. Ludwig Eisenlöffel, principal of the Beroea Bible School of the *Arbeitsgemeinschaft der Christengemeinden in Deutschland,* sums up the doctrine of classical Pentecostalism as follows: "According to the doctrinal teaching of most Pentecostal churches a distinction is to be drawn between the reception of the gift of the Holy Spirit at regeneration and that at Spirit baptism. The promise of the Comforter (John 14-16) is not connected with baptism in the Spirit, although He came for the first time on the Day of Pentecost. Our teaching is that the Holy Spirit effects divine life in us when we are born again, and anoints us for service in the baptism . . . In the teaching of most Pentecostal churches the new tongues are seen as the initial sign of Spirit baptism, which must be followed by further evidences in the life, service and conduct of those who have been baptized in the Spirit. They are distinguished from the special gift of new tongues mentioned in 1 Cor. 12:10, since not every Christian rceives the new tongues as an abiding gift (1 Cor. 12:30)."[49]

Neo-Pentecostalism, i.e. that part of the charismatic movement which in large part follows the theology of classical Pentecostalism, likewise abides by these statements in the main. Dennis and Rita Bennett write: "You have received Jesus as your Saviour . . . now you're ready to pray to be baptized in the Holy Spirit . . . This being so, you can receive the Holy Spirit anywhere, anytime . . . 'But do I have to speak in tongues?' . . . We have shown that speaking in tongues is indeed a common denominator in examples of the baptism in the Holy Spirit given in the Scriptures. It seems obvious also that the early believers had a way of telling immediately whether or not their converts had received the Holy Spirit . . . If they had had to wait until they observed fruit or change of character in the person's life, it would have taken months and years to evaluate. Apparently the early Christians had a simpler way, and it isn't hard to see what it was."[50] Merlin Carothers, like Bennett a much-read writer of the neo-Pentecostal movement, describes in his autobiography "Prison to Praise" his own baptism in the Spirit in terms consistent with the theology of both classical and neo-Pentecostalism.[51]

In contrast to these writers the *Christlicher Gemeinschaftsverband Mülheim an der Ruhr* departs from this conception of baptism with the Spirit, and may be described as a church of the charismatic renewal. In 1930 Jonathan Paul wrote: "Speaking in tongues is of course a spiritual gift, but the Person is more than all His gifts, and it is extraordinarily dangerous to regard speaking in tongues as the mark of baptism in the Spirit. To do so is to disregard the central fact, which is 'Christ in us, the hope of glory'."[52] The official teaching of the *Christlicher Gemeinschaftsverband* of Mülheim is now expressed as follows: "In the *Christlicher Gemeinschaftsverband* . . . we mean by the term 'baptism in the Spirit' what other groups of Christians describe as 'coming to a living faith', 'conversion', 'regeneration' or 'anointing from on high' . . . Hence our concern is not to draw attention to some special Pentecostal experience of Spirit baptism, recognized only by speaking in tongues, as distinct from regeneration: rather it is, in obedience to the word of God and under the guidance of His Holy Spirit, to bear witness to the necessity of a deeper filling with the Holy Spirit for a life of service as disciples of Jesus Christ."[53]

The movement of charismatic renewal frequently makes clear in its literature and in its practice that it does not share the Pentecostal doctrine of baptism in the Spirit. Thus Arnold Bittlinger says: "We Christians are not waiting an additional experience of receiving the Spirit in terms of being 'sealed' or 'baptized' by the Spirit. We know that the Holy Spirit lives in every Christian, and is able and willing to make himself manifest in every Christian."[54] All the same there are some difficulties of definition, particularly because in the early days of the charismatic renewal the vocabulary of classical Pentecostalism was widely used, and some of the confusions thus caused have not yet been removed. On the whole, however, it is clear that the theologians of the charismatic renewal are separating themselves more and more clearly from the theology of Pentecostalism. They do not however regard this theology as *demonic*, and generally no longer regard Pentecostalism as a sect; they prefer to carry on a debate with the Pentecostals in the same way as with other churches and theological viewpoints.

The Jesuit Herbert Schneider tries to analyze what the two schools have in common and what distinguishes them: "The term 'baptism in the Spirit' describes the experience of the love of God which transforms and makes over anew, and at the same time the power which equips a man for service in the church. This doctrine is common to all groups, from the holiness movement to the Catholic charismatic movement. It also includes the insight that the experience of the Holy Spirit and the fact of being a Christian belong together. In classical Pentecostalism baptism in the spirit denotes a second experience of salvation subsequent to baptism . . . This experience is shown to be authentic when it is accompanied by glossolalia. In the Protestant charismatic groups, and within the Catholic church, people speak of a vitalizing of the Spirit and His gifts which were given to the Christian at his baptism. It is therefore not so much a second experience of salvation that we are talking about as a renewal."[55] After examining the New Testament teaching, Schneider draws the following conclusion: "The gift of the Spirit is not an additional experience for someone who is already a Christian. In the New Testament it is neither a second blessing nor a subsequent experience of sanctification nor an equipping for service. Everyone becomes a believer through hearing the gospel, surrenders himself to Christ, testifies to this through baptism, and receives the gift of the Holy Spirit. That is the testimony of the New Testament."[56]

The following outline sums up the principal doctrines of Pentecostalism:[57]

1. In their doctrine of scripture and their general theological outlook most Pentecostal groups belong to the evanglical wing of Christianity, with a tendency towards fundamentalism. Faith begins with an experience of personal regeneration. This is also a precondition for baptism in the Spirit.

2. The born again Christian must play his own part in creating the conditions for receiving Spirit baptism. At this point there is no single, agreed doctrine, but in general three points set out by Donald Gee appear to be representative:

surrender, or submission to the will of God;
prayer, and an earnest desire for the gifts of the Holy Spirit;
belief in the promise of Spirit baptism, and personal expectation of receiving it.

On this Werner Skibstedt writes: "Those who want to experience baptism in the Spirit according to the scriptures must continue steadfastly and intently to seek it until the fire falls upon them. They must not allow other things of secondary importance to come in the way, for they will only kill their desire and send their souls off the right track."[58]

3. Although the activity of the Holy Spirit in a man begins with regeneration, baptism in the Spirit is the personal entrance of the Holy Spirit within him. "A new subject, another Person comes in to be with us, to make His dwelling with us and to take control of us, so that from now on he can illuminate, teach, guide and rule us. It is a matter of a person to person relationship, not merely of an inpouring of heavenly power or holiness."[59]

4. Views differ as to whether Spirit baptism is necessary for salvation. Some groups who do not so regard it nevertheless hold it to be necessary if one is to live a power-filled life in the Spirit. Donald Gee requires all office-bearers in the church to be baptized in the Spirit. Other groups see in Spirit baptism the condition for membership of the bride church. Others regard it as absolutely essential for salvation.

5. Nearly all groups see glossolalia as the evidence that a person has been baptized in the Spirit. As a result many groups make a distinction between the special appearance of this gift at the moment of Spirit baptism and the abiding gift of speaking in tongues.

6. The intensive pursuit of baptism in the Spirit and of the exercise of charismatic gifts heightens the emotional level of expectation and generally leads to a high degree of emotion in public worship and in personal spirituality. "The radical Pentecostal churches however nurture such ecstatic states . . . in order to bring about a highly charged atmosphere at their meetings. They let the expectation build up to a climax and then discharge it in explosive outbursts."[60]

7. The experience of speaking in tongues generally causes the person concerned to feel that he is being taken over by another power, causing his own personality to be suppressed. Here too there are of course wide variations of experience, but on the whole speaking in tongues in the Pentecostal churches seems to tend in the directon of ecstasy.

8. In moderate Pentecostal groups, speaking in tongues has its place mainly in the context of private prayer. It is less frequent in services, and more closely associated with worship and contemplation than with prophecy. In other groups it appears predominantly in the form of prophecy, the giving of promises, exhortation and the revealing of sins, and it frequently forms part of public worship. Such prophecies are often prefaced by the words "I, Jesus . . ."

9. Other prophecies are in the form either of words or of visions; they too are often given in the first person. Some groups have introduced a recognized method by which the gathered congregation can test the prophecy; in others there is no testing whatever. Prophecies which are original in language, imagery or form, and which are compelling to listen to, seem to be rare. Often the same clichés of language and imagery are found as in ordinary preaching.

10. There is a recurrent tendency to supernatural visions, encounters with spirits, angels or Christ himself, though only among those groups which exercise gifts in an ecstatic manner.

11. The origin of Pentecostalism in the holiness movement may be recognized by a certain tendency to perfectionism. This turns the baptism with the Spirit into the "second blessing", reducing all those who have not received it to the rank of second-class Christians.

In a later part of this book we shall discuss the theology of the Pentecostals and compare it with the teaching of the New Testament. It has been necessary however to set out this tentative summary of their theological position at this point, so that we may see both the connections and the differences between Pentecostal theology and that of the charismatic movement.

What is the present size of the Pentecostal movement? None of the figures available are very accurate, firstly because the Pentecostals are the fastest growing branch of the Christian church today, and secondly because the movement is divided into very many splinter groups, which do not all produce statistics. Hollenweger produced the following figures in 1971:[61]

Africa (missionary churches)	1,277,500
Africa (African churches)	6,799,500
North America	3,170,000
Latin America	7,055,700
Europe	1,512,400
Asia (not including China)	1,350,000
Australia and Oceania	23,500

That makes a total of more than 21 million; if one adds the number of regular church attenders and sympathizers, one must assume that more than 30 million Christians are to be reckoned as connected with the Pentecostal movement, quite apart from the rapidly growing number of people from the traditional churches who follow the charismatic movement.

It is also by no means true that in every country Pentecostal churches are a small minority. In some countries, from numerical point of view, they have almost reached the proportions of a national church. The following table shows what percentage of each country's population must be reckoned as belonging to the Pentecostal movement:[62]

Chile	36.0%
South Africa	23.5%
Trinidad	23.0%
Jamaica	17.6%
Brazil	16.4%
Rhodesia	13.2%
Liberia	12.6%
Norway	5.7%
USA	4.9%
Finland	4.5%
Indonesia	3.1%
USSR	1.0%
West Germany	0.4%

In order to distinguish between the various groups of Pentecostals and charismatics and their differing theological views, Walter Hollenweger has further made the following analysis.[63]

1. Pentecostals who teach a way of salvation in two stages

Stage 1 is regeneration, stage 2 baptism with the Spirit. This is the category to which the majority of groups belong.

Assemblies of God (USA and Great Britain)
Assemblées de Dieu (France)
Elim Pentecostal Church (Great Britain)
Congregacao Crista do Brasil (Brazil)
Arbeitsgemeinschaft der Christengemeinden (Germany)
The majority of English and American charismatic movements

2. Pentecostals who teach a way of salvation in three stages

There are three steps: regeneration, sanctification and baptism with the Spirit.

Church of God (USA)
Pentecostal Holiness Church (USA)
Gemeinde Gottes (Germany)

3. "Jesus only" Groups

These groups baptize only in the name of Jesus and reject all Trinitarian formulas.

United Pentecostal Church (USA)
The majority of black Pentecostal churches in the USA
The majority of Indonesian Pentecostals

4. Independent Pentecostal Churches in Africa

The propriety of reckoning these among the Pentecostals is disputed, but since they practise e.g. speaking in tongues, they belong to them as far as their spirituality is concerned.
Zionists (South Africa)
Aladura, Seraphim and Cherubim Churches (West Africa)
Kimbangu (Zaire)

5. Pentecostals of the Apostolic Type

Here the offices of apostle and prophet are institutionalized.
Apostolic Churches (Denmark, France, Germany, Great Britain)
Gemeinde für Urchristentum (Switzerland)

6. Pentecostals and charismatics following the theology of a traditional church

These groups have retained their traditional theology, but have introduced in addition an emphasis on the exercise of charismatic gifts. They are familiar with the experience of baptism in the Spirit, but do not regard it as an essential stage in spiritual development.
Pentecostal movement in Chile (Methodist theology)
Christlicher Gemeinschaftsverband Mülheim/Ruhr (Reformed and Lutheran)
Charismatic movement in Germany and France (retaining the traditional theology of the churches from which individuals come, e.g. Lutheran, Reformed, Baptist)
Catholic movement of Charismatic Renewal (Roman Catholic)

The theological diversity of the Pentecostal movement makes it obvious that one should certainly not pass judgment on it blanket fashion, without making distinctions. In practice the distinction between the ecstatic and non-ecstatic exercise of gifts is of particular importance. It also makes a great difference what theological significance is attached to the charismatic experience. The charismatic movement has demonstrated that it is possible to harmonize charismatic experiences with the theology of almost any church. An answer to the theological questions which are raised by the Pentecostal movement will not be attempted until a later part of this book, since this will involve a careful comparison between the New Testament teaching and the theology and practice of both Pentecostalism and the charismatic movement.

CHAPTER FOUR

The Charismatic Movement

Dates and Events

To date no one has written a history of the charismatic movement. Nor, probably, is it really possible to do so, for we are still in the midst of the events. In order to give an outline of the most important stages in the development of this movement, I have in the section which follows brought together some of the more striking events in its life so far. I make no claim to completeness nor to having achieved a true balance. In the main I have used material about which I have some personal knowledge and with which I have been concerning myself during the last ten years.

I use the term "charismatic movement" to refer to groups whose members have had consciously charismatic experiences, and in which these experiences have become formative for the group life. I am omitting those belonging to Pentecostal denominations, even if they are small groups with only a weak ecclesiastical structure. Problems of differentiation are of course scarcely avoidable. This section will avoid any kind of comment: an outline of the chief theological emphases of the charismatic movement follows later.

1905
Founding of the *Bruderschaft vom gemeinsamen Leben* ("Brothers of the Common Life"), in which during the years which followed a rich charismatic life developed, though without any over-heightening of emotion or ecstasy. The majority of Protestant Brotherhoods and Sisterhoods in the post-war period had their origin in this evangelical community with its strong emphasis on the church.

1947
Founding of the *Evangelical Sisters of Mary* by Mother Basilea (Dr. Klara) Schlink. According to their own testimony charismatic experiences have played an important part in the life of this community, although they are very consciously integrated into the total experience of faith, with the result that like other

communities within the official Protestant Church they have never been regarded as a charismatic group.

1948
On Good Friday a revival in Schwarzenbach on the Saale led to the formation of the *Christusbruderschaft* ("Brotherhood of Christ"), which is now based in Selbitz. The brotherhood is firmly anchored to the Bavarian Lutheran Church, and combines in exceptional measure consciously charismatic experience with practical, down-to-earth service.

1951
David du Plessis, a Pentecostal pastor from South Africa, felt inwardly called, as he himself testifies,[64] to give his testimony before the leaders of the World Council of Churches. This was the first contact between the Pentecostals and the World Council, and it was of great significance for the charismatic movement in the traditional churches.

1953
Demos Shakarian, a rich Pentecostal businessman, founded the *Full Gospel Businessmen's Fellowship International*. Strictly speaking this group belongs to the Pentecostal movement, but it has played the role of an intermediary between Pentecostals and the charismatic movement.

1957
Beginning of the *Vuur Movement* in the Reformed Church of Holland (*vuur* = fire). This was probably the prototype of the new charismatic movement, since it combined the traditional theology of the Dutch Reformed Church with consciously charismatic experiences and an attempt to revive charismatic *offices*.

1958
The Pentecostal preacher David Wilkerson began his work among young drug addicts in New York. His book *The Cross and the Switchblade*, which describes his experiences in this work, was to become one of the motivating factors behind the Catholic movement of charismatic renewal.

1959
At Whitsuntide *Pope John XXIII*, announcing the Second Vatican Council, said that at this council "all bishops of the Church . . . are to be gathered together as at a new Pentecost".

Later he prayed: "Holy Spirit, sent by the Father in the name of Jesus, be present in the Church and lead her continually. We beseech you to pour out the fullness of your gifts on this ecumenical council. Renew your wonders in this our day. Give us a new Pentecost."[65]

1960
A sermon preached by *Dennis Bennett*, an Episcopalian priest in Van Nuys, California, on 3 April 1960, in which he said that he had received the baptism of the Holy Spirit and the gift of tongues, set off a chain reaction. Not long after this 700 members of his church had had the same experience. The press and the television gave the events full coverage, and even showed Bennett speaking in tongues. The way that these events acted as a kind of public signal has caused them generally to be regarded as the beginning of the charismatic movement in the U.S.A.

1961
Larry Christenson, a Lutheran pastor, experienced a charismatic breakthrough in his church at San Pedro, California. He maintained a closer adherence to the traditional theology of his church than Dennis Bennett.

1962
Arnold Bittlinger, a German Lutheran, went to the U.S.A. at the invitation of the Lutheran World Federation, and there met Larry Christenson and so came into contact with the new charismatic movement. On his return to Germany he related his experiences to various groups, in particular the religious communities and younger movements.

1962
Michael Harper, an Anglican priest in London, had similar personal experiences of a charismatic kind and founded the Fountain Trust, which became the most important rallying point of the charismatic movement in Great Britain.

1963
In August of this year Arnold Bittlinger invited some 80 leading figures from various groups and movements within the national church and the free churches in Germany to a conference at *Enkenbach* under the title "The work of the Holy Spirit today". Larry Christenson was invited to speak. The result was an outbreak of charismatic experiences in many groups and movements within German Protestantism. Together with the Charis-

matic Renewal in the Roman Catholic Church, the charismatic movement in German Protestantism has been the part least affected by classical Pentecostalism.

1965
At the invitation of Michael Harper, Dennis Bennett (who in the mean time had left his church because of growing tension over the charismatic phenomena) came to England for a lecture tour. He had the opportunity of visiting some of the most influential circles of the Church in England, and was invited by several bishops to address groups of clergy. As a result the charismatic movement gained ground rapidly in England, and was strongly influenced by the theology and experience of the movement in the U.S.A.

1965
In July a great ecumenical conference took place at *Königstein* on the subject of charismatic growth in the local church. The conference theme was "Church and Charisma". Among the speakers were Bishop Johannes and Dr. Paul Verghese from the Orthodox Church; Wilhelm Schamoni and Eugen Mederlet, O.F.M., from the Roman Catholic Church; Dr. R. F. Edel, Arnold Bittlinger, Michael Harper, Larry Christenson and Dr. Walter Hollenweger from the Protestant Churches; and Wilhard Becker from the Free Churches.

1966
The great revival began in *Indonesia,* with its centre at Batu Bible Institute. This revival has developed a rich charismatic life, with very independent features of its own. It does not emphasize speaking in tongues.

1966
Study of the Acts of the Apostles and the book *The Cross and the Switchblade* by David Wilkerson caused Roman Catholic professors and students at *Duquesne University, Pittsburgh,* to be confronted with the question of the existence of charisms in the present-day church.

1967
In February of this year the *Pittsburgh Group* met for a weekend conference to do some study on the Holy Spirit. Members of the Protestant charismatic movement were also present and took part. They remained together in prayer from 10pm until 5am next morning. During this time some obviously

charismatic experiences occurred. "Some praised God in unknown languages, others quietly wept for joy, others prayed and sang."[66] This occasion formed the beginning of the movement of *Charismatic Renewal* in the Catholic Church.

1967
What has become known as the *Jesus Movement* arose in various places in the U.S.A. Little detailed research has been done into the connection between the Jesus People and the charismatic movement, but in some cases the young people known in the press as Jesus People have had charismatic experiences.

1968
In the summer of this year the *Lebenszentrum für die Einheit der Christen* (Life Centre for Christian Unity) was founded at Schloss Craheim in Lower Franconia (Germany). Here live and work together the Catholic Eugen Mederlet, OFM, the Protestants Dr. R. F. Edel and Arnold Bittlinger, and the Baptists Wilhard Becker and Siegfried Grossmann. There has been a development of thoroughly charismatic experiences and Schloss Craheim has become one of the important centres of the charismatic movement in Germany.

1969
From April 25-27 at *Notre Dame University*, South Bend, Indiana, there took place the first meeting of members of the Charismatic Renewal in the Catholic Church to attract supporters of the movement from all over the U.S.A. 450 took part.

1969
On 14 November the American Roman Catholic bishops issued a declaration concluding that the charismatic renewal movement should not be hindered at that point in its development.[67]

1970
19-21 June the second annual conference of the Roman Catholic movement of Charismatic Renewal took place, with 1,279 participants.

1971
4,500 people took part in the third annual conference of the Charismatic Renewal, 18-20 June. Among the participants were supporters of the movement from Australia, Korea and Israel, and two Catholic bishops: Bishop Stephen A. Leven and Bishop

Joseph C. McKinney.

1972
The fourth annual conference brought together more than 11,000 people in the campus of Notre Dame, 2-4 June.

1972
In Zürich-Horgen, 20-24 June, a meeting took place between the Roman Catholic Secretariat for Christian Unity, leading members of several Pentecostal churches, and leading representatives of the charismatic movement. In the chair were the Pentecostal pastor David du Plessis and the Roman Catholic Kilian McDonnell.

1972
About a hundred representatives of the charismatic movement from England, Scandinavia, Holland, Germany, Switzerland, Austria, Italy, France, South Africa, Australia, Canada and the U.S.A. met at Schloss Craheim, 26-30 June. The participants came from national Protestant churches, and the Roman Catholic and Orthodox Churches, as well as from Protestant free churches and the Pentecostals.

1972
At the end of the year three theological study conferences took place in rapid succession at Schwerte, Berne and Munich, at which well-known Protestant and Catholic theologians met to think about the question of the Holy Spirit and the modern charismatic outbreaks. These conferences resulted in the book *Erfahrung und Theologie des Heiligen Geistes*,[68] to which among others K. Rahner, W. Schmithals, H. Schlier, O. Dilschneider, W. Pannenberg, J. Ratzinger, H. Mühlen, H. R. Müller-Schwefe and A. Bittlinger made contributions.

1973
The fifth annual conference of the Catholic Charismatic Renewal took place at Notre Dame, 1-3 June, and brought together over 22,000 people. The plenary sessions took place in the football stadium in the presence of Cardinal Suenens, including the final mass at which 500 priests concelebrated.

1973
9-13 October, 130 delegates from 34 countries met in Grottaferrata, near Rome, for the first international conference of the Catholic movement for Charismatic Renewal. Among them

were Cardinal Suenens and Bishop McKinney. At an audience held for 11 representatives of this conference, Pope Paul VI said: "We rejoice with you, dear friends, at the renewal of spiritual life manifested in the Church today, in different forms and in various environments."[69]

1974
3-5 March, a world conference on the Holy Spirit took place in Jerusalem, which was attended by representatives both of the Pentecostal churches and of charismatic groups within the mainstream churches. Influential personalities at this conference included David du Plessis and Kathryn Kuhlmann.

1974
280 leaders of the Charismatic Renewal in the Catholic Church from 16 Latin American countries met at Bogota.

1974
The seventh conference of the Catholic Charismatic Renewal in the U.S.A. was held in the football stadium at Notre Dame. The magazine *Time* reported: "First, men in business suits or sports coats carrying banners aloft: THE SPIRIT OF JESUS AMONG US emerging from the football team's tunnel on to the Notre Dame field; then the double moving line of priests in white robes and clerical stoles singing; their arms raised heavenward, hands open, palms up. The excitement of the crowd built, issuing into applause. Then as eight Roman Catholic bishops followed by Léon-Joseph, Cardinal Suenens of Belgium . . . came into view, the clapping exploded into a mighty roar. From 25,000 voices 'Alleluia! Alleluia!' rocked the stadium."[70]

1974
1,400 people came to the "congress with an open door" held near Chalon-sur-Saône and organized by leading members of the French charismatic movement.

1974
A new memorandum from the American Catholic bishops again spoke positively about the Charismatic Renewal, but was more careful to point out the dangers clearly than did the first one. Emphasis was laid on the need to integrate groups already existing into church structures, so that effective communication might be maintained.[71]

1975
John Stott, a leader among evangelicals in England, called for a fruitful dialogue with the charismatic movement. Stott regretted on the one hand the fact that in past years the two movements had avoided one another, and gave his support to more thorough-going dialogue; but on the other hand he defined the points over which there are serious disagreements between evangelicals and charismatics.

1975
At Whitsun 10,000 Catholics from 63 countries met for the third international congress of the Catholic Renewal in Rome. Cardinal Suenens celebrated the Eucharist at St. Peter's, with 750 priests and 12 bishops concelebrating. "This was the first charismatic service St. Peter's had seen. Pentecostal 'singing in the Spirit' echoed around the huge building; a layman spoke a prophecy 'as Christ's representative' which was 'confirmed in its authenticity' by long applause from the whole congregation."[72]

1975
By now 3,500 Catholic prayer groups, with more than 400,000 members, exist throughout the world, in 50 different countries. Other estimates speak of half a million Catholic charismatics. In West Germany there are said to be 150 groups with 6,000 members, in France 400 groups with 20,000 members. No exact figures are available for the Protestant groups, and in any case the borderline between charismatics and Pentecostals is a fluid one. Probably the numbers are somewhat lower than those of the Catholic Charismatic Renewal, but of a similar order.

1976
29 February — 3 March, the newly formed *Evangelisch-theologische Koordinierungsausschuss* (Theological co-ordinating committee for the Protestant national church) of the Charismatic Renewal met at Würzburg. There theological guidelines were worked out which make it clear that the aim is a theological and practical integration of the Charismatic Renewal in the Protestant Church into the life of the existing churches.

1976
In the Southern Baptist Convention there are some 20,000 members who have active contact with the charismatic movement. Some 100 churches can be described as charismatic churches. The association in the State of Texas has expelled two

charismatic churches. The North American Baptist Federation concludes that the charismatic movement "often brings together its followers from across denominational frontiers, but frequently divides members of a local chuch from one another."[73]

1976
From 11-14 October the council of the Methodist Central Conference of Europe held a congress at Arnoldshain on the theme "Charisma and Renewal of the Church". The conference emphasized that every Christian has charismatic gifts, and recommended that greater liberty ought to be given for their expression in the local churches.

Theological Assessment

Our historical survey reveals so many links between Pentecostalism and the charismatic movement that it is difficult to draw a clear dividing line between them. At the same time the differences in theology and charismatic practice are so great that the two movements cannot simply be brought together under a single heading. We must look for a screen which will make it easier to see finer differentiations than the broad categories of "classical Pentecostalism" and "new charismatic movement" allow.

The only unambiguous distinction between classical Pentecostalism and the new charismatic movement lies in the fact that Pentecostalism has developed clear denominational structures of its own, whereas the charismatic groups have remained within their churches and have so far been allowed to remain there. But this is to say nothing of their theological position. The *Christlicher Gemeinschaftsverband Mülheim/Ruhr*, for example, adheres theologically much more strongly to the Reformed tradition than to the theology of classical Pentecostalism; yet because it has it own denominational structure, it is counted as a Pentecostal Church. On the other hand great parts of the Protestant charismatic movement in the U.S.A., e.g. the groups influenced by Bennett, ought to be reckoned as belonging theologically to Pentecostalism. They are however regarded as part of the charismatic movement because they have not formed themselves into a separate denomination.

My starting point is that the theological principles of a group are of much greater importance for purposes of classification than questions of denominational allegiance. Hence in the following paragraphs I shall make theology the chief factor in drawing up my categories, although differences of denominational structure will also be considered as a minor point. This way of looking at the question leads me to find two main groups, each of which must be further sub-divided. At the same time I should like to stress that any classification can only be approximate, since many of the dividing lines are fluid.

1. The Pentecostal Movement

In this category I class all groups which have adopted as their main emphasis the theology of classical Pentecostalism, teaching that baptism in the Holy Spirit is a separate stage along the way of salvation, and that it is always evidenced by speaking in tongues. Usually only the nine gifts mentioned in 1 Cor. 12:8-10 are recognized as gifts of the Spirit. Baptism with the Spirit, with the implication of a two- or three-stage salvation, and the exercise of the Corinthians *charismata*, are regarded as sufficient grounds for separation, whether to form a denominational structure of their own, or to exist as a Pentecostal group within one of the traditional churches. Charismatic activity takes a highly emotional form, and spectacular gifts like prophecy, healing and speaking in tongues receive the most attention.

In developing this kind of life the Pentecostal movement has departed from the basic teaching of the New Testament in two important respects. In the first place the doctrine of Spirit baptism as an independent stage along the way of salvation reduces the role of regeneration and in effect makes Spirit baptism the central experience of the spiritual life. Here an idea of stages has been introduced which is totally foreign to the New Testament: the born-again Christian is at the first, general stage of being a Christian, which will it is true bring him salvation, but which will not equip him for a power-filled spiritual life; only the person who has been baptized in the Spirit reaches the higher stage of being a really authentic Christian, a category reserved for a chosen group.

Moreover the full range of *charismata*, emphasized over and over again by St. Paul, is effectively narrowed down to the nine gifts named in 1 Cor. 12:8-10, in other words to those gifts which tend to be associated with fanaticism and open to emotional deviations, and to those which emphasize the word rather than action.

As a result of this, exaggerated pressure is put upon Christians to expect the longed-for baptism with the Spirit. This has led to whole strategies being developed to help people prepare themselves, by human effort, for reception of the baptism. These may even include the suggestion that certain verbal exercises will make it easier to receive the gift of glossolalia. The expectation of a baptism in the Spirit experienced in a highly emotional way, and the limitation of charismatic gifts to include only those mentioned in 1 Cor. 12:8-10, has led in many Pentecostal churches and in some charismatic groups to a fanatical tendency in the spiritual life. This is understandable enough when one considers the largely unemotional and over-intellectual character of the church, but the effects on the individual Christian and on the life of the church are highly dubious, since they are often associated with a departure from sound teaching and practical Christian living.

Part II of this book will discuss the theological questions in detail, while in Part III we shall try to find a true balance which avoids the dangers both of "over-heating" and of "under-cooling" in the exercise of charismatic gifts.

1. 1 Classical Pentecostalism

In this category I place those groups of Pentecostals who have formed denominations of their own. In official church circles they have been regarded as sects, and they for their part strongly reject the national churches. "When the Babylonian character becomes still more clearly and transparently evident, the last of those who belong to Jesus will leave the church — unless they wish to be judged along with her."[74] Among others this group includes the following: Assemblies of God, Elim Pentecostal Churches, several Brazilian Pentecostal Churches, the Church of God, the Pentecostal Holiness Church, the United Pentecostal Church, many of the black Pentecostal churches in the U.S.A. and of the independent Pentecostal churches of Africa, and in Germany the *Arbeitsgemeinschaft der Christengemeinden*, the *Volksmission entschiedener Christen*, the *Gemeinde Gottes*, the Apostolic Church in Germany *(Urchristliche Mission)*, and many "house churches".

1. 2 Neo-Pentecostalism

Some of the groups which come under the general label of the "charismatic movement" derive their basic theological doctrines and their manner of exercising charismatic gifts from classical Pentecostalism. Some things are differently formulated, or even adapted outwardly to the patterns of the traditional churches but in the central issues of their theology and of the activity of the Spirit these groups are nearer to classical Pentecostalism than to their native churches. I categorize as neo-Pentecostal the greater part of the Protestant charismatic movement in the U.S.A., e.g. the groups associated with the names of Dennis Bennett and Merlin Carothers; the Full Gospel Businessmen's Fellowship International; the greater part of the charismatic movement in the United Kingdom (although *Michael Harper* disagrees with the Pentecostals on some points); and a considerable proportion of the Jesus People both in the U.S.A. and in Europe, where they claim definite charismatic experiences. Many smaller groups might be mentioned as well, but it is safe to say that a substantial part of the charismatic movement in Germany, France and Holland is more properly classified under the heading of "charismatic renewal".

2. Charismatic Renewal

Under this heading I want to include all those groups which in their theology and manner of expressing charismatic gifts have gone a different way from the Pentecostals. It is however difficult to classify accurately each individual group, because there are many links between the theology of Pentecostalism and the position of the Charismatic Renewal, and some groups have not taken up a clearly defined position.

In so far as the expression "baptism in the Spirit" is used in the Charismatic Renewal Movement, it refers not to an independent stage in the way of salvation but rather to a realization of the Holy Spirit's indwelling and to an awakening of the charismatic powers which were given to the Christian when he was born again, but which only now — often as a result of some kind of breakthrough experience — begin to function. (The reason why such a breakthrough experience occurs at all, often a long time after a person has been born again, is that in the traditional life of the churches there is scarcely any expectation of the visible working of the Holy Spirit.) The gift of tongues is seen as one gift among many: relatively common, it is true, but not overemphasized and generally restricted to private use. There is an expectation of all the *charismata* mentioned in the New Testament, not solely those of 1 Cor. 12:8-10. Spectacular gifts are not excluded, but they are exercised quietly and in moderation, and so divested of their spectacular (and surely human) overtones. The theologians of the Charismatic Renewal are working at integrating their experiences into the theology of their respective churches. They are striving to find a middle way which will avoid both the *obsession with the Spirit* characteristic of Pentecostalism and the *forgetfulness of the Spirit* which has characterized the traditional theology and life of the mainstream churches.

2. 1 Churches of the Charismatic Renewal

To this category belongs a relatively small number of churches which do not on the one hand adopt the theology and practice of classical Pentecostalism, but which on the other hand have developed clear denominational structures. In the U.S.A. there are some Pentecostal churches with a Quaker theological tradition, and the greater part of the Pentecostal movement in Chile is based on the theology and church organization of Methodism. In Germany the *Christlicher Gemeinschaftsverband Mülheim/Ruhr* returned after an initial period of uncertainty to the theology of the Reformation, but finds itself isolated both by the Pentecostals and by the traditional churches. It is also a special case in another respect, in that it does not have a thoroughgoing denominational structure: those who join are not required to leave the churches to which they have hitherto belonged. Nevertheless it does in practice have a quasi-denominational organization, for which reason it is included here among the churches of the Charismatic Renewal.

2. 2 The movement towards Charismatic Renewal of the Churches

In the majority of groups charismatic experiences were not much reflected upon at first, and to some extent the terminology of the old Pentecostal movement was unthinkingly used to describe them. Separate groups were formed because there was no opportunity given for charismatic expression in the churches to which the members belonged. Today however most of the groups we are about to mention are on the way to becoming integrated into their own churches. Many responsible church leaders probably opened up the way to integration at first only because they feared splits and extremism. Since then it has become evident that the charismatic renewal in the traditional churches has raised some fundamental questions, e.g. the question of making a personal decision for Christ, the relationship of charismatic gifts to offices in the church, or to the sacraments, the distinction between clergy and laity, and even the possibility of overcoming Christianity's division into different denominations. These questions conceal some very explosive issues, so that if the integration of the charismatic renewal continues and is successfully achieved, we must expect some changes in the original churches.

The group which is both numerically the greatest and has the greatest influence upon its native church is the Charismatic Renewal in the Catholic Church. Everywhere this is involved in developing a church-integrated theology. It is unequivocally under episcopal control, and it has the support of the Pope. Among Protestant groups in the U.S.A. and in the United Kingdom only fairly small groups belong within this classification, such as those which have been influenced by Larry Christenson. The category of charismatic renewal further includes the Indonesian revival, the Dutch *Vuur* movement and most of the charismatic movement in France. In Germany many communities, brotherhoods and sisterhoods have had charismatic experiences of the sort associated with charismatic renewal, as have also the groups influenced by Arnold Bittlinger and the Enkenbach conference mentioned above, the *Lebenszentrum* at Schloss Craheim, and the *Rufer* movement, through which charismatic experiences have flowed widely into the evangelical free churches. In East Germany mention should be made of the charismatic movement which emanated from the *Schniewindhaus* and the late Pastor Jansa. Today there are strong links between the Charismatic Renewal movements in the Catholic and Protestant Churches, and these have found expression in some joint publications. Both movements have set up their own information centres.[75]

Effects of the Movement

The emergence of the neo-Pentecostal movement and of the movement for Charismatic Renewal can today no longer be regarded as a passing fashion at the fringe of the churches. It has set in motion developments which have raised new questions in many of the traditional churches. Although everything is still in a state of flux, this chapter should not close without some attempt to sketch in some of the important effects of the charismatic movement.

1. The classical Pentecostal churches have changed in the esteem of the traditional churches from being regarded as a sect to being welcomed as a partner. True, most of the theological reservations remain, but one can no longer pretend that the other side does not exist, since the new charismatic phenomena in the larger churches are suddenly indicating some common ground which was not there before. At various levels, therefore, a new dialogue has begun, in many cases for the first time. There are conversations within the framework of the World Council of Churches; there are a great number of bilateral relationships; and finally there are consultations between the Roman Catholic Church, the Charismatic Renewal and classical Pentecostalism. It is already becoming clear for all to see that classical Pentecostalism is slowly emerging from its ghetto. Phenomena like speaking in tongues and healing are suddenly

news and are being discussed quite openly. When a bishop speaks in tongues, it is no longer so easy to write off the ordinary man in the street as backward and over-emotional. Will the new contacts between the Pentecostal movement and the traditional churches now lead to the opening of those mutual discussions which ought really to have taken place 70 years ago?

2. The Pentecostal churches and the charismatic renewal movement are both overwhelmingly evangelical in their doctrine of scripture and in their spirituality. Thus, by the roundabout route of the charismatic movement, a new Pietism has invaded the great churches, be they Lutheran, Reformed, Anglican or Catholic. Links are even being established with the Orthodox Church. Interesting new questions have arisen, especially in those areas where Pietism in its new, charismatic form has penetrated churches of a totally different tradition, such as the Roman Catholic Church.

3. Baptism in the Spirit, understood as a personal experience and frequently an emotional one, is in many traditional churches touching on an area which has received little attention before. This is the area of personal experiences in faith, of conscious, personal decision and a definite act of commitment, of personal relationship with Jesus, of free, personally formulated prayer and of private Bible study. The charismatic groups have suddenly discovered from their own experience the meaning of what is known in evangelical circles as "conversion". While they have been unwilling to accept the whole of evangelical theology, they have felt it necessary to subject this new experience to theological reflection. In the Charismatic Renewal movement in Germany the term "conversion", with its pietistic overtones, is gradually being replaced by the expression, "fundamental Christian experience".

An information leaflet about charismatic renewal in the Catholic Church begins thus:

> The charismatic renewal is a form of evangelization in which on the basis of the common priesthood of all believers Christians lead each other by means of their personal witness to the faith to a direct encounter with Christ himself. Its essence is the conversion that is a necessary pre-requisite for baptism, a missionary liturgy, and the renewal of the Spirit.
>
> Many people who are Christians merely by virtue of infant baptism and their upbringing have found their lives changed by the personal growth prompted by this renewal.
>
> They talk about God and Christ on the basis of a real personal encounter and are set free to bear personal witness to their faith in a world that has grown indifferent or even hostile to Christianity.

> Many, often to their own surprise, experience in themselves a new love for scripture and for prayer, a new openness to other people's problems and needs and for a social commitment founded in Christian motivation.[76]

The same statement goes on to say later:

> "Conversion is the renewal of our human spirit, of our emotion, will, intellect, of our whole person, in the power of the Holy Spirit. Its starting-point is surrender to God's plan and will, and an initial acceptance of one's own death — the latter the pre-condition for all charismatic activity . . . such conversion is something that takes place at a very profound level in our lives and that cannot be repeated with the same effect but nevertheless must continually be renewed."[77]

4. Now that the charismatic movement can no longer be overlooked by the great churches, theology too has been carried along with the tide. Genuine, lasting integration of charismatic experience into the various church traditions demands new theological work in the field of pneumatology. The challenge this presents has in fact already had some evident effects. The Holy Spirit has once more become an important subject in the most recent theology. It is still too early to give even an outline summary of how this latest theological theme is being handled. One can only hope that it is not merely a theological fashion. For the experiences of the charismatic movement are there, and with them the challenge to explore their meaning.

5. There is another point as well at which theology has been drawn along by the charismatic tide, and that is in the field of ecclesiology. This is not quite so obvious, because the urgency of this subject has long been recognized. Heribert Mühlen describes very emphatically the task which has arisen. For him the most important characteristics of our time are a communal experience of God based upon personal encounter with Jesus Christ, and the movement towards a community church of convinced Christians. He writes: "What is happening in the newly formed prayer groups is not in any sense a return to an idealized primitive church without regard to history, but a historically motivated response to a world which has become secularized in the bad sense, or to an atheism which is the product of theological development. Only when we have realized that modern atheism represents an attack upon the fundamentals of Christianity shall we be able to recognize the truly foundation-laying and renewing power which is at work in the renewal of the charisms."[78]

6. One final point remains to be made: the charismatic movement is leading in many places to a new *ecumenism of*

experience. For a long time the main emphasis was upon an *ecumenism of theologians and church leaders*, in which the attempt was made to reconcile the doctrinal systems of the various churches. This was in turn succeeded to a large extent by an *ecumenism of world changers*, which attempted to find the one church by tackling the problems of the one world. Today the individual initiatives which really are breaking new ground seem to be based on an ecumenism of experience. Of course there have always been common experiences of faith — for example in the Second World War — but they have arisen from unusual situations. Today members of churches as far apart in tradition as the Roman Catholic, the Lutheran and the Protestant free churches are experiencing a common crossing of barriers from stiff, churchy forms of church life to new, spiritual experiences. In comparison with the new, spiritual experiences which these people have in common, the divergent doctrines which each has brought along seem to be of secondary importance. What will result from this new ecumenism of experience is not yet clear, but it should be carefully watched, for it will probably prove to be the driving force of ecumenism in the years ahead.

All in all the charismatic movement and the Pentecostal movement present a variegated and confusing picture. Some find this a positive aspect, a sign of the many-sidedness of the Holy Spirit's work. At the same time I believe that when we are faced with such a wide range of theological insights and actual experiences, it is also a sign that much that is merely human has flowed into this new charismatic stream. Whenever such a mixing takes place it results in a clouding of issues and tendencies to extremism. The question then arises: where is there a danger that, because of unscriptural teaching and practice, situations will develop which could open the gate to forces opposed to God?

In 1907 the evangelist Elias Schrenk, then 76 years of age, wrote in great concern: "If we look back at many movements of the Spirit in the last few centuries, we get the impression that God's hand was stretched out mightily to bless. But His church showed herself insufficiently mature to receive the blessing and to retain it . . . Shall we this time pass the test?"[79] The church of those days did not pass the test. Schrenk later disassociated himself from the Pentecostal movement which arose out of the split in 1909, because it had become too extreme.

CHAPTER FIVE

The Charismatic Movement and the Spirit of the Age

The charismatic movement ought not to be considered without reference to contemporary trends of thought. The Holy Spirit works within the situation which he finds among men. Since every awakening contains both Spirit-given and merely human elements, it is important to know the intellectual climate within which an awakening occurs, with what currents of thought it is associated, and against what trends in contemporary life it opposes itself. In what follows I shall describe only those trends which have some connection with the charismatic movement.

The various intellectual movements, aims, hopes and anxieties of our day are characterized by a deep-going *crisis of orientation*.Our world has become so complicated that even the experts can no longer understand it thoroughly, since their competence is confined to a limited field. Moreover any kind of orientation requires firm and immovable points of reference. Today there is a far-reaching lack of generally accepted values and norms. And so hopes, promises and expectations for the future are beginning to lose their lustre, and frustration is on the increase. The philosopher Günter Rohrmoser comments: "A far-reaching change is clearly discernable in the fundamental attitude of our age in relation to its future. It will not be possible for much longer to escape by means of utopian expectations from the insecurity caused by the disintegration of all traditional standards of reference."[80]

What are the reasons for this crisis of orientation? Futurologists discovered one of the causes some time ago. They call it "accelerating change". Even the layman is able to observe that changes follow one another with ever increasing rapidity. Social changes which formerly took decades now take place in a year or two. If circumstances are changing faster and faster, new knowledge is also more quickly outdated. Scarcely is a new piece of knowledge developed to the point where it can be put into practical use, before it is overtaken by other developments. As the rate of change accelerates, anxiety about the future grows, because more and more frequently one finds that people are unable to cope with the changes — whether they be in economics or politics, work or leisure, marriage and the family, or the search for personal identity in the face of changes which tumble over one another. Thus the scene is set for a conflict of orientation.

Two areas of development in particular have severely shaken people's faith in the progress of mankind. Uninhibited industrialization and the plundering of earth's resources have so fundamentally destroyed the ecological balance of nature that many experts believe it can no longer be restored. Herbert Gruhl emphasizes the seriousness of the situation when he writes: "Therefore those nations which continue to pursue the fetish of growth will be the first to find themselves faced with unexpected disaster, unless they resolve to destroy others — in other words to conduct wars of extermination."[81] While the pollution of the environment has made the conflict of orientation a political issue, there is a parallel development, more closely related to the personality, which today is already affecting the individual at a very personal level. Jürgen vom Scheidt calls this "pollution of the inner world" (*Innenweltverschmutzung*).[82] By this he means the poisoning of the human mind by false feelings, deceptive hopes and unreal fantasies. As the most significant symptoms he mentions dependence upon drugs, psychosomatic illnesses, neuroses, mental disorders and the polluting effect of the media, e.g. through advertising and television. All these phenomena are signs of the inner crisis of orientation.

The problems of orientation have a particularly strong penetrating power because most people lack the personal protection of religious experience. Many people have substituted belief in progress for the Christian faith they have lost, and now that this new faith is in the process of being destroyed the situation has become explosive. "The latest 'religion' of mankind — followed with equal devotion by capitalist and communist — is faith in material progress. Today, in the light of hard facts, we see the dissolution and reduction to zero of this faith."[83] The younger generation especially, being generally more sensitive to the spirit of an age than their elders, who have adapted themselves to it, has responded to the orientation conflict in a variety of ways. Our media often over-simplify by calling this reaction a flight from the society based on achievement, because this is the aspect which is in fact most evident. In reality this flight is frequently a despairing cry for help in finding the way. People drop out of a society which has become complex in the hope of making for themselves a simple world, only to discover that this does not bring them the happiness they hoped for when they set out on their search. Superficially it looks like a mere fashion, but for many it is a sign of genuine despair.

The magazine *Der Spiegel* (no. 8/1972) describes the situation in terms which emphasize the religious aspects: "After pilgrimages to Marx and Mao, Buddha and Krishna, after excursions into black magic, Satanism and agriculture, after a total self-surrender to sex and drugs, and after a painful awakening from the illusions of revolution and narcotic fantasies, part of the rock and pop generation in its flight from the achievement-orientated society has now arrived in biblical Galilee. For, as the LSD saint Timothy Leary has already preached to them, 'the only purpose in life is the search for God'."[84] But the middle-aged and older generation also shows clear signs of having been shaken by the crisis of orientation. The increase in psychosomatic diseases, the loss of certainty about sexual roles, the growth in the divorce rate, the increasing incidence of mid-life crisis, the breaking-off of careers because of a lack of self-confidence and the sharp increase in alcoholism are signs of a universal crisis of orientation, affecting people of every generation.

Two basic attitudes to life have developed which look contradictory, but which are frequently found in combination. The ever-increasing perfection of life, if one looks at the surface only, has led to a largely unconscious *claim of a right to be happy*. The social services must be tied up until the net is absolutely secure, for every problem there must be some kind of advice and solution, for every bodily ailment there must be an appropriate medicine, every future uncertainty must be nullified by taking out an insurance. The thought of death, which is a factor not catered for by the general perfection of medical remedies — the most one can do is to postpone it — must be suppressed. It has become one of the strongest taboos of our time. There is a claim to perfect happiness in the inner life as well: emotional imbalance, exhaustion, nervousness as a result of strain — all may be overcome by taking the right tablets. The claim to happiness has led to conditions of life in which certain areas of the personality which are necessary to life are unable to develop because of over-indulgence.

Parallel to this claim of a right to happiness there seems to be a deep feeling of *purposelessness*. One reason for this is that the realities of life come nowhere near to satisfying the demand for happiness. Secondly, over-indulgence has prevented the capacities of will-power, perseverance and meaningful adaptation to actual circumstances from being properly developed, so that it is scarcely possible to take even one step towards the achievement of a goal. In addition there is the absence of a real spirituality, which alone can give someone an abiding sense of purpose — for unless we pass beyond our human level of existence to the level of *transcendence*, no real purpose can become evident.

Viktor E. Frankl describes the basic situation in the following way: "Today we psychiatrists have fewer problems with the classical forms of neurosis than we do with a new type, of which . . . the most obvious characteristics are an absence of interests and a lack of initiative . . . weakness of motivation is characteristic of the neurosis of today. The underlying cause, according to my own research, is a bottomless feeling of meaninglessness . . . It would be equally true to say that today it is no longer the case, as it was in the days of Sigmund Freud, that neurosis is the result of the sexual frustration which his psycho-analysis so often revealed as the root cause. Today's neurosis is in many cases a result of an *existential* frustration, the lack of fulfilment for the human need for as meaningful a life as possible."[85]

It is understandable that many people react to this crisis of orientation and meaning by flight: flight from respectability, flight into drug addiction (not forgetting alcohol, the most widely available drug), flight into unrealistic philosophies or political ideologies, flight from marriage, and finally, most radical of all, flight from life itself. Others, especially young people, react by protest. There are several levels of protest, from wearing a beard or unconventional clothes to taking part in demonstrations, and on in perilous escalation to the extreme of underground terrorism. The protest movement, which began in the universities, is one of the most significant indications of the orientation conflict; taken together with the drug scene, probably the most significant. Hermann Lübbe analyzes it as follows: "The new youth movement has been from its outset a religiously motivated movement. In saying this I do not mean to deny or even question the political aspects. But the motivation behind political engagement was from the start religiously structured. It included mourning for the world, i.e. society as a whole; the search for a teaching which would answer all questions about the origins and future of society; the identification or unmasking of the real enemy of mankind, who opposes the eschatological dawn of the new age; the suppression of reason and pragmatism and adoption of fanaticism; the refusal to be taught and contradiction of reality."[86]

In addition to flight and protest there are many attempts to develop new religions without God. Led by the correct apprehension that meaning in life has something to do with transcending our human sphere of existence, many people have arrived at the wrong destination and have turned experiments with extra-sensory experiences into a substitute religion. Others have gone in the opposite direction and have tried to find spiritual guidance by means of meditation. As a method of crossing the barriers which separate us from our own inner life meditation can of course be thoroughly helpful, because it can enable us to form balanced judgments about ourselves and about the world, but it is not capable of solving existential questions. Another concept which means a great deal to people today is creativity. The same is true here as in the case of meditation: creativity can play an extremely important part in the development of a person's individual gifts; it can contribute to inner release and to wholeness; but it is incapable of solving questions like that of the meaning and basic purpose of life.

From all the many contemporary trends I would like to pick out one more attempt to solve the crisis of orientation: the group. Without any doubt man is so inherently social in his make-up that without the orientation given by a relationship between two people, or a family, or a group, he is scarcely likely to find his way within the greater world of society at large. How strong among young people, especially, the longing is to find a group which will be their real home, we may see from the disquieting upsurge of cults or youth religions like the Unification Church (Moonites), the International Society of Krishna Consciousness, the Children of God, or Transcendental Meditation. All these movements offer meaning and orientation through a simple doctrine which answers all questions, and which at the same time promises through a course of intensive and generally very expensive exercises the achievement of a state of happiness. Even more interesting however is the fact that all these new youth religions force upon their members a radical group discipline, demanding absolute obedience, total separation from their previous environment, and total surrender of their possessions and ability to work. The great number of young people who join these groups gives clear evidence of the extent to which the spiritual movements of the present day have been produced and shaped by the crisis of orientation. For only in a situation of disorientation from which there is no escape would anyone be prepared to enter a state of total dependence. Perhaps they do so for the very reason that it means a complete break with the familiar freedom of their life hitherto, which has failed to free them from their orientation conflicts.

What answer has the church to give to the crisis of orientation which expresses itself in these currents of thought, anxieties and inappropriate attempts to find solutions? Here again we cannot go into all the many attempts at reform and restructuring of the churches. We can only outline the main ways in which the churches have reacted to the spiritual situation of our times. Though there are some differences, it is generally true to say that the traditional churches have all given verbal replies.

In the Protestant churches, which have always felt themselves to be "churches of the word", the answer has been very polished, intellectually motivated and culturally up-to-date. The result is clear if one takes a glance at the statistics: nowhere are the churches so empty today as in the Protestant churches of Europe. The Catholic Church has fared somewhat better, in that in the sacrament it offers a kind of sign of the experiential presence of God, but on the whole it has been unable to make the sacred, tradition-laden status of the sacraments relevant to the experience of modern man. Here too the consequences are easy to see: churches are less well-filled, priests are losing confidence and in increasing numbers abandoning their vocation, and even the monasteries are no longer able to attract enough novices. Groups of Christians having an evangelical and therefore originally experience-centred background have likewise verbalized and analyzed the central experience of conversion, out of a fear of emotion. Here too in many cases stagnation has set in.

Ernst Benz interprets these facts as a historical development: "Every genuine religious experience is in essence an experience of the *presence* of God . . . of contact in the here and now with the overwhelming, joy-bringing, terrifying, saving and judging power of the transcendent. The traditional, church-centred Christianity of today, which has undergone a lengthy process of theologizing, historical analysis and intellectualization, sees this presence as being mediated by the word. But the word itself has undergone a certain devaluation. The word which is meant to mediate the presence of God has been reduced to the level of colourless information."[87] Something similar has happened with the sacrament. "The sacrament also, especially in Western Christianity, has been talked to death and devalued by progressive theologizing, in the increasingly determined attempt to interpret the mystery of the Eucharist in rational categories."[88]

The progress of mankind, which had its origins in scientific knowledge, has become bogged down by the problems of pollution in the environment and in the inner life. The progressive rationalization of the Christian faith has led it too into a similar cul-de-sac. The blind cannot lead the blind — and therefore it is understandable that when modern man is faced with a crisis of orientation and meaning, he does not go to the church for the answer. Rather he seeks out substitute religions which promise him the presence of God, even if the God in question is only a substitute deity created by men. Because of the rationalistic watering down of the Christian faith which has been going on in increasing measure for centuries now, emotional outbreaks have been blazing with ever-increasing intensity at the church's walls, e.g. the Pentecostal movement and the multitude of sects both large and small which appeared at the beginning of the 20th century.

The great shake-up brought about by the Second World War resulted in the appearance in post-war Europe of many new religious communities, brotherhoods and sisterhoods, which re-discovered the area of religious experience within the frame-work of a firm community life. Loosely organized movements also appeared in the Protestant free churches, and in groups like the Y.M.C.A., because there a certain measure of living fellow-ship had been preserved at the local level. Everywhere there were the first signs of a new awakening, moving Alfons Rosen-berg to a prophetic utterance: ". . .the Church as the great brotherhood, which will be built up out of countless cells con-sisting of free or disciplined brotherhoods and sisterhoods — a type of fellowship among Christians which is much closer to the pattern of the gospels than is the hierarchical structure of the church. As church history shows, the latter could only really be established and maintained on the basis of continual violation of the commands given to us in the gospels. But in the future it will at last be possible to give the full stamp of official recog-nition to the many attempts to organize Christianity in the form of a brotherhood, which in the past have remained outside the legal structures of the church or have been declared heretical."[89]

These unresolved questions have been made relevant and topical once more by the "Jesus movement" — for suddenly here was a movement displaying overflowing emotion, deeply personal experience leading people to break down and begin their lives completely anew, which was able to heal an amazing number of drop-outs from their dependence on drugs through an insurgence of emotion which went equally deep, but which unlike drugs offered the chance of finding a way out of the cul-de-sac of the orientation crisis. In the words of one seventeen-year-old drug addict: "When the situation had become quite hopeless, someone took me along to the Jesus People. They had just finished a prayer meeting . . . And this prayer was spoken as if Jesus were there himself — as if I were sitting right next to him. Suddenly I was quite still. I wasn't aware of myself at all. All at once I started to cry. My whole body began to tremble, there was such a power in me. I thought I would explode at that moment. And I knew that Jesus was really there. And then I started to laugh. I was so happy. And since that day I have been free. From that moment I needed no more drugs."[90]

Not all drug addicts were cured, not all people released so easily. Many hopes which people had placed in the Jesus movement were not fulfilled. Nevertheless, in many parts of the world groups have survived which are still having these experiences. One might think of the Jesus movement as a sign that we need definite experiences with God, that we must experience personally the nearness of Jesus and the power of the Holy Spirit if we want to live life with a meaning. We must not pose a false alternative between reason and experience. What is needed is a healthy balance between theology and practice, between the word and the Spirit, between church tradition and present experience, between intellect and emotion. Where in this context should we place the charismatic movement? Can it help to bring Christianity back to the middle way between continuity and spontaneity which was there at the start? Or does it belong among the fringe of substitute religions and sects, which only prolong the fruitless search for a solution to the crisis of orientation and meaning?

It is clear that the charismatic movement offers something which exactly fits the gap which has been left unfilled in a Christianity preoccupied with reason. Ernst Benz concludes: "Today, when Christianity has come to the end of the road of intellectualism, when theology has found at the end of her own process of purely formal dialectic an atheism into which she herself has in some cases toppled over, those churches which with great scorn and disdain have excluded the pre-rational and irrational *charismata* are gradually beginning to recognize that the achievement of a high level of development in the theology of the word has not prevented them from remaining at a lamentably low level of development in the realm of spirituality. They look perhaps a little enviously at the Pentecostals, who display with an almost unruly lack of inhibition those gifts which they have so systematically driven out of their midst. Indeed they would perhaps even be prepared to accept speaking in tongues if they could have the other gifts of the Spirit as well."[91]

The fascination of the charismatic movement derives from the direct experience of God, which moreover manifests itself in apparently supernatural signs, be they speaking in tongues, as in classical and neo-Pentecostalism, or as in the charismatic renewal movement other signs of the Holy Spirit's power, such as healing, inspired speech, the word of wisdom or the gift of administration. True, it is widely known today that all these phenomena occur outside Christianity as well and they are not therefore in every case cogent evidence of the presence of God. Nevertheless it remains true that these signs have appeared in the charismatic movement not as a result of some kind of occult activity or "trips" into the hippy world, but following prayer for filling with the Holy Spirit. When a person makes a personal decision for Jesus Christ and thereby undergoes the *fundamental Christian experience* of being filled with the Holy Spirit, it is not just his intellect but every level of his personality that is involved. Nor is it only people of little education who thus find a dimension of depth in their experience of God, but also intellectuals, for it is more likely to give them real orientation and a sense of meaning in life than is a uni-dimensional acceptance of the faith based on reason alone.

In the charismatic movement there appears a new inner depth and originality of expression of faith which is lacking as much in the over-intellectual churches of the word as it is in those churches which have complex liturgies. For in both these cases expressions of faith are merely repeated — expressions which once, long ago, were original but on which the dust of history has settled. Both the pure emotionalism of many Pentecostal churches and the spontaneous yet reverent exercise of charismatic gifts in the prayer meetings of the charismatic renewal possess something of the originality and freshness which we associate with the way children express their faith. The youth scene of the last few years represents one long search for such spontaneity of life, without which one would perish in the technological mass society of the 20th century. So it is not surprising that both the Jesus movement and the charismatic renewal have attracted young people to a particularly marked extent.

It is not only however the individual's expression of his faith which is fresh and real in the charismatic movement: the same is true of the group experience. That has been especially evident in the Jesus movement. But also in the prayer groups of the charismatic movement, which often consist of middle-aged, middle-class people, and in the Pentecostal churches, which draw much of their membership from a working class background, spontaneous group experience is to be found. Often of course this takes the form of following a leader in hand-clapping, singing or bodily movements, in a highly emotional atmosphere; but in smaller groups which have grown more slowly it increasingly takes on the pattern of the Pauline concept of the body of

Christ, where an organic structure develops through the exercise of variety of spiritual gifts. Such a group will also possess healing and direction-giving abilities.

Finally it is confirmed from many sources that a direct experience of God accompanied by the visible working of the Spirit not only causes things to happen, but also releases energies which give greater power to a person's spiritual life. Thus many people are given a deeper love for Jesus Christ, which enables them to live in a continual state of listening for the guidance of the Holy Spirit; a greater love for the Bible, which transforms Bible reading from a dry obligation to a genuine matter of the heart; or a direct love for the church as a whole and for their own local fellowship, enabling them to work responsibly within it in spite of criticism.

These positive aspects are matched by the dangers which accompany every spiritual movement, because of the overlapping or mixing of Spirit-given elements with human and Satanic influences. A movement as direct and spontaneous as the charismatic renewal is especially prone to such dangers.

The accompanying charismatic phenomena can make a person's experience of God more direct and deeper, and release power to help him master his life, but they must never be made into a *touchstone* for the activity of God. They can, after all, come from sources other than God. Those who see charismatic phenomena alone as the sign of the activity of the Holy Spirit are easily in danger of striving for the gifts alone, rather than for an experience of God. When the accompanying signs become the centre of attention there is a danger of addiction to miracles, something which frequently is derived from egoistic motives.

Experiences of the power of the Holy Spirit are not to be embellished. Those who only ever speak of miracles, failing to mention the times when God has not acted according to a person's wish or desire, degrade the activity of God to the level of a human technique. There is a specal danger of this in the neo-Pentecostal movement, where there is a tendency to expect every kind of help and every kind of miracle to follow on baptism in the Spirit.

The claim of modern man to a right to happiness carries with it the danger of always looking for easy success, even in the spiritual realm. Spectacular charisms allow people to forget the problem of daily striving against sin and temptation, and lead into a spiritual dream world from which there is usually a sudden and rude awakening. This danger can best be avoided by a clear realization that the charisms are *service* gifts, not intended in the first instance to help me overcome my problems, but to help me to serve others.

There is a further danger that the emotional freshness of charismatic expressions of faith will be short-lived. This is not too serious, provided that the foundation on which our spiritual experience rests is not the presence of charisms but our second birth, and the faith in Jesus Christ which results from it. If we find that some time after a special experience we lose our spiritual power again, we can always pray for it afresh, or we can examine ourselves to see whether there is some sin standing between us and God. Or perhaps we are unable to recognize any of the Holy Spirit's works of power in our lives because we are living only for ourselves and so leaving him no opportunity of blessing us with gifts to be used in the service of others.

A direct and deep-going experience of God will release love for Jesus, but not a love which will last for the rest of one's life. Such gifts of God's grace must undergo a change of emphasis related to spiritual growth, a change from the level of direct experience of the Spirit to that of the fruit of the Spirit. As a result of the continual working of the Holy Spirit, the various aspects of a person are gradually transformed until they accord with the will of God. The person who does not live in such a process of spiritual growth will find sufficient motivation to go on believing only if he has overwhelming spiritual experiences at frequent intervals. Over a long period however this is impossible, for elemental experiences of God have a wearing down effect if they happen too often. The Holy Spirit does want to lay hold of us again and again, deeply and totally, but not in such a way that we hold on desperately from one spiritual "peak" to the next. He wants, rather, to dwell within us.

In an age characterized by a desperate loss of orientation and also by an exaggerated intellectualism on the ecclesiastical scene, we need the charismatic renewal of the churches. By this I do not mean that everything should turn upon the charismatic phenomena, but rather that the powers of the Holy Spirit, released in people's lives, should lead to exemplary living and responsible behaviour in the context of the orientation crisis. Only a sensible and controlled spirituality in the power of the Holy Spirit, embracing all areas of life, can be the basis of a lasting charismatic renewal in a church which is in the process of being transformed from a *preaching* church into a *community* church — in lively local congregations which have developed a charismatic structure which corresponds to the New Testament picture of the body of Christ.

Part Two

CHARISMATIC GIFTS AND THE HOLY SPIRIT IN THE NEW TESTAMENT

CHAPTER SIX

The Gift of the Holy Spirit

The thoughts which follow are not intended as an exhaustive *pneumatology*, or systematic study of the doctrine of the Holy Spirit. That could be written only by bringing together the various statements of the Old and New Testaments (which only in the rarest of cases are intended to be systematic) with a great deal of human sagacity and scientific attention to detail, to form a coherent, logical system — and it would leave open the question as to whether this doctrinal construction was really faithful to the intentions of God's word. In the pages which follow we shall be asking what the New Testament has to say about the reception of the Holy Spirit for it is on this central point that the theological front lines are hotly embattled.

Who is the Holy Spirit? His person and his nature are hard to put into words: the Spirit blows where he wills. Let us therefore begin with the words which the various languages have used in their attempts to describe the Holy Spirit. Both the Hebrew term *ruach* and the Greek *pneuma* have as their primary meaning "air in motion", so that in the New Testament two images are of particular significance. The first is the image of human breath, which suggests the Holy Spirit as the *giver of life*. The second is the image of the wind, portraying the Holy Spirit as a *power for change*. But the German word *Geist* also suggests an important characteristic of the Holy Spirit. According to recent research,[92] it appears to have developed from a primary root meaning "to be driven, to be startled, to be beside oneself". Hence it emphasizes the Holy Spirit's function of *challenging* and *crossing boundaries*. All three meanings are, according to the Bible, associated with the chief activities of the Holy Spirit.

Man receives *life* from the breath of God. "Then the Lord God formed man of dust from the ground, and breathed into his nostrils the breath of life; and man became a living being" (Gen. 2:7).[93] The risen Christ passes on the Holy Spirit to his disciples in the same way. "And when he had said this, he breathed on them, and said to them, 'Receive the Holy Spirit' " (John 20:22). The creator Spirit is the basis of all life, beginning with the creation of the world, but he is in a special way the creator of the new life in Jesus Christ.

In the Pentecost event the inward activity of the Spirit- wind, which worked so powerfully to change people and circumstances, is also experienced in an outward form. "And suddenly a sound came from heaven like the rush of a mighty wind, and it filled all the house where they were sitting . . . And they were all filled with the Holy Spirit and began to speak in other tongues, as the Spirit gave them utterance" (Acts 2:2,4).

The Holy Spirit also undoubtedly brings experiences of being "beside oneself". In the account of Peter's vision in connection with the conversion of Cornelius this is called a "trance" (Acts 10:9-23). Here the connection between vision and the guidance of the Spirit is emphasized: "And while Peter was pondering the vision, the Spirit said to him, 'Behold, three men are looking for you. Rise and go down, and accompany them without hesitation; for I have sent them' " (Acts 10:19-20).

Creation of life, transforming power and the crossing of boundaries are activities of the Spirit of God, through which God is revealed as the God who acts. Hence the New Testament repeatedly bears witness to the Holy Spirit as Person and power. "For the Holy Spirit is God Himself in His freedom to be present with His creation as a gift and power . . . Therefore we must add also that the Spirit is the risen Christ's testimony to Himself. He is the power which creatively gives life and renewal, by means of which people are taken, brought together and united within the fellowship of believers, the church."[94]

Christians have always tended, and especially so since the appearance of the great revival and holiness movements, to be more interested in the question of the Holy Spirit's spontaneous activity than in his continuing presence and his indwelling. The Pentecostal doctrine that there are two or three stages of salvation and that one of these is the Spirit stage has made the question of the indwelling of the Holy Spirit, how it begins and what are the signs of its authenticity, the most pressing question in the field of pneumatology.

The term "Spirit baptism", or "baptism in the Holy Spirit" does not occur directly in the New Testament at all — only an experience which is described by the words "to baptize with the Holy Spirit". Thus John the Baptist says: "I have baptized you with water; but he will baptize you with the Holy Spirit" (Mark 1:8). The risen Christ refers again to this promise at his ascension (Acts 1:5). This event — the reception of the Holy Spirit — is however alluded to in many other phrases:

"when the Holy Spirit has come upon you" (Acts 1:8)
"I will pour out my Spirit" (Acts 2:18)
"you shall receive the gift of the Holy Spirit" (Acts 2:38)

"the Holy Spirit fell on all who heard the word" (Acts 10:44)
"giving them the Holy Spirit" (Acts 15:8).

Is "being baptized with the Spirit" a special stage in the reception of the Holy Spirit, or only one phrase among many for the *indwelling* of the Spirit?

The study of the New Testament evidence which follows does not claim to provide ultimate clarity on all questions concerning reception of the Spirit. I hope however that it may help us to get things into perspective and at the same time stimulate readers to study the scriptures for themselves. Conversion, regeneration, water baptism and reception of the Spirit form in the New Testament one united whole (cf. J. D. G. Dunn: *Baptism in the Holy Spirit*, London, SCM, 1970). This does not mean that all these things have to happen at exactly the same moment, but they are near to one another in time and in experience, and belong together from God's point of view. All the accounts in the New Testament which speak of longer intervals between these events are dealing with unusual situations.

This unity is most strongly emphasized by Jesus himself in his conversation with Nicodemus (John 3:1-21). God gives us the opportunity of a new birth: "You must be born anew" (7). Nevertheless it is expected of a man that he for his part will provide the precondition of faith: "For God so loved the world that he gave his only Son, that whoever believes in him should not perish but have eternal life" (16). Conversion and regeneration are indissolubly linked, since they are two sides of the same event: conversion is man's response to the call of God, regeneration is the divine acceptance of this decision. Jesus puts both into the context of water and Spirit: "Unless one is born of water and the Spirit, he cannot enter the kingdom of God" (5). The conversation between Jesus and Nicodemus states in concentrated form something which is attested again and again in the New Testament, that the fundamental Christian experience consists of conversion and regeneration, water baptism and the reception of the Holy Spirit.

In the New Testament there is a very close connection between these events, not only in the sense of their inner association, but also in terms of time. Nevertheless exceptions to this basic principle are recorded, so that we can assume that while there is a normal sequence of events, there is no rigid law. The events described in the New Testament which have to do with the fundamental Christian experience are, therefore, closer or more distant *approximations* to a normal course of events. We find an example of this normal course of events in the reaction of the hearers to Peter's sermon at Pentecost. "And Peter said to them, 'Repent, and be baptized, every one of you, in the name of Jesus Christ for the forgiveness of your sins; and you shall receive the gift of the Holy Spirit' " (Acts 2:38). The order of the events which depend on man's decision is plain in the New Testament: first repentance, then baptism. Equally plain is the way in which God reacts to this human decision: by forgiveness of sins, and the fundamental acceptance of a person as a child of God, through regeneration and the reception of the Holy Spirit. It is unnecessary to try to lay down an exact order of events at this point: the decision of man is followed by the gift of grace and of the Spirit, and these are in a direct inner relationship which is generally evident also in their timing.

The Pentecostal churches do not of course deny that the Holy Spirit plays a part in regeneration. Because however they associate the really decisive reception of the Spirit with the visible gift of speaking in tongues, they stress those occasions in the book of Acts where (visible) reception of the Spirit and regeneration are separated in time. Thus they arrive at the doctrine of Spirit baptism. Here two questions must be asked:

1. Do the "two-stage" examples represent the normal case, or can they be regarded as exceptions because of the special circumstances in which they occur?
2. Is the reception of the Spirit marked in every case by speaking in tongues?

To the first question the New Testament gives an unequivocal answer. All the passages which record a wide separation in time between regeneration and the visible reception of the Spirit are describing exceptional situations. The promise of Jesus in Acts 1:5 ("Before many days you shall be baptized with the Holy Spirit") was given *before the Pentecost event*. Before the fundamental breakthrough of the Holy Spirit had taken place, it could not happen to individual people either. The same can be said of the disciples of John at Ephesus (Acts 19:1-7). John's baptism did not involve any necessary connection with the Holy Spirit, and so it cannot have been preceded by a conversion in the full sense. The conversion of these disciples was completed through the ministry of St. Paul, who had first to point them to Jesus. God gave them a second birth, and only then could baptism in the name of Jesus be administered and a visible reception of the Spirit follow.

The conversion of the Samaritans and their later reception of the Spirit (Acts 8:4-25) seems at first sight to present the greatest difficulties, since they did not receive the Spirit until the apostles intervened. When we remember however the enmity which existed between the Jews and the Samaritans, we can see that here too was an exceptional situation. It was absolutely essential that the reception of the Spirit should take place under the aegis of the apostles, for otherwise the awakening in Samaria would probably not have been recognized by the church in Jerusalem. Similar conditions applied in the case of the conversion of Cornelius. Peter went to him only because he had received a clear vision telling him to do so. When Cornelius and his friends received the Holy Spirit, Peter could not refuse them baptism. Without their having received the Spirit in a visibly evident way, he would probably have refused to baptize them.

None of these incidents alter the basic connection between regeneration and reception of the Spirit. To be "baptized in the Holy Spirit" is simply another way of saying "to receive the Holy Spirit". If we want to use the expression "Spirit baptism", we can use it only to describe the reception of the Holy Spirit which occurs when a person is born again. Neither the particular accounts referred to in Acts nor the total witness of the New Testament support the doctrine of Spirit baptism as a second stage of salvation in the sense of an anointing for service or as the real, empowering experience of the Spirit.

What about the connection between receiving the Spirit and speaking in tongues? The various accounts in Acts do not present a clear picture. Some of them are totally lacking in details, reporting only that people came to believe, e.g. following Peter's sermon at Pentecost (Acts 2:41). In the case of the Samaritan awakening the visible nature of the coming of the Spirit is emphasized. "Now when Simon saw that the Spirit was given through the laying on of the apostles' hands, he offered them money . . ." (Acts 8:18) — because he too wanted this gift. Perhaps the sign here was speaking in tongues, but elsewhere other charisms are mentioned when people first receive the Spirit, viz. glossolalia *and prophesying* at Ephesus (Acts 19:6), the rushing wind, tongues of fire and glossolalia at Pentecost. In the latter case speaking in tongues has a different function from that of the gift described in 1 Cor. 12-14. There it is incomprehensible and must be interpreted; here it is actually an aid to understanding. Finally, at the conversion of Cornelius, speaking in tongues is mentioned alone as the sign of the reception of the Spirit (Acts 10:44-46).

Thus it is scarcely legitimate to conclude from the texts we have mentioned that speaking in tongues was the regular and certain sign of having received the Spirit. Two things in particular tell against such a view. Firstly, as we have already emphasized, all the above-mentioned passages describe exceptional situations which required an especially clear confirmation tha the Spirit had been received. In three cases this was certainl speaking in tongues; on the other occasions it must have been a least a recognizable charism — or simply overflowing joy an praise, for this too is a visible sign. Secondly, Paul says i 1 Cor. 12:30 that not all who have received spiritual gifts hav that of speaking in tongues. Glossolalia is regarded throughou 1 Cor. 12-14 as a charism like any other — and thus here too th principle applies that the charisms are distributed so that no on possesses all the gifts. Only to the whole church is the promis of a full complement of gifts given. Classical Pentecostalism ha sought to answer this objection by means of the hypothesis tha there are two kinds of speaking in tongues, the glossolalia men tioned in 1 Cor. 12-14, which is not given to everyone as permanent gift, and the glossolalia mentioned in Acts, which i a kind of *sign of initiation* when someone has been baptized i the Spirit and which is therefore associated with the experienc of breakthrough and not with the continuing indwelling of th Holy Spirit.

This view is not supported by the New Testament, since th accounts in Acts, which only sometimes record exact detail about the events connected with reception of the Spirit, are no intended to form the basis for any doctrine of "stages" in th reception of the Spirit, but rather to bear witness to the workin of the Spirit in the formation of the first churches. The onl thorough discussion of charismatic gifts in the New Testament i found in the writings of Paul (especially in Rom. 12 and 1 Cor 12-14), and he does not assign to speaking in tongues any func tion as a sign of the reception of the Spirit. Experiences withi Pentecostalism and within the charismatic renewal differ at thi point. Even the neo-Pentecostals, because they have this set o expectations, find that their Spirit baptisms are accompanied b tongues in the same way as the classical Pentecostals, wherea for the charismatic renewal movement glossolalia is simply on charism among others — given, it is true, to a relatively larg number of Christians, but of secondary importance in practica Christian living. Since speaking in tongues can also occur as a purely human phenomenon, it is reasonable to suppose tha where people expect it as an essential sign of Spirit baptism what they often experience is in fact a merely *emotiona* glossolalia, a function of the human unconscious. That this i the case becomes even clearer when it is deliberately *practised*, as is normal in some parts of the Pentecostal movement.

The fact remains, however, that in the book of Acts it i repeatedly made clear that the experience of the Holy Spirit i accompanied by visible signs and clearly recognizable events. A person does not become aware of the indwelling of the Holy Spirit only after years of spiritual growth; already at the moment of regeneration he finds that the reception of the Holy Spirit includes this element of signs and special experiences. The signs are not confined to speaking in tongues, but may be any of the many different charismatic gifts promised in the New Testament; or they may take the form of an experience of overflowing joy, deep penitence or total surrender.

It is the fault of the churches that the doctrine of Spirit baptism as an independent experience of salvation has developed. For the expectation of a visible and perceptible reception of the Spirit at the time of regeneration has been lost in almost all the churches, in spite of being so well attested in the New Testament. When people then have this experience later, the false conclusion is easily drawn that conscious reception of the Spirit is an independent experience of salvation called "Spirit baptism".

The doctrine of Spirit baptism as held by the classical Pentecostal movement had its origins in the holiness movement. It was not developed by people who had engaged in intensive theological study and who then went on to discover a corresponding set of facts in practice, but by people who had had practical experiences and then subjected these to theological reflection. It is the general absence of any concrete experience of the Spirit in our churches which has led to the separation of this part of the fundamental Christian experience as a doctrine in its own right. The charismatic renewal movement, which has once again brought these experiences into the mainstream churches, provides an opportunity of reintegrating the experience of the Spirit as part of the fundamental Christian experience. This integration will however be possible only if the present-day expectations of the churches with regard to the conscious reception and actual working of the Holy Spirit are once again brought into line with the expectations of the New Testament, especially as they are recorded in Acts.

This would mean that conversion, regeneration, and reception of the Spirit would again be brought into the connection which we find existing between them in the New Testament. But we have still said nothing about water baptism. In the churches which practise infant baptism the experience of water baptism disappears completely, since an infant cannot have such an experience. Both the precondition of conversion and regeneration, and the precondition of human consciousness, are lacking. A subsequent recognition of one's baptism is only a weary attempt to integrate it into the totality of the fundamental Christian experience, since it takes place at an intellectual level and not at the level of experience. The question of baptism as a conscious experience also becomes acute today for another reason: as we discussed more fully above, in our present crisis of orientation the intellectual level which is addressed in preaching does not suffice to give orientation and meaning in life. Hence, too, a conspicuous aspect of the Jesus movement, which was a revolt from the grass roots against the total intellectualization of Christianity, was the baptism of adults as an immediate act of confession following the experience of conversion and regeneration. Often the reception of the Spirit was experienced as a breakthrough at the time of baptism.

Those churches which practise believers' baptism of converted adults have also made it difficult by their current practice for people to experience the totality of the fundamental Christian experience. Thus for example in the Baptist churches in Germany, and in other similar churches, conversion mostly takes place as a result of special evangelistic preaching which does not encourage an expectation of receiving the Spirit. Conversion and regeneration therefore lack in general any conscious experience of receiving the Spirit, and the newly converted are often given the misleading impression that a later baptism with the Spirit is a special stage in salvation. Baptism too is separated from the experience of conversion and regeneration. A person may apply for baptism at a later date, often planned long in advance for organizational reasons, where he testifies to his faith before the assembled church and is baptized. Frequently, therefore, baptism is seen not as part of the fundamental Christian experience, but only in its partial function as an act of reception into the church.

Both national churches which practise infant baptism and free churches which practise believers' baptism ought therefore to reflect together on the nature of the fundamental Christian experience in the early church. Churches which practise believers' baptism ought really to find it easier within their own structures to re-establish the fundamental Christian experience in its original sense. In our age of the orientation crisis it is especially important that the Christian life should begin with a conscious experience involving every level of the personality — not with a purely intellectual decision nor with a purely emotional event. The fundamental Christian experience, with its full content of conversion, regeneration, water baptism and reception of the Spirit, with its balance between the action of God and the action of man, between word and sign, between intellect and emotion, is worthy of being preached and practised afresh in all its original power.

The rediscovery and proclamation of the fundamental Christian experience in its totality is also important for another reason — to minimize the danger of an independent and one-sided experience of Spirit baptism. For the reduction of the fundamental Christian experience to Spirit baptism and concentration on this has a harmful effect on the spiritual growth of the young Christian, as of course does also a neglect of the dimension of the Holy Spirit.

Let us then list the main negative results of a doctrine and practice of Spirit baptism as a separate stage in the way of salvation.

1. Concentration on Spirit baptism easily detracts from the central importance of regeneration. Often the recognition of sin is lacking in depth, because the fundamental event of forgiveness of sins on the basis of a personal and total confession of sin does not have the central place in a person's experience.

2. Because the experience of a later baptism in the Spirit often goes much deeper than the experience of being born again — especially in children from believing homes, who frequently experience conversion and regeneration as a process rather than as a datable event — the central significance of the fundamental Christian experience with its many aspects (e.g. sin, forgiveness, power, confession) is transferred to the signs accompanying the experience of the Spirit. Assurance of salvation is therefore based no longer on the acceptance of forgiveness at regeneration, but on charismatic signs.

3. In Spirit baptism the experience of power and ability becomes the central experience, while the areas of self-recognition, acceptance of salvation, forgiveness of sins and confession become secondary. This can easily result in spiritual schizophrenia: so long as the "objective" facts of being filled with the Spirit are present in the charismatic gifts, the life of sanctification and the development of the fruit of the Spirit can be neglected.

4. The reception of the Spirit takes on the character of a universal remedy. Preachers are apt to suggest: "If only you experience the baptism of the Spirit and break out into speaking in tongues, all your other problems will be solved." This is applied to the problem of illness, to other problems of life, to the problem of doubt and to faults of character.

5. Because Spirit baptism generally takes place at an emotional level, it can easily be imitated by experiences which

involve purely human feelings. This leads to the danger of demonic distortion.

It would however be utterly wrong to conclude that, because of the dangers inherent in a limited doctrine of Spirit baptism, the working of the Holy Spirit should be avoided altogether as "dangerous". For if the dimension of the Holy Spirit is lacking there are other and different consequences for the spiritual life which are equally dangerous. The only conclusion we can draw is that we need to restore the various aspects of the fundamental Christian experience to the balance we find in the New Testament.

CHAPTER SEVEN

Charisma: The Term and its Meaning

Since the question of charismatic gifts has become one of the most pressing theological questions of the present day, it will also form the major emphasis of this book. The danger thereby arises of disregarding other aspects of the Holy Spirit's work. Since it would be beyond the scope of this book to include a comprehensive treatment of the Holy Spirit, his nature and his activity, let us at least look briefly at some main aspects of the work of the Holy Spirit.

1. The universal activity of the Holy Spirit

The creation story makes it plain that the Spirit of God was the power through which the creation took place — in other words, the Holy Spirit is God as power. "In the beginning God created the heavens and the earth. The earth was without form and void, and darkness was upon the face of the deep; and the Spirit of God was moving over the face of the waters" (Gen. 1:1-2). In his sermon at Pentecost Peter takes up the prophecy of Joel and says: "And in the last days it shall be, God declares, that I will pour out my Spirit upon all flesh" (Acts 2:17). Since Pentecost the Spirit of God has been at work everywhere, though only when people give him opportunity to work. Therefore Peter draws from the prophecy of Joel the following conclusion: "Repent, and be baptized every one of you in the name of Jesus Christ for the forgiveness of your sins; and you shall receive the gift of the Holy Spirit" (Acts 2:38). It is a liberating secret when we discover that we do not have to see the universe and our world under the "minus sign" of Satan (although he is still able to work), but that we may see it under the "plus sign" of the Holy Spirit, which has been "poured out on all flesh" and becomes operative in every born again Christian.

2. The indwelling of the Holy Spirit

The Holy Spirit can develop his proper activity only when he finds a home in a human personality. Thus Paul says to Timothy: "Guard the truth that has been entrusted to you by the Holy Spirit who dwells within us" (2 Tim. 1:14). "Dwells" in this context means that the Holy Spirit is given the opportunity to work continually in us and through us. Before we were born again the Spirit of God was only able to influence us occasionally *from the outside*; now he works *from the inside*, provided we do not resist his working. He seeks to guide us and to form us into the image of Christ.

3. The gifts of the Holy Spirit

These are not special distinctions conferred on a privileged few, for every Christian is gifted by the Holy Spirit. "All these are inspired by one and the same Spirit, who apportions to each one individually as he wills" (1 Cor. 12:11). The individual is like a vessel, for he receives gifts for the sake of others — for the profit of the church (1 Cor. 12:7). They are not rewards for good behaviour, nor signs of having reached a certain stage of holiness, but tools for service. They are to be exercised with discretion, and subject to the correction of the church. There are three lists of "charisms" (from *charisma*, meaning gift of grace) in Rom. 12, 1 Cor. 12:8-10, and 1 Cor. 12:28, but further gifts of the Holy Spirit are mentioned in various places. From the context of these lists in the New Testament it is fair to conclude that these were not intended to be an exhaustive catalogue, and that further gifts of the Holy Spirit are possible, perhaps with varying centres of emphasis at different times.

4. The fruit of the Holy Spirit

Charisms appear spontaneously; fruit only comes following a process of growth. The fruit of the Holy Spirit is not the result of our own efforts and toil, but of the formative power of the Holy Spirit within us. It grows through a personal walk with God, in stillness before God, in contemplation of God, in silent prayer. The fruit of the Spirit does not objectify itself in actions but in the nature of our personality, not in superficial signs but in essential qualities of character which are derived from a change at the deep levels of our being: "The fruit of the Spirit is love, joy, peace, patience, kindness, goodness, faithfulness, gentleness, self-control" (Gal. 5:22).

5. The guidance of the Holy Spirit

Jesus himself speaks of the Holy Spirit as Counsellor. "But the Counsellor (lit., the one called alongside to help), the Holy Spirit, whom the Father will send in my name, he will teach you all things, and bring to your remembrance all that I have said to you" (John 14:26). The Holy Spirit is not a drill serjeant but a counsellor who advises us if we are open to his guidance. He expects obedience, but he does not compel us. If a man opens himself to him, he will receive counsel in the form of recognizing God's will for his life and in the quite practical decisions of every day, and by having his eyes opened to himself, his sins and his situation. The guidance of the Holy Spirit consists however not only of such practical wisdom but also of an unfolding of great spiritual truths ("he will teach you all things") and a bringing to mind of the word of God ("and bring to your remembrance all that I have said to you").

The term *charisma* occurs relatively seldom in the New Testament. It clearly has several meanings, and in the places where it is used only part of the total meaning is to be found. It is for this reason that theologians produce such very differing interpretations of it. It is understandable that the charismatic movement has frequently concentrated only on the practical aspects, for there are several difficulties about the theory. It is however dangerous to use the term *charisma* and the phenomenon it denotes without defining it and specifying its nature, for where this is done neither the tasks and aims nor the limits of charismatic activity can be clearly determined. We shall therefore attempt at least to draft some guidelines as to the concept and nature of *charisma*, so that our later statements on the practical aspects have some kind of firm basis on which to rest.

Apart from 1 Pet. 4:10, the term *charisma* is used in the New Testament only by Paul (and even he does not use the word with complete consistency). Sometimes *charisma* means simply an ordinary gift or present, thus more or less following secular hellenistic usage, although outside the New Testament the word was evidently seldom used and not clearly defined. Thus in Rom. 1:11 Paul probably does not mean a special charism in the sense conveyed in his later lists, but rather a spiritual present: "For I long to see you, that I may impart to you some spiritual gift to strengthen you . . ." In Romans 5 the salvation given by Christ is described as a *charisma* and as a gift of grace, evidently again in a general sense meaning simply a free gift from God. The meaning of Rom. 6:23 (where eternal life is called a gift of grace), and 1 Cor. 7:7 (where marriage and the single state are described as *charismata*), is debated. Some interpreters emphasize the ordinary sense of gift, others include these gifts among the special charisms. From the uncertainty as to the word's meaning and from the fact that there are differences between the list of charisms in Rom. 12 and that in 1 Cor. 12 I draw the conclusion that all the charisms mentioned there are taken simply as examples. Probably there are yet more forms which spiritual gifts received by grace can take than those mentioned in the New Testament. Conversely, one cannot always place the charismatic workings of the Holy Spirit in a tidy pigeon hole within a list of charisms. The Spirit blows as he wills, and he works as he wills. What is important is that we understand and accept in principle the nature, the purpose and the offer of the *charisma*. The infrequency and scattered nature of references to this word in the New Testament urge us to caution, not of course with regard to the actual workings of the Holy Spirit, but with regard to all human attempts to over-schematize them.

Charisma is most accurately rendered "gift of grace", for it is derived from the verb *charizomai*, "to give freely", and related to the noun *charis*, "grace" (and also incidentally to *chara*, "joy"). Thus a *charisma* may be regarded as a gift or ability which gives rise to joy and amazement. The same association of ideas is known to us in German, where we speak of a *begnadeter Künstler* (gifted, lit. grace-given, artist). The gift produces surprise, not in the sense of fright or of being caught unawares, but the surprise associated with ability and joy.

The source of the *charisma* is the grace of God, the effective agent the Holy Spirit. "To one is given through the Spirit the utterance of wisdom, and to another the utterance of knowledge according to the same Spirit . . ." (1 Cor. 12:8). The term *pneumatika*, spiritual gifts, is used much less frequently than the term *charismata*, gifts of grace. From 1 Cor. 12 one gains the impression that the Corinthians themselves talked of "spiritual gifts", no doubt in order to emphasize the importance of their gifts, while Paul quite deliberately uses the expression "gifts of grace", in order to make it clear that no one ought to become conceited because of his gifts. The danger exists undiminished today: so let us follow him in sticking to the term *charisma*, since it is after all the more common and better attested term.

Let us now examine the practical meaning of this New Testament term. What is a charism? Hans Küng writes: "We have seen that charisms are everyday rather than fundamentally exceptional phenomena, that they are various rather than uniform in kind, and that they are found throughout the Church rather than being restricted to a particular group of people . . . In its widest sense (charisma) signifies the call of God, addressed to an individual, to a particular ministry in the community, which brings with it the ability to fulfil that ministry."[95] Siegfried Liebschner on the other hand lays more emphasis on the spontaneity of the individual charismatic activity: "Whether one finds the charismatic gifts unusual, disturbing or wonderful, they at any rate bring us closer to the level of something tangible than do other aspects of the Spirit's work which proceed more quietly and steadily, like the ethical aspect of sanctification, for instance."[96] Gotthold Hasenhüttl strikes a similar note. "For Paul . . . the source of the gifts of grace is not an inexplicable spiritual power, but the objective, historical Jesus Christ. Hence he does not interpret as the work of the Spirit extraordinary manifestations alone, but also and particularly everyday events in the life of the church."[97]

The New Testament makes it clear that every believing Christian is also a charismatic, since he received the Holy Spirit when he was born again. But even in those days — and still more so in ours — it is clear that not every born again Christian lived in the awareness of having received a gift of grace or various charisms. There is no difference as far as the *reception* of the gift is concerned, except that different kinds of gifts are given, but there certainly is a difference in the degree to which people are aware of their gifts and accept and use them. This is the only way of explaining the fact that over and over again in the history of the church, and especially in our own day, charismatic movements have appeared — a kind of movement which from a New Testament point of view is absurd, since in the church of those days the charisms were given to the church and never made the basis for the self-identification of an independent group. Like Timothy we need today to be challenged "to rekindle the gift of God that is within (us) through the laying on of . . . hands" (2 Tim. 1:6).

Paul further makes it clear that the idea of the individualistic, isolated charismatic is a nonsense: firstly such a person would become extreme in his views, since his charism would not be open to correction and supplementation through the charisms of others, and secondly his charism would be useless, in that charisms are given not for our own profit but for that of the whole church (1 Cor. 12:7). Both in 1 Cor. 12 and in Rom. 12 Paul therefore links his review of the charismatic gifts with the picture of the body of Christ. "For as in one body we have many members, and all the members do not have the same function, so we, though many, are one body in Christ, and individually members one of another" (Rom. 12:4-5).

Jürgen Moltmann calls the charisms "the energies of the new

life".[98] Extending this line of thought, one could describe the fruit of the Spirit as the quality, and the church as the communication, of the new life.

Paul himself describes the charisms in 1 Cor. 12 by considering them, so to speak, from three angles. First he calls them *charismata*, gifts of grace, so drawing attention to their *source*. Then he calls them *diakoniai*, ministries or forms of service, and so defines their *purpose*. Finally he calls them *energemata*, operations, and so makes it clear that their *task* is to manifest God's power at work. The charism will be capable of being exercised in a way that is edifying only if it possesses all three of these attributes. If the visible gift has as its source not the Holy Spirit but human ability, sooner or later it will let us down. If it is not employed in some form of service, merely being present but having no purpose, it will soon cease to be of any help and turn into a weapon to be used against others. If it is without power, it will lead only to stress, not to service. These three characteristics of a charism may be thought of as being like a triangle of forces, which is stable only when all three fields are operative. As soon as one of the characteristics disappears, the whole collapses.

Many — I believe mistakenly — see the necessity of choosing between the two alternatives posed by the question whether the charisms are "natural" or "supernatural" gifts. If one decides for the alternative that they are natural, one must presuppose that the charisms which have been released were already present in the genetic structure of the person concerned, and have merely been further developed by the Holy Spirit. If one decides for the alternative that they are supernatural, then the presupposition is that the charisms which appear have nothing to do with the person's own natural talents, but represent miraculous powers of God. Both opinions are strongly held. Werner de Boor writes: "There are many natural 'gifts' which the Lord can use and sanctify in His service. 'Spiritual gifts' or 'charisms', however, are something different from such natural 'talents'!"[99] Heribert Mühlen on the other hand holds the opposite view: "By a charism we mean a natural gift which has been released by the Holy Spirit and set to work for the building up and growth of the Body of Christ."[100]

Must we choose between these alternatives? I believe not, and therefore would agree with Gotthold Hasenhüttl when he points out that Paul knew nothing of this distinction. "Paul does not discuss this question, because the continuity between a person outside the charismatic experience and the person under its influence does not come within his purview. The problem is unknown to him in this context because to him the whole person, with all his abilities, disposition and gifts, has become a new creation through the salvation event."[101] But we cannot be content to stop there, for one extreme brings about negative effects just as much as the other. Those who make a fundamental distinction between all charismatic gifts and all natural abilities will over-emphasize those charisms which look more supernatural than others, for example speaking in tongues, healing, mighty works, prophecy and suchlike. Those charisms which (at least as far as their outward appearance is concerned) also occur without the help of the Holy Spirit, like administration, mercy, sharing of possessions and service will be undervalued; indeed frequently they are not reckoned as charisma at all. Those on the other hand who regard the charisms as no more than natural abilities released by the Holy Spirit at once greatly narrow the range of people's expectations, for everyone knows roughly where his own abilities lie and will be led to expect no more than a strengthening and further development of what he already has. Moreover the charisms of action will tend to be given preference over those which work in supernatural ways.

If we go along with Paul in his three-sided view of the gifts of the Holy Spirit as gifts of grace, ministries and manifestations of God's power, we shall conclude that there is truth on both sides. The first essential factor is that the source of the gift lies in the grace of God. God is just as able to set free a natural gift which is there but which has been blocked, as he is to create something new which previously was altogether beyond the person's range of abilities. It is quite impossible for man to discern what God has actually done in any individual case. For no one can demonstrate, when a charism appears, that it was not present in the person's genetic structure, any more than he can establish that it was. It is also vitally important that the gift has the nature of service to others, and that it operates in a way corresponding to the will of God.

Hasenhüttl writes on this point: "Even though the life of the believer has become a life of service for Christ in the new nature created by the Spirit, and even though a man has received his life from the Christ event, this does not preclude his natural dispositions from progressively changing into charisms as they are perfected through God's sovereign power . . . This however means neither that the natural abilities were charisms all the time, nor that it is the natural ability which makes possible the gift of grace."[102]

The way in which Paul deals with the subject of charisms and gifts of the Spirit in his letters makes it evident that there can be no absolute certainty about our definitions of terms, our descriptions of the nature of each gift, and our classifications. In the end only the effect produced by the exercise of charisms can give the clue as to whether they are genuine gifts of the grace of God or counterfeit activity resulting from people acting on their own authority or from the incursion of Satanic powers. Moreover there is always the possibility that genuine charisms will produce negative results because of a lack of spiritual maturity or because of sin which has not been cleansed. Hence it is important to think often about the standards which Paul has given us for judging the effects of charisms:

1. Charisms result in Jesus being attested as Lord. "Therefore I want you to understand that no one speaking by the Spirit of God ever says 'Jesus be cursed' and no one can say 'Jesus is Lord' except by the Holy Spirit" (1 Cor. 12:3). Certainly he is not referring only to verbal confession here, but also to the testimony of a person's life.

2. Charisms are given for the edification of the church. "When you come together, each one has a hymn, a lesson, a revelation, a tongue, or an interpretation. Let all things be done for edification" (1 Cor. 14:26). Charisms are neither a game to be played nor a means of asserting oneself. They must contribute to the growth and furtherance of the church, for growth is visible — even if not at once.

3. Charisms do not lead to disorder, but to peace. Paul emphasizes that the spontaneity of the charisms carries with it the danger of disorder. Therefore he writes: "The spirits of prophets are subject to prophets. For God is not a God of confusion but of peace" (1 Cor. 14:32-33). The authenticity of a charism can be recognized by its willingness to be brought into line, so that the prophet who goes beyond the mark is capable of entrusting himself to the guiding hand of another prophet.

4. Charisms possess the character of witness to unbelievers. If a charism ceases to be intelligible, it becomes ridiculous, but if it has the character of a manifestation of God's power, it will convince the unbeliever. "But if all prophesy, and an unbeliever or outsider enters, he is convicted by all, he is called to account by all, the secrets of his heart are disclosed; and so, falling on his face, he will worship God and declare that God is really among you" (1 Cor. 14:24-25).

5. Charisms without love are of no value. "If I speak in the tongues of man and of angels, but have not love, I am a noisy gong or a clanging cymbal" (1 Cor. 13:1). Charisms are not independently active — they cannot be separated from the cir-

cumstances in which they are exercised. A charism without love does not fulfil the qualitative condition for spiritual activity: it is indeed "ability in the Spirit", but it does not fulfil the function which is God's will for it. Love in this context stands for the whole range of fruit of the Spirit, for every fruit of the Spirit is an aspect of love.

6. Charisms lead to God being glorified. ". . . Whoever speaks, (let him speak) as one who utters oracles of God; whoever renders service, as one who renders it by the strength which God supplies; in order that in everything God may be glorified through Jesus Christ. To him belong glory and dominion for ever and ever" (1 Pet. 4:11). When our speech and our actions are charismatic, when they are a gift of God's grace, then the circle is complete: what comes from God flows back to him again, and sets him through Jesus Christ in the central place. This is the fundamental rule for all charisms: God must remain, through Jesus Christ, the standard of reference.

A certain tradition of theology constantly reproduces the view that some of the charisms ceased when the New Testament canon was complete. Fritz Hubmer writes: "With the creation of the New Testament and its availability to the faithful, the revelation of God as such was complete. Three of the original Christian gifts of the Spirit, namely the revelatory gifts of speaking in tongues, prophecy and charismatic knowledge, had now fulfilled their function. After the appearance of the New Testament they were, in accordance with 1 Cor. 13:8, removed from the list of early Christian charisms and have ceased . . . The 'perfect' of God's revelation (1 Cor. 13:10) is now there."[103]

1 Cor. 13 is the only place where it is said that the charisms will cease, and there it is placed in the context of perfection. "When the perfect comes, the imperfect will pass away . . . For now we see in a mirror dimly, but then face to face" (1 Cor. 13:10,12). "The perfect" cannot possibly refer to the writing of the New Testament, for even today, despite the wonderful gift of the New Testament, we do not yet see "face to face". We are still dependent on the Holy Spirit, and on prophecy and knowledge, for the exposition and application of the word of God, though well aware that all this is "in part". For the word translated as "perfect" is the Greek work *teleion*, which is related to *telos*, end, so that the translation ought properly to read: "When the end comes . . ."

Others hold the view that the miraculous gifts were given only for the apostolic age, whereas the gifts of service have continued to this day. Paul makes no distinction of this sort; both in Rom. 12 and in 1 Cor. 12-14 he sets miraculous powers alongside the gifts of service and confirms that they belong together by using the picture of the body of Christ. Neither is any distinction of this sort to be found in Mark 16:17-18, which says nothing of a cessation of the gifts: "And these signs will accompany those who believe: in my name they will cast out demons; they will speak in new tongues; they will pick up serpents, and if they drink any deadly thing, it will not hurt them; they will lay their hands on the sick, and they will recover." No one maintains that demons can no longer be cast out today; why then should healings or mighty works (both of them miraculous gifts) have ceased?

To close this chapter I quote the sensible, practical and down-to-earth conclusions of Walter Hümmer about the spiritual gifts of 1 Cor. 12.

"1. These spiritual gifts are scriptural. Paul does not oppose them. He is only concerned that they be rightly used.

2. These gifts serve exclusively the building up of the body of Jesus. They are service gifts.

3. They all need 'electronic base control', i.e. supplementation and correction by a living church.

4. Spiritual gifts must always be combined with humility. They have nothing to do with fanaticism. 'The spirits of prophets are subject to prophets.'

5. They provide no kind of evidence for the quality of our Christian life. They are essentially tools for the job. Every gift can be used to do mischief.

6. God's purpose for us is not that we should be charismatic, but loving, self-giving and priestly (1 Cor. 13).

7. When practised by immature Christians under immature leadership, spiritual gifts not uncommonly have disastrous effects. When practised by mature Christians under mature spiritual leadership, they mean an enrichment of the life of the church."[104]

CHAPTER EIGHT

The Variety of Gifts

The multiplicity of charismatic gifts cannot be forced into any tidy scheme. It is idle to argue about the question of how many charisms are mentioned in the New Testament. The two lists in Rom. 12 and 1 Cor. 12 are neither of them intended as exhaustive catalogues, but simply as lists of examples. Furthermore the term *charisma* does not have one consistent meaning. As we have already seen, Paul sometimes uses it in the general sense of a present, and sometimes as a technical term meaning "gift of grace". In some cases therefore it remains a matter of interpretation whether one speaks of a charism or of simply a gift of God.

Of fundamental importance is the question whether, like the Pentecostals, we speak of only the nine gifts mentioned in 1 Cor. 12:8-10 as charisms, or whether we take as our starting-point the whole spectrum of gifts in the New Testament. It is clear that Paul uses the term *charisma* in the sense of "gift of grace" not only in 1 Cor. 12 but also in Rom. 12 and probably in other places as well. Moreover the total context of the New Testament always suggests a multiplicity of gifts, especially through the image of the body of Christ. It is therefore a distortion of the biblical evidence to centre our expectations of charismatic activity one-sidedly on 1 Cor. 12:8-10. I believe that there are far more charisms than we find listed in the New Testament, that there are fluid distinctions between the individual gifts of grace, and that we therefore ought to start with a broad definition of charism so as to avoid over-hastily limiting the multiplicity of gifts by classifying and delineating them.

The list of individual charismatic gifts which follows should not be interpreted as setting limits to the range of gifts, but rather as indicating their multiplicity. It is not my intention to make a catalogue of the gifts of grace, but by listing them to encourage people not to narrow down their range of expectations to anything less than the charisms as they existed in the New Testament. The problems which have arisen in connection with individual, spectacular and emotionally exaggerated charisms are there only because the totality and variety of the gifts mentioned and promised in the New Testament has been lost from view. The scope of this book, which is intended to take a wide-ranging look at our subject, covering it at various levels and in answer to various sets of questions, rules out for reasons of length the possibility of describing the individual charisms exhaustively. Here we are concerned simply to outline the main aspects of the various gifts, in order to indicate the breadth and balance of the New Testament pattern from which we start.

Gifts of God's grace in a general sense

Are *eternal life* (Rom, 6:23), *marriage and the single state* (1 Cor. 7:7) and *meeting* (Rom. 1:11-12) gifts of grace? All three are associated with the Greek word *charisma*. Gotthold Hasenhüttl reckons them as charisms in the strict sense, and goes so far as to regard the charism of meeting and that of eternal life as the "fundamental charisms".[105] In the charismatic renewal movement marriage and the single state, and eternal life, are likewise generally reckoned as gifts of grace. Other writers like Ulrich Brockhaus assume that in these cases the term *charisma* means a gift from God in the ordinary sense of "gift", and so ought not to be translated as "gift of grace" or "charism".[106]

We cannot go here into a thorough consideration of these differing interpretations. It is clear that Paul's use of the word *charisma* outside Rom. 12 and 1 Cor. 12-14 is not uniform, and that in most cases he evidently uses it in the ordinary sense of a "free gift" and not that of a special, charismatic gift. Secondly the reference to the church is not so explicit as in the two lists of charisms with their direct association with the image of the body of Christ. Thirdly they are not so specialized — a feature which in Rom. 12 and 1 Cor. 12-14 is an indispensable part of the doctrine of charismatic gifts. On the other hand, in the cases we are thinking about (eternal life, marriage and the single life, and meeting) the word *charisma* is found in direct relation to a definite situation which could be thought of as a gift of the Holy Spirit. Experience in the charismatic renewal has shown that marriage and the single state, meeting, and eternal life in the sense of anticipation in the present of God's promise for the future, can take on a radiance directly bestowed by the Spirit which corresponds to that of those other charisms which are listed in the "catalogues". To distinguish them clearly from the special charisms which are listed particularly in Rom. 12 and 1 Cor. 12-14, I call them "gifts of God's grace in a general sense". This makes it clear that they represent an intermediate stage between spiritual "presents" from God and the gifts of grace we call charisms.[107]

Eternal life as a gift of grace

Paul says in Rom. 6:23, "For the wages of sin is death, but the free gift of God is eternal life in Christ Jesus our Lord." Eternal life as God's free gift is the fundamental promise of God to mankind. It is firmly promised to the believer: "He who believes in the Son has eternal life" (John 3:36). The assurance of eternal life, the assurance of salvation, is a work of the Holy Spirit. "It is the Spirit himself bearing witness with our spirit that we are children of God" (Rom. 8:16). Now there is a special promise in the fact that eternal life is described as assurance and as a gift of grace, for it means that it reaches not only our understanding but also every part of our personality, that it is not a matter of knowledge only, but also of the activity of God. Thus eternal life is a gift which takes us by surprise, not an insight laboriously achieved, but a gift, a working of God's power, and something to be used for the service of others. Where the gracious gift of eternal life is visibly given, not only is a person's life determined by the future eternal goal, but it is embedded in the present reality of eternal life now.

What then is meant by eternal life as a present activity of the Holy Spirit? Because all spiritual life is related to the future in Christ, eternal life as a gift of grace means the God-given ability to live on the basis of Christ's future, to allow the long breath of eternity, with its living hope and unspeakable joy, to take form in one's life here and now. Many Christians have a very definite idea of life after death but nevertheless see their life now, on the way to eternity, as a kind of one-way street, with eternity as a *goal* which they must reach like the far bank of a river where safety lies. They do not see the traffic in the other direction, the effects of eternity on the life here and now, of eternal life as the formative power within our earthly life, eternal life as a gift.

Where eternal life becomes operative as a gift of grace, the events of life are taken out of the narrow confines of here and now and brought into their rightful place within the context of eternity. Many people for instance become embittered, begin to hate or try to get their revenge when they experience injustices which are not put right. This reaction is completely this-worldly. Eternal life as a gift of grace brings such experiences into the great context of the history of salvation. It does not take injustice so seriously, because life here and now is not the one goal towards which everything is directed. The gift of eternal life thus leads to a greater confidence in God, to a happy ability to relax. The life of most people is narrow, insular, confined, egocentric. The gift of eternal life frees people to broaden their horizons, because it directs the attention to the wider perspective of God's activity.

If at the time of conversion a person is led to expect a breakthrough of the Holy Spirit's activity, the result is often a complete, deep experience of the assurance of salvation, in which eternal life is experienced as a gift of the Holy Spirit. The charismatic gift of eternal life often releases such unspeakable joy that a person's own words do not suffice to articulate the experience. Thus it is not surprising when for some people the experience of receiving the Spirit is accompanied by the charism of glossolalia, a sign that they are crossing the frontiers of their own speech in praise of the mighty works of God (Acts 2:11). This is certainly not to say that praying in other languages is the normative sign of receiving the Spirit, but simply that it is one of the possible means by which a person's great joy at the gift of eternal life can be expressed. (As a principle I use in my exegetical work the expression "speaking in other languages" or "praying in other languages" because it corresponds most closely to the Greek expression *en glossais lalein*, lit. to speak in languages. When I am dealing with historical and phenomenological material I retain what is in my view the unfortunate expression "speaking in tongues", because it is so widely used.)

Meeting as a gift of grace

The actual gift is frequently mentioned in the New Testament and is common in our experience, but it is only put in so many words at one point in the New Testament, viz. Rom. 1:11-12. "For I long to see you, that I may impart to you some spiritual gift to strengthen you, that is, that we may be mutually encouraged by each other's faith, both yours and mine." The text makes it clear that here Paul is not thinking of one of the special charisms which he has received, believing that it will be bestowed upon the church as a result of his visit to Rome, but rather that that meeting itself is a gift. It is not stated what special effect will result from the meeting, but Paul expects that it will have the quality of a gift of grace, that it will be so deep and far-reaching in its effects as to be explicable only in terms of a direct and fascinating work of the Spirit.

There are two levels at which charismatic meeting takes place: in the encounter of man with God, and in the encounter of man with man. Many Christians have experience of meetings with God which were so intense that they took on the quality of a charismatic event. They may have been encounters with God in times of quiet, or in "charismatic silence", in the experience of being called, or strengthened, or healed, or in the discovery of some special insight. The Bible records many such encounters, which one may regard as charismatic meetings, e.g. Moses on the holy mountain, Elijah in the wilderness, Paul when he was caught up into heaven, etc. They need not always be such outstanding experiences as these, but every Christian needs experiences of God more intense than the "normal" encounter he may experience in Bible reading, preaching or silence.

We can experience our faith in the meeting of Christians with one another in spiritual fellowship, and it is indeed dependent on such meeting. The picture of the body of Christ is the most tightly knit model of communication one could think of. Usually we are content with the doctrine that every born again Christian has charismatic gifts, assuming that the communication of these gifts will begin automatically as it were. The gift of meeting is the promise that the working together of a group of people with their various charisms in the local church can have, and should have, in itself the character of a gift of the Holy Spirit. I am not talking about the development of group life on the basis of human, scientific insights, but of meeting as a spiritual gift freely given. Because of the poverty of our group relationships today and the associated problems in family, church and society, we have scarcely begun to grasp the greatness and significance of this divine promise with its offer of *meeting* as a free gift of grace.

Marriage and the single life as gifts of grace

Living a single life himself, Paul writes to the Corinthians: "I wish that all were as I myself am. But each has his own special gift from God, one of one kind and one of another" (1 Cor. 7:7). Judging by the way in which he opens the subject, it is probable that Paul means by this gift of grace first and foremost *continence* as a precondition of the single state.[108] Since however he then goes on to extend the *charisma* to marriage, he obviously presupposes that the human condition of either marriage or celibacy can undergo a spiritual transformation, that the decision (for Christians guided by the Holy Spirit) can become a gift of grace, a manner of life filled with the radiance of a gift bestowed by the Holy Spirit. If we follow this line of thought further, it seems natural to see this basic promise as extending to other fundamental structures of life which have just as distinctive a character as marriage or the single state, such as the life-shaping patterns of career, size of family or life-style in the sense of how far one develops a professional career, the degree of comfort one seeks in one's home and living standards, what hobbies one takes up, and how one combines family and professional responsibilities with involvement in the local church.

All these fundamental patterns of life are based upon decisions. One must decide whether one will marry or not, one must decide on a certain career, one must find guidelines for one's individual life-style. In this it is of vital importance to discover where one's gifts lie. God has given everyone a gift, of one sort to one person and another to another. It is not always easy to recognize the gift, but the goal is a high one, for the person who lives in harmony not only with his human but also with his spiritual gifts will find true fulfilment in life. It makes a great difference whether I make a decision concerning these basic patterns of life simply because I *must* choose one way or the other (in other words, as is so often the case, whether I make *random* decisions which I then try to justify), or whether I ask what is my gift and so put myself in the position where it is possible to make a God-given decision.

In our own day, with its crisis of orientation, it has become very obvious that it is hardly possible for someone to cope with the basic patterns of his own life without the help of God. Human efforts and an appeal to faith are not in themselves sufficient. It is all the more important that the individual Christian should live in harmony with his gifts. Hence the gifts of marriage, the single life, career and life style represent a promise of unparalleled relevance and practical significance in everyday life. It is easy to understand and freeing to know that one of God's general gifts of grace, promised to all Christians, is this taking possession of our daily lives starting with the basic patterns which shape them.

Special charisms

In addition to the general gifts of God's grace (eternal life, meeting, marriage and the single life and the other gifts implied by the latter) there are the special charisms. All of these are specialized: every Christian has one or several, but none has them all, and all of them are subject to control by the local church. They are given to complement each other, according to the principle of the body of Christ. These special charisms may be divided into two main groups: *charisms of the word*, which are all more or less closely derived from the central charism of prophecy; and *charisms of action*, which have their starting point in the charism of service. The descriptions which follow can only hint at the many and varied workings of the various charisms in the church, in the personal life, in preaching and in secular application. They are intended as an attempt to help the individual to recognize the gifts of grace which God has given him, in order that they may be put to use "according to the measure of faith" and "as inspired by the Spirit". I have already warned of the danger of unwarranted classification of the gifts, but analyses lose their danger when we become aware that the distinctions are fluid and come to regard the particular terms only as descriptions of the main characteristics and not as rigidly defined gifts and unvarying types of behaviour.

Charisms of the word

The gift of prophecy

Prophecy is the charism which underlies all the gifts of the word. The complexity of prophetic activity in both Old and New Testaments makes it difficult to give a simple and comprehensive definition. Speaking very generally prophecy means in the first place speaking under divine inspiration. At the same time it is clear that the divinely inspired word is directed to men, so that prophecy always has the effect of making something known. Gerhard Hörster puts it in the following way: "Thus prophecy is a word received by inspiration from God which bears upon the situation of the past, present and future."[109] Prophecy is a message from God for a person, for a certain situation or for a group of people. It differs neither in manner of speaking nor in language from normal human speech, but its content is of particular power, clarity and pertinence. Genuine prophecy does not seek refuge in generalities, but names real things by their names or conveys a promise applying to a particular situation.

Paul regards prophecy as a charism of very great importance. Of course it is true as well that the most important charism is always the one which is most greatly needed at the time; but even when speaking quite generally Paul gives first place to prophecy. He mentions it both in Rom. 12 and in 1 Cor. 12, clearly ranks it above glossolalia, and says that he wishes all Christians were able to prophesy (1 Cor. 14:1-25). Nevertheless he also takes care to point out that, as with all the special charisms, even this gift is not given to all. "Are all prophets?" (1 Cor. 12:29).

Paul himself gives us a more precise definition of prophecy.

"He who prophesies speaks to men for their upbuilding and encouragement and consolation" (1 Cor. 14:3). *Oikodome*, the building of a house, is a technical term in architecture. Prophetic speech is a good building material. It gives advice when there is a decision to be made. It cheers dispirited men by bringing them comfort. It broadens the horizons when bold steps have to be made into the future. Prophecy serves the further purpose of encouragement or exhortation. The Greek word for this, *paraklesis*, has to do with the act of calling someone alongside to help. The man who has a clear vision and the gift of giving an appropriate answer will be asked for help when someone is in difficulties. Since prophecy is a gift of the Holy Spirit, this is not really a case of asking a particular person because of his ability, but of asking the Holy Spirit himself for help. Thus exhortation or encouragement serves the glory of God. Finally, prophecy brings consolation, *paramythia*, which really means "reassurance". For a church or a group of people it means much to know that there is someone there who can advise them in difficult situations. It calms them, leads to greater composure and encourages them to accept the risk of living with Jesus.

The second main function of prophecy, after edification, is the disclosure of hidden things. "But if all prophesy, and an unbeliever or outsider enters, he is convicted by all, he is called to account by all, the secrets of his heart are disclosed; and so, falling on his face, he will worship God and declare that God is really among you" (1 Cor. 14:24-25). Prophetic disclosure of this sort is seen for instance in the encounter of Peter with Ananias and Sapphira (Acts 5:1-11), and in the conversation of Jesus with the woman of Samaria, who at the end exclaims: "Sir, I perceive that you are a prophet" (John 4:19). "Thus the disclosure of the heart through prophecy serves the building up of the church, for it is precisely insight into the inner being of another that forms the basis of fellowship. So long as secretiveness and dissimulation lurk in our present relationships, unity is destroyed. The prophet is therefore fundamental to church life. Without him everything would remain hidden in darkness and the fundamental structure of the church would be unable to carry anything."[110]

Thirdly prophecy is a means of commissioning for service. The most detailed account of the way in which such commissioning took place in New Testament days is recorded in Acts 13:2-3. "While they were worshipping the Lord and fasting, the Holy Spirit said, 'Set apart for me Barnabas and Saul for the work to which I have called them.' Then after fasting and praying they laid their hands on them and sent them off." Verse 1 of the same chapter makes it clear that this commissioning took place at a service of worship, and that the message came through the mouth of a prophet. Certain people not mentioned by name in the text were known and recognized in this church as prophets. God had confirmed their words repeatedly and thus acknowledged the prophetic quality of their message. It was however necessary for the church to ratify their words. This it did by carrying out the commissioning and sealing it with prayer and the laying on of hands. Prophecy is meant to take place as naturally and undramatically as that, and it should be confirmed by the church as visibly and practically as it was on this occasion.

It is in keeping with the basic significance of prophecy as inspired speech that its manner of operation should be very varied. For it is by no means true to say that prophecy can take the form only of public proclamation at a freely structured act of worship. It can help decisions to be made at a church meeting, after the pattern of Acts 13, where the prophetic word is recognized and confirmed by the church members. It has an important role to play in preaching, both at services of worship and evangelistic meetings, and it also has a place in everyday life where even conversations at work or at home, with friends and neighbours, can take on a prophetic radiance.

Prophecy may be recognized in general not by its actual choice of words, but by the prophetic quality of what they express. Certainly there are exceptions to this, for sometimes God guides a person to give explicit emphasis to the authority of the prophetic message and to use a form of words which may go something like "I, the Lord, say to you . . ." There are however great dangers in such a form of words, for it makes the prophecy harder for the church to assess and contains a hidden temptation for the speaker to use such an opening just at the times when he is not quite sure of himself. It can also develop easily into a mania which excites a person into mere outward repetition, or degenerate into a means for gaining power and deliberately manipulating others. Such a form of words must therefore be only a rare exception, permissible only when in addition to the inspired content a clear indication is given by the Holy Spirit that this kind of introduction should be used. In the normal situation it is not the responsibility of the one who utters the prophecy to recognize whether it is genuine, and so he must not manipulate such recognition by the way he phrases his message. The recognition of a word as prophecy is a matter for the hearers with their spiritual gift of discernment, and a matter for

God who confirms a true prophecy by the events which follow. When inspired speech is repeatedly recognized and accepted as authoritative in the same people, they acquire a natural spiritual authority like that of certain people who are clearly described as prophets in Acts 13.

When prophetic gifts are used in personal counselling, special reserve is called for. In general this reserve will take the form of sharing the insight given to one while taking care not on any account to *suggest* that it has prophetic authority. Here too there may be exceptional situations when one is clearly guided to claim prophetic authority, but they will be rare. Reserve will help the counsellor to avoid creating an unhealthy degree of dependence, taking over too much decision-making from the person he is counselling, or making mistakes which have even more disastrous effects than they would otherwise have because what was a merely human piece of advice was made to appear like a prophecy. If we bear in mind that prophecy in the counselling situation is given mainly for the help of the counsellor and not as an instrument for influencing the counsellee, we shall find that God confirms whether what we say is inspired, giving it, in the effect it has on the recipient, that prophetic status which the counsellor has deliberately refrained from giving it explicitly in his form of words.

Mother Basilea Schlink sums up the place of prophecy, its significance and its dangers, in the following way: "Because prophecy is such a sacred gift and because it has been entrusted to men in all their human weakness, the apostle Paul gives clear directions as to how to distinguish between true and false prophecy. Prophecy is to agree with Scripture. It must always be confirmed by one or two other prophets and weighed by the rest (1 Cor. 14:29, 1 Thes. 5:21). The prophet is to prophesy in proportion to his faith (Rom. 12:7). It is also his responsibility to produce nothing from his own mind, vanity or desire for power and to provide absolutely no opportunity for the spirit of Satan to enter, for it is written that the spirits of prophets are subject to the prophets (1 Cor. 14:32). Because the prophet takes part personally, his personality is not switched off in the act of prophesying, but he is responsible for what he says."[111]

The gift of revelation

Revelation is in essence only a form of prophecy, so that what we have said about the charism of prophecy obviously applies to this gift as well. The underlying Greek word *apokalypsis* is used by Paul in 1 Cor. 14:26: "When you come together, each one has a hymn, a lesson, a revelation, a tongue or an interpretation. Let all things be done for edification." *Apokalypsis* means literally "removal of a veil" and clearly refers here to prophecy in the perceptible form of a vision, or less commonly an "audition", i.e. something heard at the normal level of speech. According to the record of Acts revelations were frequent occurrences. Peter announces that this will be so in his Pentecost sermon: "And in the last days it shall be, God declares, that I will pour out my Spirit upon all flesh, and your sons and your daughters shall prophesy, and your young men shall see visions, and your old men shall dream dreams" (Acts 2:17). Here prophecy and revelation are seen in the close association in which they belong.

Peter experiences such a vision when he is commissioned to go to the Gentile centurion Cornelius ". . . and (he) saw the heaven opened, and something descending, like a great sheet . . ." (Acts 10:11). This is then followed by an audition. "While Peter was pondering the vision, the Spirit said to him, 'Behold, three men are looking for you . . .' " (Acts 10:19). The book of Acts is full of such accounts in which very definite guidance is given. Other visions seem to draw aside for a short time the veil which hangs between our earthly world and the heavenly one. Stephen at the moment of death sees heaven open. The scenes described in the book of Revelation also point in this direction.

In practice the gift of revelation frequently manifests itself at a prayer meeting which allows plenty of time for silence and at which there is an atmosphere of expectancy about the exercise of charisms. A member of the group sees an image in his mind. He describes the vision in quite down-to-earth language, as one might describe a painting one was looking at. Another member gives the interpretation, telling what the picture means. The interpretation generally has some reference to the particular group present at the time. Visions are subject to control in the same way as prophecies, but they are easier to share in a group than explicitly prophetic utterances, since they need further interpretation and are therefore tested in effect in the process. In the field of personal counselling the same caution is called for as with prophecy: often visions simply because of their form enjoy from the outset an even higher status than spoken prophecy, and are therefore more dangerous. They too can be taken up by the counsellor as an aid to clarifying the situation, without any need for the counsellor to *claim* that his advice results from a gift of revelation.

The gift of counselling

The Greek word *paraklesis* means "encouragement" or "exhortation", lit. "calling someone alongside to help". As far as the term is concerned, it is hard to draw a dividing line between this and other charisms. We have already met with *paraklesis* as one of the effects of prophecy (1 Cor. 14:3); Paul also links it with teaching (e.g. 1 Tim. 6:2b, "Teach and urge (*parakalei*) these duties"). Paul regards counselling as so important a charism that in Rom. 12:8 he mentions it as a gift of grace in its own right (the gift of exhortation); prophecy and teaching are both mentioned separately.

The word *paraklesis* makes it clear that the heart of this gift of counselling is the giving of help. Thus this gift of grace is not in the first instance determined by its content but by its effects. *Encouragement* is pointing to Jesus the great helper, it is comfort, it is proclamation of his presence and the help that brings, it is also pointing to the Holy Spirit whom Jesus describes as the "Paraclete" or comforter. *Exhortation* is bringing the presence of Christ to bear on a person's situation, telling him where he stands, calling his sins by their name and challenging him to repent. Charismatic counselling will always establish the relationship in both directions: from the person towards Jesus, to receive help and encouragement, strength and comfort; and from Jesus towards him, exhorting, revealing where he stands and calling him to repentance.

Since the charism of counselling is derived from the gift of prophecy it will always have this prophetic basis of inspired speech and action. This does not mean that the counsellor will generally avail himself of prophetic *terminology*: the presence and activity of the Holy Spirit will be confirmed by the power and authority of the counsel given, by the special appropriateness of the counsellor's words which will lead the other to exclaim "Yes, that's it!"

It is in counselling perhaps that it becomes most obvious how closely interwoven are the gifts and the fruit of the Spirit. The charism of counselling can only begin to function where there is spiritual maturity. Without love it becomes ineffective, for no trust can develop. Only on the basis of trust can the prophetic word reach the place where it will be effective: the person in need feels drawn to a Christian because he expects him to be able to help him. Where charismatic counselling operates, all beating about the bush comes to an end. There is no need to spend many words talking about Jesus Christ, for he is present in his Holy Spirit.

The word of wisdom

The two expressions in 1 Cor. 12:8, "word of wisdom" and "word of knowledge", are somewhat problematical. To what extent do they denote separate gifts, to what extent are they merely different aspects of the same gift? We shall not go any further into this question here, but simply deal separately with the two terms, although they are very closely related to each other. In this way we shall be able to describe them more concretely.

As Gilbert Murray points out in *Euripides and his Age*,[112] the word *sophia* embraces wisdom, knowledge, skill and culture. Not only is there no English word corresponding to it: the various words used for its different aspects have lost their poetry. Clearly, however, the term emphasizes wholeness. Wisdom is more than knowledge, more than skill; the concept of wisdom is one of integration, of knowledge given its proper place in a wider context. Paul obviously intends these connotations when he uses the word in his list of charisms, for in the previous chapters he has unequivocally attacked *human* wisdom, i.e. knowledge which is not integrated into God's creative order, skill which is not integrated into God's purposes. G. Hasenhüttl writes: "The word of wisdom is the word of the cross, and it has meaning only when it is produced for the benefit of the church. That was overlooked by the charismatic speakers at Corinth. Christian wisdom consists in becoming foolish; for God has not called the wise and those learned in the scriptures but the 'fools', in order to put to shame the wisdom of this world. The power of God is shown in weakness . . ."[113]

The word of wisdom is no ordinary wisdom achieved over the course of a long life as a result of many insights and experiences, but a spontaneous ability given by the Holy Spirit to grasp the depths of the riches of God, to recognize the real coherence of events and as a result to throw light on the will of God. The great sermons in Acts by Peter, Stephen and Paul are examples of this charismatic wisdom, which suddenly throws light on the relations between things and makes intelligible various otherwise seemingly unconnected and incomprehensible insights. This is why Paul can say of himself: "And I was with you in weakness and in much fear and trembling; and my speech and my message were not in plausible words of wisdom, but in demonstration of the Spirit and of power, that your faith might not rest in the wisdom of men but in the power of God." (1 Cor. 2:3-5).

The word of wisdom has another function too, of which there

are many examples in the Bible and in our own actual experience. This is the gift of a key word in a difficult situation, a kind of quick-wittedness which does not originate in polished human wisdom but reveals the hidden wisdom of God. We find this kind of presence of mind both in Solomon — when he has to settle the dispute of the two women who both claim to be the true mother — and in Jesus when faced with the trap question set by the scribes, whether it is lawful to pay tribute to Caesar. The Spirit of God frees us from the difficult situation and at the same time puts God in the centre of the stage. "And all Israel heard of the judgement which the king had rendered; and they stood in awe of the king, because they perceived that the wisdom of God was in him" (1 Kings 3:28). A similar sequence of events follows the various trap questions set for Jesus by the scribes.

The word of wisdom meets the problem exactly, it releases the tense atmosphere at once. In the answer given a higher wisdom is to be seen, something more than what one's own considered thought could produce. A typical sign of this function of the word of wisdom is the spontaneous agreement of others. If someone constantly speaks such an appropriate and helpful word in all manner of different problem situations, a relationship of trust will develop. This is something stronger than fellow-feeling, for it is based on confidence in the ability of the one who possesses the gift of the word of wisdom. This confidence will result in trust in God, for the charism gives central prominence to the Originator of the gift.

The word of knowledge

In the case of the charism of knowledge there is dispute not only about how it differs from the word of wisdom, but also about the content of the gift itself. One could certainly find general agreement to the proposition that the charism of knowledge is a spirit-given sharing in the all-embracing knowledge of God, just as the word of wisdom is a sharing in the wisdom of God, but this leaves the actual content of the charism very unclearly defined.

Harold Horton formulates the conviction of the classical Pentecostal movement in the following way: "The Word of Knowledge is the supernatural revelation by the Holy Spirit of certain facts in the mind of God. God keeps ever before Him in the storehouse of His mind all the facts of heaven and earth . . . The Word of Knowledge is the revelation to man by His Spirit of some detail of that All-knowledge. The revelation, perhaps, of the existence, condition or whereabouts of some person or object or place, of the location or occasion of some event."[114] A publication sympathetic to the charismatic renewal movement says on the other hand: "In the word of knowledge the exalted Lord reveals to the church and its members an understanding of the theological threads of His message."[115]

I regard it as possible that both these aspects may somehow be included in the Pauline concept of the word of knowledge, but I see the main emphasis as undoubtedly being on the theological side. Supernatural knowledge of unknown facts is a marginal phenomenon both in the New Testament and in present-day experience and it easily degenerates into a charismatic *game*. Where it occurs as a genuine gift of the Holy Spirit it could more appropriately be classed as prophecy or revelation, or in some cases included among "works of power". In 1 Cor. 14:24-25 it is classified as an effect of prophecy, which causes "secrets of the heart" to be disclosed. It does of course impinge upon the sphere of the word of knowledge, but this is not its chief emphasis, and it is not by any means to be regarded as one of the important gifts of grace.

The word of knowledge, therefore, is essentially the charismatic interpretation of the word of God for a particular situation. Like the word of wisdom it is a word which surprises, instantaneously and convincingly illuminating the message of a Bible passage for the hearers. The gift is not a negation of theological study: rightly understood, the two activities are complementary. Theological study uncovers the basic statements of the Bible, and the word of knowledge applies them to the actual situation of the hearers. It does not always have to refer to a particular biblical text, however; it can also interpret in a relevant fashion quite general statements of the Bible. Because it is always addressed to a particular situation, it must not be given absolute authority. It is a direct impulse of the Holy Spirit, but this does not automatically give it general validity in the realm of theological thought.

This meaning of the word of knowledge is what Paul has in mind in 1 Cor. 2:12-13, when he writes: "Now we have received not the spirit of the world, but the Spirit which is from God, that we might understand the gifts bestowed on us by God. And we impart this in words not taught by human wisdom but taught by the Spirit, interpreting spiritual truths to those who possess the Spirit."

The gift of teaching

This gift of grace appears last in the list of charisms in Rom. 12.

The term used there, *didaskalia*, is the Greek word from which we derive our word "didactic". When we read in 1 Cor. 12:28-29 of "teachers" the same root is involved. Teaching here denotes therefore not only the content of what is taught but also and more particularly the manner in which it is transmitted: instruction, didactic teaching. It is this insight that leads Gerhard Hörster to write: "The gift of teaching consists of passing on biblical material in a way that is easily remembered, vivid and readily comprehended."[116]

In contrast to the word of knowledge, the gift of teaching is not a spontaneous inspiration making the word of God suddenly relevant and applicable to the situation of the hearers, but the Spirit-given ability of a teacher to awaken in those taught an understanding of God in his word and in his works. Although the gift of teaching is in essence a permanent gift it is not fully at the disposal of the one who has it but is constantly dependent on inspiration from the Holy Spirit. When Jesus began to preach and to travel around, the first thing which struck people was his gift of teaching. "And they were all amazed, so that they questioned among themselves, saying, 'What is this? A new teaching! With authority he commands even the unclean spirits, and they obey him' " (Mark 1:27). The gift was always present, but it showed itself only on the particular occasions when the pertinence of his inspired teaching fascinated the people and made the charism obvious.

In our day, when difficulties of communication are especially marked and the Christian church presents the appearance of a body torn apart by many differences of opinion in doctrine, the charism of teaching is particularly necessary. The essential contents of the divine message are, it is true, recorded in scripture, but because of the great distance in time by which we are separated from Bible days they are not immediately capable of being understood.

What does being a Christian mean in objective terms today for the individual in his own particular situation, for a group, for a denomination, for the whole Christian church? It is the task of the charismatic teacher to make the word of God understandable in our age. At the same time the charism of teaching is more than a general teaching ability. For example, the answer to a contemporary question which someone may give on the basis of his abilities as a teacher may in itself be perfectly correct, and yet fail to provide clear direction in the typical situation. Charismatic teaching on the other hand is always to be recognized by the way in which it exactly fits the situation, bringing to it a genuine and deep understanding.

The gift of glossolalia

Discussion of this one charism has become so extensive that here I shall give only a summary of the different aspects in tabular form. An exhaustive assessment of the various points of view and types of experience would go far beyond the scope of this book and would in any case give the misleading impression that the gift of glossolalia was the most important of all the charisms.

1. Speaking in other languages is a gift of grace which does occur today but which does not have a unique role. Some Christians possess this gift and others do not. In certain situations its use is appropriate, in others inappropriate.

The view is always being put forward, especially in Pentecostal circles, that speaking in other languages is a gift all Christians should have, since Paul says in 1 Cor. 14:5, "Now I want you all to speak in tongues . . ." But Paul also says, in 1 Cor. 12:30, "Do all speak with tongues?" Moreover glossolalia is included in verse 10 of this chapter as one in the list of charisms of which it is said that one person receives one gift, and another another — clearly implying that none of the gifts mentioned there is promised to every Christian. How then are we to understand 1 Cor. 14:5? First of all it is obvious from the context that this verse was not written in order to single out speaking in other languages as especially important, but rather to emphasize the greater importance and value of prophecy. "I want you all to speak in tongues, but even more to prophesy." If one gives this verse the emphasis which the context shows Paul to have intended, it means something like this: "Speaking in tongues is an important gift, but prophecy is an even more important one." Every gift of the Holy Spirit is so good and so important that we should wish everyone to have it. This does not however mean that everyone will receive every charism whether speaking in other languages or prophecy.

2. The Greek word *glossolalia* is usually translated into English as "speaking in tongues". Although the word *glossa* can mean either "tongue" or "language", the term "speaking in tongues" is unfortunate. For it gives the impression that glossolalia consists of ecstatic babbling, whereas Paul makes it clear that it means speaking (or at most praying) in a language not familiar to the one who is speaking, and that its beginning, ending and emotional peaks are all subject to the will of the speaker. Frequently therefore Paul uses the expression *en glossais lalein*, to speak in languages.

3. Particularly in a missionary situation (as indeed on the

Day of Pentecost) it sometimes happens that this speaking in other languages is done in a language spoken by the hearers, although the speaker has never learned it. It has also proved possible to identify in glossolalia languages spoken in earlier times. Usually however it is a case of *artificial* languages which do nevertheless display a genuine linguistic structure with root words and derivatives, grammatical rules, common words and rarer ones — in other words, not a structure that someone could simply have "invented". I would regard such a semantic structure, at least in primitive form, as an essential mark of authentic glossolalia.

4. Glossolalia originates in deep levels of the personality. "If the Jungian idea of the collective unconscious is accepted, speaking in tongues makes real sense, as a breakthrough into consciousness of a deep level of the collective unconscious similar to the dream. Linguistic patterns belonging to the past, to some other part of the present, or to some other level of being take possession of the individual and are expressed by him."[117] This of course says nothing about its ultimate origin: glossolalia is equally likely to occur in cases of mental illness or demonic oppression as in the form of a gift of the Holy Spirit. It does however mean that speaking in Spirit-given languages provides an important opportunity for God to reach down to and heal our unconscious mind.

5. In 1 Cor. 12-14 Paul sets up something approaching a basic set of rules for the use of the gift of glossolalia. He takes more care over this than he does in respect of other charisms, evidently because there is a greater possibility of abuse. The following are the main points in this set of rules:

12:10	Speaking in other languages is one gift among many. Some members of the church possess it, others do not.
12:12ff.	The picture of the body of Christ tells us that the importance of a gift depends on its being needed at the time. This is true of glossolalia as of the other gifts.
14:2,5	The classic use of speaking in other languages is in praying to God — the Spirit praying through me. This charism generally therefore belongs to the sphere of private prayer.
14:4	Glossolalia has a very important function in the personal realm. It edifies the person who exercises it.

14:13	Speaking in other languages also has a function in the church, provided it is interpreted. Hence as far as the local church is concerned, interpretation is the more important gift.
14:27	Glossolalia is subject to the will of the speaker. Otherwise there would be no sense in the rules Paul makes for its use. The exercise of this gift of grace is to be kept within limits (at most three speakers one after another) and must not create any disorder ("each in turn").
14:29	Since interpretation is a variant form of the gift of prophecy, it too is subject to evaluation by the church.

Paul himself sums up this set of rules with the words: "So, my brethren, earnestly desire to prophesy, and do not forbid speaking in tongues" (1 Cor. 14:39).

6. The charism of glossolalia can be *under-estimated,* especially when it is denied that it can still be a gift of the Holy Spirit today. For instance W. G. Broadbent writes: "In the early part of the apostolic period all those who belonged to the groups of whom it is reported that they spoke in tongues did so. By the middle of the apostolic age it was only a few, not everyone. When however the New Testament was complete and became available to the believing community, 'the tongues ceased'."[118] Others do not go quite so far as this but nonetheless feel that glossolalia is somehow a *disreputable* gift which it would be better not to receive.

7. Equally, the charism of glossalalia can be *over-estimated,* especially when it is assumed that every Christian can receive this gift, as is generally taught in the Pentecostal churches and also in the neo-Pentecostal movement. Larry Christenson, for example, believes that while God calls only certain people to speak in tongues in a meeting, nevertheless every believer can be blessed through the personal edification conferred by the gift when used in private devotion. The gift is available for every Christian who desires it and asks the Lord for it.[119] Over frequent use of the gift in public worship, particularly in a highly emotional atmosphere, can likewise be an indication that the gift is being over-valued.

8. Various dangers go with the charism of glossolalia. Some of these apply to all charisms, and will be described more fully at a later stage of this book, but some of them are peculiar to this gift. Where people regard glossolalia as a sign clearly

indicative of Spirit baptism and so of a higher status in the kingdom of God, it is easy for an unhealthy anxiety to develop, producing a passion for this charism and attempts to bring about a "breakthrough" by the use of various exercises and forms of psychological conditioning. Frequently the result which follows is an ecstatic counterfeit experience, associated with crying, shuddering, shaking, falling down, clapping and shouting. Such phenomena can be a sign of demonic activity, but often they indicate mere human adjuncts resulting from an urge to be accepted, psychological instability, a breakthrough of repressed emotions or something of that sort — in other words, symptoms of personal immaturity. These forms are never divine in origin, for "God is not a God of confusion but of peace" (1 Cor. 14:33).

Those who speak in tongues often make a claim to authority in the church, a claim which has its origin in an arrogant attitude towards those who do not speak in other languages. Human dependence and splits in the church fellowship result. But the person who uses his gift only for his own benefit is also in danger. He may come to think that the breakthrough of glossolalia means he has reached a higher stage in the spiritual life, where he no longer needs to strive for further sanctification and growth in the faith.

9. What are the benefits we can weigh up against these dangers? Paul concentrates mainly on the importance of glossolalia in the personal prayer life of the individual. Here it can be of considerable help. "He who speaks in a tongue edifies himself" (1 Cor. 14:4). In personal prayer we continually become aware of the limitations of our speech and our own perception. "Likewise the Spirit helps us in our weakness; for we do not know how to pray as we ought, but the Spirit himself intercedes for us with sighs too deep for words" (Rom. 8:26). Praying in other languages can thus open up a new dimension in worship and praise as well as in intercession, where often so many problems crowd in upon us that words fail us. Because glossolalia makes us more clearly aware of the reality of God than many other experiences, it is able to break through the disinclination, monotony and resignation of our prayer life. So too in difficult situations where we no longer find it possible to pray with understanding, the Spirit can pray in us. Ultimately the Holy Spirit finds through prayer spoken in other languages a direct way into our unconscious mind, which is constantly in need of being cleansed and refilled.

In public worship glossolalia can be of help only when it is interpreted. Then, as in private prayer, it can help to express the inexpressible in worship, praise and encouragement. For in the interpretation of a prayer in another language we often find that the words have a power of expression, a depth and originality, which we should not find in the rational speech of the person who interprets.

Glossolalia can be of great help in situations of persecution. Corrie ten Boom writes: "A missionary in China was subjected to brainwashing. He resisted and struggled against it with all his might. But the moment came when he was at the end of his strength. Then he began to speak in tongues. This relaxed relationship with the Lord was his salvation. The enemy could no longer influence his spirit. Has the Lord at this time given this gift to many children of God in various churches because it is a strong weapon and a powerful defence in the final struggle?"[120]

The interpretation of glossolalia

The ability to interpret prayers in other languages is an important gift as far as the church is concerned, for without it glossolalia cannot have its proper effect. The Greek word *hermeneia* does not mean "translation" in the philological sense, but rather interpretation. Glossolalia is not reproduced word for word: the Holy Spirit gives the interpreter a sensitivity to that which has been said in the prayer uttered in another language. Sometimes it has to be expressed by a circumlocution, because there are often no corresponding terms and images available in our language which are exactly equivalent to those of a spiritual message. Accordingly an interpretation may well be considerably longer than the prayer in another language to which it corresponds. Sometimes too only the main thought is indicated, or it happens that a second interpreter has understood a further part of the thought expressed and so adds his interpretation to the first one.

In general the content of such interpretations consists of praise and worship, encouragement and exhortation, but not with the direct sharpness of prophecy. God has given a special charism for that purpose. It is however sometimes the case that glossolalia is immediately followed by a prophecy which at first appears to be an interpretation, but which is then recognized by the interpreters present as an independent prophecy. Since the charism of interpretation of glossolalia is closely related to prophecy, it is in my opinion included in Paul's ruling that it must be subject to the control of the church. For the false interpretation of prayers in other languages can do the church as much harm as prophecy which is not inspired by God or is distorted by man.

It is also possible to experience interpretation of a kind in connection with the private practice of glossolalia. Someone may, for example, be faced with an unexpected decision he has to make. He prays quietly in another language. If he is suddenly filled with a great inward sense of clarity, enabling him to make an accurate decision, he has experienced an interpretation of his own incomprehensible prayer. Or if as a result of frequent prayer in other languages a person becomes aware of certain sins because his unconscious mind has come more strongly under the influence of the Holy Spirit, the effect is the same as that of a direct interpretation of a prayer spoken aloud in another language: the Holy Spirit's message has been understood.

Singing in the Spirit

The various Greek expressions used in the New Testament to refer to this all place emphasis on praising God. Paul distinguishes two kinds of song: "I will sing with the spirit and I will sing with the mind also" (1 Cor. 14:15). Singing with the mind is the singing of songs already written down. Such songs may well have been charismatic in their origin, but they have subsequently been written down and have become part of the church's heritage. An interesting story is told of how Ambrose's great hymn *Te Deum Laudamus* came to be written. When Augustine was baptized at Easter 387, Ambrose and Augustine are said to have sung this hymn responsively: moved by the Spirit, Ambrose began, and then likewise moved by the Spirit, Augustine replied with every second line.[121] That is singing in the Spirit.

In public worship it can happen that during a period of silence someone suddenly begins to sing in his own language or in the form of glossolalia. Others join in although they do not know the song. Sometimes charismatic song can be sung in several parts or as a round. Usually the charismatic singing is led by people who would be incapable of composing or writing a song with their *mind*. The musical and literary quality of these songs is generally mediocre, but often it is very original or strange. Nevertheless the singing has a beautiful effect. In its spontaneity it can convey the great conciseness of a spiritual utterance: it seems as if the church is taking part in the worship of heaven. Thus singing in the Spirit can become an inspiring medium of worship and praise.

The gift of prophetic leadership

The gift of leadership often overlaps with other gifts of grace such as the word of wisdom and of knowledge, prophecy or service. But when we talk of leadership we are talking of a greater responsibility, such as the running of a local church or a group of Christian workers, or a position of responsibility in public life, e.g. in a business concern, a teaching post or political office. The leadership of a group of people is a difficult and complex task. If the person responsible for it possesses the charism of leadership, all that he does will have an evident confidence, a natural authority, a clear direction, which will constantly be proved right by events. Even the charismatic leader will make mistakes, but his leadership is of a different quality from that of someone who has purely human gifts of leadership.

The great variety of leadership functions is recognized even in the New Testament, in that two different words are used for the charism of leadership. In Rom. 12:8 it says: "If you are a leader, exert yourself to lead" (NEB). *Prohistemi*, to lead, means literally "to stand before", hence to "look after" — it comes from the language of banking and is a technical term in the civil service. This charism I call "*administrative* leadership", and it will be described in a later section. In 1 Cor. 12:28, on the other hand, we have the word *kybernēsis*, literally "steering with a rudder". It is an expression borrowed from nautical language, and it is concerned not with the administration of funds or other valued items, but with the making of decisions, with steering. Charismatic leadership chooses the right course out of several possible ones and takes the whole group along in that direction. Therefore I call this charism "*prophetic* leadership".

The Greek word *kybernēsis* also underlies the modern term "cybernetics". This is the word for the science of control techniques and programming, the principles of which have made possible the development of the computer. The cybernetic system can be appropriately programmed so that decisions are made as the programme directs and taking into account the special facts of each case. The charism of prophetic leadership would on this analogy be the ability to make decisions in individual cases on the basis of divine programming. The centre of the programme is the Bible itself, but the Bible is far too general to be capable of giving clear answers to every particular problem. The charism is in this case more precise and to the point, but it does not go beyond the basic principles of the biblical programme. It provides as it were God's personal programme for a certain person in a particular situation.

All forms of spiritual guidance are constantly at risk from the side of man himself. The word of God often gives only a general answer to a particular problem, an answer which in the process of being applied to that particular case can be distorted by human ideas and motivations. Equally risky is the practice of listening for an "inner voice", even where this is accompanied by prayer and Bible reading. Even the word of another Christian can deceive, for here too it is possible for human, Satanic and divine elements to be mingled. Unequivocal spiritual guidance will be found only in a church, or in a spiritual fellowship of similar structure, where the various charisms such as the word of wisdom or of knowledge, prophecy and counselling are brought together and activated by the charism of prophetic leadership.

Charisms of Action

The gift of service

Gifts of the word have always enjoyed a higher standing in Christianity than gifts of action, all of which are derived to a greater or lesser extent from the charism of *service*. Gerhard Hörster writes: "It is of course firmly anchored in the minds of Christians that prophecy and teaching are gifts of God's grace. Many however have not yet discovered the truth that practical gifts are likewise free gifts of God. The fact that Paul sets the two kinds of gifts alongside one another ought to give food for thought. Anyone who studies the gifts of grace in the New Testament is freed from the necessity of imagining that 'charismatic' is synonymous with 'ecstatic speaking in tongues'." *Diakonia* (service or ministry) is a word which has several meanings in the New Testament. In 1 Cor. 12:5 it is used as a general description of all the gifts of grace, the three terms "charism", "operation" and "ministry" appearing as interchangeable. Paul also uses *diakonia* to denote certain offices in the church. Thus in 1 Tim. 1:12 he writes, "I thank him who has given me strength for this, Christ Jesus our Lord, because he judged me faithful by appointing me to his service" — by which he obviously means the office of an apostle. Finally *diakonia* is used to denote a particular charism which is included in the list in Rom. 12: ". . . if service, in our serving" (v.7). In Acts 6:1-7 it is stressed that the practical task of caring for the widows calls for men who are "full of the Spirit and of wisdom". This gift of service appears in effect also in 1 Cor. 12, though under a different name, *antilempsis*, which is generally rendered "ability to help" (NEB). Literally the word means "receiving in exchange": Paul is here using a word from the language of trade, which describes the task of the person whose duty it is to see that people keep their side of the contract.

The charism of service has to do with all man's practical needs. Today this includes a wide area: food, housing, health, business life, employment, energy supply, conservation of the ecological balance of nature, care of the elderly and the various tasks of administration. It is a belittlement of *diakonia* to take the word as referring only to the care of the sick. Health is a basic need of man and certainly an important concern of God. It is natural therefore that Christian movements have always put intensive efforts into caring for the sick. But this must not be seen as representing the whole of the "deacon" 's task. Today there are quite new problems emerging, the solution of which is essential for the survival of man.

There is nothing spectacular about this charism of service. The action it involves appears quite natural and normal. It is only the surprising appropriateness and straightforwardness of the action which reveals its origin in the working of divine power. God gives more than man by nature possesses. The workings of the Holy Spirit exactly meet the needs of man, and they remain at the same time in constant harmony with the will of God. The charism of service is administration, provision of help and spontaneous organization through the power of the Holy Spirit. This gift is very much needed in our highly organized world, for it breaks through the egoism of bureaucracy which revolves only around itself.

The evidence for the gift of service is that what is necessary actually gets done, and that properly. The purpose behind any kind of help is to serve another person. The help given must therefore be appropriate. The help given by the Good Samaritan was of this quality, for it included everything that the man who had been robbed and wounded really needed. In genuine service nothing is superfluous, for what is unnecessary is inappropriate. Appropriateness depends on recognizing truth and reality, but inappropriateness is unloving, usually having something to do with a person's desire to draw attention to himself. Genuine service therefore undertakes what is necessary without fuss, and is often inspired by the spontaneous prompting of the Holy Spirit. If I make a fuss it is for my own sake: it is inappropriate, because it is aimed at serving me and not the person in need.

In the symbolic act of washing his disciples' feet Jesus made it clear that service is essentially the gift of selflessness, because it relates all that it does to the need of the person requiring help. Is not selflessness a greater miracle than works of power, speaking in other languages or words of wisdom? Is not the power of the Holy Spirit more greatly needed here than for the charisms of the word? Perhaps the *simple* charisms of service, sharing possessions, mercy and the faith which moves mountains are in reality the *great* charisms, which have done far more to build up the Kingdom of God than many a charism of the word.

Sharing possessions

"If you give . . . give with all your heart" (Rom. 12:8, NEB). Here, in the list of charisms in Rom. 12, we meet the gift of sharing possessions, or, as Hasenhüttl puts it, the "charism of ability to share".[123] In 1 Cor. 13 it is mentioned again: "If I give away all I have . . . but have not love, I gain nothing" (v.3). The charism lies neither in the fact that I have something nor simply in the fact that I give it away, but in a manner of sharing my possessions which is motivated by *diakonia* and is in keeping with the will of God.

The man who is gifted with this charism looks at things this way: God has given me what I possess in order that I may use it to serve others. It is not a matter of distributing my possessions indiscriminately nor is it a matter of distributing things so that in the end everyone will have the same amount. The starting point of this form of service is that possessions, like every gift of God, are the basic materials for a task. I have money, land, influence, artistic and creative skill, because God entrusts these things to me, to be used in an appropriate way. My possessions and my abilities belong to God; I am there in an administrative capacity. My thoughts and my discoveries are the work of the Holy Spirit; it is my responsibility to use them properly.

Possessions are not linked to money and material things. Everything which I have freely at my disposal belongs within this category. Intellectual abilities, accumulated knowledge, creative thought are my possessions just as is the treasure-store of the experiences I have undergone. One of the most precious possessions is time, because today it is in short supply. This makes time an area which is especially hard to administer in such a way as both to serve my own practical needs and to minister selflessly to the needs of my fellow men.

Much giving takes place today, but there is still much need in the material realm and more still on the emotional level. Many people have to be cared for constantly: they do not find the way out of this dependence and they never achieve an autonomous life-style. Some of them could be helped if they were provided not only with material possessions but also with genuine love. Here the charism of sharing possessions is lacking: the gift of being able to give in such a way that another's life is changed for the better and his personality strengthened.

The charism of sharing possessions is the wisdom to give at the right time and in the right quarter. Only so will the right thing be done without fuss and bother, and the action be a *diakonia*. In this way even material possessions can be integrated in the life of a Christian. This also applies however to those who are not rich, for all people have possessions, things to which they cling. Giving away possessions means being able to share. Here is a great secret of growth. Just as an amoeba multiplies by dividing itself, so everything we possess becomes more when we share it — but only if the process is not brought to a halt by our wanting suddenly to hold on to what we have newly acquired. Ability to share as a principle of life is very difficult: it is scarcely attainable by human strength alone and is probably possible only when it is given to us as a charism, a free gift of the Holy Spirit.

The charism of mercy, or compassion

This gift is described in Rom. 12:8: "He who does acts of mercy, (let him do them) with cheerfulness." This is the gift of compassion, the ability to put oneself in another's place. It is expressed well by the German word *Barmherzigkeit*, which contains the word *Herz*, heart, and reminds us that the heart is involved. This charism is the fruit of a strong, inner compulsion. He who possesses it finds it impossible to pass by on the other side. Compassion is also more than sympathy, for sympathy may be the result of a weak emotional constitution. Compassion means rather the ability to bear the need of another from within. People who have it are able to benefit a person in need of help by the way they approach him, and to find the right balance between helping and challenging.

Most people keep themselves apart from the sick and the weak. In their eyes the need of such people is the responsibility of the institutions set up for that purpose. Compassion has therefore become a rare virtue. It is all the more important therefore that the charism of compassion should be awakened and developed. If somewhere in a church, a factory, a housing estate or a tower block there is someone who possesses this charism, there is great hope for many who are sick, weak and backward. Compassionate people will however soon be overwhelmed by the sheer number of people in need, and therefore it is particularly important that all those who possess this charism should use it.

Compassion has a healing function, for it releases love and so creates a real relationship between people. Jesus had this gift in a quite exceptional way. He says of himself: "Come to me, all who labour and are heavy laden, and I will give you rest." (Matt. 11:28). His compassion gives people inner peace. Jesus leads people out of the distress into which the soul is plunged by any kind of need. Thus the sick are not only healed but strengthened afresh at the emotional level as well. The tax collectors and adulterers do not merely receive good advice for the journey of life, but by personal encounter with Jesus are released from the spiritual distress into which their status as outcasts in society had brought them.

People in material need today receive social assistance. But that alone does not release the poor man from his personal problems. He needs new self-confidence, help to help himself, new hope. This does not come about through material help alone, but much more as a result of human contact arising from true compassion. The same applies to a man afflicted by mental distress or physical illness. He can get the right medicines and find an environment which will contribute to his recovery. But for the same reason he is all the more in need of personal contact. He needs people who will invest a deep commitment in their relationships with him, people with the gift of compassion.

The charism of faith

At first it may seem strange that Paul should include faith among the list of charisms in 1 Cor. 12:9 ("to another faith by the same Spirit . . ."). He cannot mean saving faith, for that is a precondition to the reception of the Spirit. True, it is clearly stated in Eph. 2:8 that a decision of faith cannot be made without the grace of God: "For by grace you have been saved through faith; and this is not your own doing, it is the gift of God." The Greek word here used for "gift" is not however *charisma* but *doron*, a sacrificial gift which one brought if one wished to approach God. For all God's help, this gift remains always associated with man's own prior decision. The kind of faith Paul is talking about in 1 Cor. 12 when he speaks of the charism of faith is revealed in the passage which follows in the next chapter: "and if I have all faith, so as to remove mountains, but have not love, I am nothing" (1 Cor. 13:2).

The charism of faith is primarily a charism of power, related to the gift of miracles. Joseph Brosch writes: "Thus the charism of faith is nothing other than . . . the power bestowed by the Holy Spirit, and working through the individual, to carry through God's will despite all natural obstacles; in particular the power to triumph over a world opposed to God."[124] The gift of faith is also however a prophetic gift. "The Christian who is endowed with this gift of grace has a supernatural ability to sense that in a particular, real-life situation God is going to reveal His power, His righteousness and His mercy."[125] Thus faith is both an unspeakable knowledge that God will intervene in a specific situation, and the gift of becoming the means by which the intervention of God's power takes place. So the gift of faith can make the impossible possible, though only when what is said and done is truly inspired.

Faith as a charism is the firm knowledge that here and now God will do a miracle. This knowledge leads to action; in other words, the person who has faith acts as if the expected intervention of God were already a reality. Perhaps this causes him to make decisions which seem irrational to others around him, going beyond the confines of a purely human perception of reality. But where the charism of faith is present, he is carrying out God's will, even though it may be in the face of massive opposition.

Where is the borderline between the victorious assurance of faith and human pig-headedness? The first characteristic by which the charism of faith may be recognized is that God vindicates it by events. Success alone is not however sufficient evidence, for occasionally human stubbornness will be proved right in spite of all experience to the contrary. Charismatic action displays as its motive love for one's fellow man, not mere self-assertion. Love is the only mark whereby charismatic faith can be distinguished from human stubbornness. The adventure of faith is always marked by a divine clarity and a happy, relaxed attitude, not by unintelligibility and obdurate eccentricity.

The gift of miracles, or works of power

This charism is associated with miracles of every sort. In the New Testament we read in particular of miracles of nature (e.g. Acts 16:26), the exorcism of demons (e.g. Acts 16:18) and the raising of the dead (e.g. Acts 9:40). It is difficult to define the exact scope of this gift, since the charisms of miracles, faith and healing are closely related. Even the Old Testament records a large number of events in which works of power were to be seen, and in the case of Jesus this aspect is very strongly marked. It is therefore reasonable to suppose that the charism of miracles still has a considerable importance for us today, where it is allowed to develop. It is noticeable that there are many impressive examples of this gift throughout Christian history, especially at times of revival and of persecution.

In early Christianity missionary preaching without works of power was unthinkable. Paul writes concerning his own ministry: "My speech and my message were not in plausible words of wisdom, but in demonstration of the Spirit and of power" (1 Cor. 2:4). Joseph Brosch writes: "From every quarter, wherever the messengers of Jesus had gone, the reports came back that they had been given the gift of miracles. In keeping with the promise given by the Lord when He issued the Great Commission, it was practically a criterion of the young church that it came in Spirit and in power. Though the instruments chosen by God for the proclamation of the Good News might be weak, God worked all the more powerfully through them by His own mighty arm, and so brought to nothing the wisdom of this world."[126]

In addition to their role in missionary preaching, miracles had for the earliest Christians a very special significance in times of persecution. When the young Christian church at Jerusalem underwent her first crisis, with Peter and John being arrested by the Council and formally forbidden to say any more about Jesus, they remembered the promise of Jesus that he would perform works of power: " 'And now, Lord, look upon their threats, and grant thy servants to speak the word with all boldness, while thou stretchest out thy hand to heal, and signs and wonders are performed through the name of thy holy servant Jesus.' And when they had prayed, the place in which they were gathered together was shaken; and they were all filled with the Holy Spirit and spoke the word of God with boldness" (Acts 4:29-31). The book of Acts shows us many examples of how signs and wonders took place in order to protect the way of the young church. It also reminds us however that miracles did not always take place: the Spirit blows where he will.

Why is it that so little can be said about the gift of miracles in practice today? Whereas healings and works of power constantly accompanied the church in its early days and in later revival movements, our present-day preaching is too rigidly confined to the word. Up to a point there are good reasons for this: there is always a danger that a miracle will detach itself from the preaching context and become an end in itself, so that works of power cease to be signs following the word and become its content instead. The New Testament however never gives us permission to prevent the wrong use of a charism by making no use at all of the gift. In a disciplined manner therefore we should broaden the scope of our expectations to include once more the gift of miracles, and allow the charisms which God has bestowed to fulfil their rightful function.

The gift of healing

When this charism is mentioned in 1 Cor. 12:9, the phrase used means literally "gifts of healings". This double plural is clearly chosen deliberately, for it is retained throughout the chapter (cf. verses 28, 30). *Gifts* — that means that there are several quite distinct forms of healing, e.g. prayer with laying on of hands, prayer for a sick person in his absence, or anointing with oil. *Healings* — the use of this plural is harder to explain. Probably it means that every healing is to be regarded as a charism in its own right, as a separate gift of God's grace, whereas in the case of the other gifts it is the ability itself which is described as a charism. Thus it is a matter of indifference who actually possesses the "gifts of healings" — for that some *do* exercise this gift repeatedly may be concluded from the fact that it is included in the list of charisms in 1 Cor. 12:8-10. This is also confirmed by the experience of the church both throughout its history and at the present day. What does Paul want to achieve by this indifference? I take it that he wants to urge upon us a particular modesty as far as this charism is concerned. There are speakers in other languages, there are deacons, there are prophets — but there are no *healers*, only people who find that their ministry has a special tendency in this direction. It does not lead to a charismatic *office*. This may also help to explain Jesus' reserve in the matter of healing, which he never used (unlike miracles such as the feeding of the five thousand) as an open manifestation of the power of God.

Illness is not simply a matter of physical disorder. That is made clear even in the healings which Jesus performed. He did not merely heal the sickness, he blessed the whole person. He forgave sins, he purified and sanctified every part of the person. Modern medicine has again revealed the very close connection between body and soul, so that in the case of many diseases the doctor must concern himself with the emotional life of his patient or with his social environment. Both can have a profound influence on his condition. Of course the healing of the sick is primarily a matter of curing physical disorders, but mental disabilities, which are rapidly increasing today, are also a part of the same field. I would also include the peripheral emotional disorders, such as nervousness, anxiety, restlessness, agitation, problems of orientation, as well as the whole area of social disorder. Many people are already so damaged in this respect that "normal" forms of counselling or therapy are no longer able to help them. Prayer for healing has just as much of a place here as in the area of physiological disorders. Even in the Old Testament we are told that God does not heal every illness, even when it is made a matter for prayer. The same is true of the experience of the earliest Christian churches. Paul was probably sick throughout his life; it is recorded also that Timothy was sick for a while and was not healed at once. It is still true today that the person who exercises the charism of healing has no assurance that he will be successful. Roland Brown, for example, never tells a person that he will be healed through prayer, nor that God will make him well if only he can have enough faith and pray hard enough. The person exercising the gift of healing never knows what God will do or when he will do it nor how. What can be said is that God desires the good of the sufferer and that he is able to heal. It is possible to trust God and ask for his healing not knowing what the outcome will be but hoping for healing.[127]

Occasionally it happens that a sick person is promised healing, as in the case of the lame man in the temple (Acts 3:6). Here the gift of healing is coupled with the gift of prophecy. The gift of faith may also be present, i.e. the knowledge that God will do a miracle in this situation, as with the raising of Lazarus. But it is essential that there should be a special authority and inner assurance before anyone is given a direct promise of healing.

Many diseases are not healed immediately. Often the prayer of blessing over a sick person is just the beginning of a process. The prayer brings his whole person into the sphere of God's activity. Perhaps to begin with he is given a deeper recognition of sin, or he gets to know God better through deeper experiences in prayer. After a long process it may be that healing finally comes, but it may equally be the readiness to say "yes" to the disease. If the healing is immediate there is a danger too for the person who has offered the prayer. Perhaps he will associate the healing too closely with his own person, or perhaps others will do so, causing the healer himself rather than God to stand in the forefront. Recognition of the danger of an immediate healing must not however mean that one should never expect it. God does not let himself be pressed into any mould: the Spirit blows where he will.

What forms does prayer for the sick take in actual practice? If a sick person expects nothing from God, because he has not a living relationship with him, one cannot pray aloud and obviously for that person. Here there is a place for the silent prayer of blessing. I can lay my hands on the sick person in my imagination. This has no magical efficacy, for God is not in the least dependent on my gestures, whether they are made in fact or in the imagination. But the imaginary laying on of hands helps me to form a closer relationship with the sick person, for the gesture of imposition expresses a strong human contact.

Another form is the communal prayer of a group of Christians for a sick person. It often happens that a whole group of people, be it a house group or a local congregation, is deeply moved by the illness of someone who is near and dear to them. The group therefore prays together for the one who is sick. There are some groups which evidently have great power through their prayers, and who may therefore be said to exercise the charism of healing as a group. In particularly difficult situations it is appropriate to make use of prayer and fasting. Starting from the realization that we have no authority to dispose over the charism of healing, we may follow literally the example of Jesus. "This kind cannot be driven out by anything but prayer and fasting" (Mark 9:29).

Wherever possible one should pray with the sick person. Here the laying on of hands is a great help. If the sick person is not familiar with this kind of prayer one should explain it to him and ask him if he wants it. In explaining the action care should be taken to make it clear that the laying on of hands has no magical effect. It is a sign of sympathy and of a human relationship into which one enters in order to stand alongside that person before God. If there is a danger — as there may be especially with unstable people — of an unhealthy dependence resulting from the laying on of hands, the action should be avoided and done simply in the imagination.

Prayer for healing also has a place in the life of the local church, for the charism of healing, like all the gifts of grace, has been placed within the sphere of the church's responsibility even when it is exercised through personal contact. There is therefore a danger in special healing centres which are separated from the life of the church, and even more so in travelling healers. The gift of healing should find its home in the natural structure of the local church, the pastoral ministry or a church group, and in the worship of the church. Heribert Mühlen writes: "If someone comes forward in a service and asks for healing, all are deeply affected and see this as a test of their faith. 'Should we and may we ask God now to heal this man? Will He show His power?' When one experiences a situation like this for the first time the first reaction is one of consternation, perhaps even revulsion. Many people need a long process of surrendering themselves to God before growing into the attitude of simple trust which is associated with prayer for healing and with acceptance of the gift of healing."[128] A special form of healing through the ministry of the church is the anointing of the sick with oil, as described in Jas. 5:11-16. The decisive factor here is probably that the local church not only provides the general spiritual background for the prayer for healing, but also appears in a quasi-official form in the persons of the elders. If we study the passage in detail, we shall observe that behind this practice there lies rich pastoral experience. "The faith of the sick person, his humble obedience in calling for the elders . . . and their readiness to be called; the mutual confession of sins; the anointing with oil; the prayer with laying on of hands . . ."[129] — all are steps which help to give the event a symbolic setting and lead to a deep communication between the sick person and the elders.

Our age is an age which makes people ill. Medicine has developed many good drugs; medical skill has reached a high level. Nevertheless the charism of healing is not in any sort of competition with the doctors: the two kinds of healing are complementary. In spite of medical advances the charism of healing is as necessary now as it ever was, both in those situations where the doctors come to the end of their skill and in those where the guidance of the Holy Spirit makes it clear that God intends to heal. Not only this, but the prayer for healing brings the whole person into the sphere of God's influence, whereas medicines generally affect only a particular area of the body. Many cases of physical, mental and social disorder can be transformed through the prayer of a Christian for God's blessing.

The significance of all the charisms which are concerned with our fellow men, such as service, sharing possessions, compassion and healing, is summed up by the New Testament in Heb. 13:16. "Do not neglect to do good and to share what you have, for such sacrifices are pleasing to God." Paul brings it into an even greater context: "Bear one another's burdens, and so fulfil the law of Christ" (Gal. 6:2).

The gift of martyrdom

In 1 Cor. 13:3 Paul includes martyrdom among the charismatic gifts, for it is mentioned here in the same breath as other charisms like speaking in other languages, prophecy, faith and sharing possessions. "And if I deliver my body to be burned, and have not love, I gain nothing." Charismatic suffering and death acquire a convincing power which for the person who suffers is an undeserved gift, a grace. Many of the records of the deaths of martyrs agree that there was a mysterious power about their dying, that the suffering did not lead (as one might expect) to tension and contorted expressions but to calmness, relaxed expressions and peace. Where this happens suffering and death is a gift of grace. It also has the effect we have come to associate with a charism, of making the character and power of God convincingly clear. Christ is glorified.

Such outward manifestations are of course not an infallible sign of a charism. In exceptional cases they could result from above-average will power. The only really distinctive mark is the motive: a strong love for God. It is Jesus who must be glorified in my suffering, not myself nor my ideology. Sadly there have often been Christians who have suffered only a physical martyrdom, because they have clung in false confidence to their own convictions. Their deaths were a tragedy but they did not reveal the grace of God. Obstinacy can lead to suffering, but such suffering does not glorify Jesus.

Thus martyrdom too needs to be corrected and completed by the other charisms. Prophecy, the word of wisdom, ability to discern spirits and faith are gifts which can show us whether at a particular juncture resistance should be made for Jesus' sake or not. If the events leading up to martyrdom have been subject to correction and development through other charisms and have been ratified by the local church, God will give grace and the Holy Spirit will be effective in the suffering and death. Church history has demonstrated that such martyrdom surpasses every other kind of proclamation in power and effectiveness.

In our own contemporary experience there are few situations in which confession of Jesus brings physical suffering or death in its train — though this could change at any time. Nevertheless even in our own day in the democratic nations the basic principle of martyrdom is still there: only the form has changed. Suffering for Jesus' sake may for example take the form of unjustified loss of reputation, of integrity, of influence. Although loss of reputation cannot be compared with loss of one's life, it remains hard enough for a person throughout his life to have to endure misrepresentation of his achievements and motives. Here charismatic suffering means the bearing of this situation for Jesus' sake in such a way that God is glorified.

The gift of administrative leadership

We have already examined the different words used for the gift of leadership (in the section on "The gift of prophetic leadership", pp. 114ff. above). Administrative leadership is mentioned in Rom. 12:8: "If you are a leader, exert yourself to lead" (NEB). *Prohistemi* can be translated "to take care of": it is a matter of administering what is there and if possible increasing it. This is best done "with zeal", with strong commitment and reliable consistency. The task is described in Heb. 13:17: "Obey your leaders and submit to them; for they are keeping watch over your souls, as men who will have to give account. Let them do this joyfully, and not sadly, for that would be of no advantage to you."

Administrative leadership is a matter of organization and management, and is to be exercised with zeal and faithfulness. It is part of the shepherd's task. It sees the people who are there and tries to show them the place in the total life of the church or group which it is God's will for them to take. It has the educative task of helping people to find their appropriate place in life, of caring for them and giving each individual the ideas and suggestions he needs at the time. This care extends not only to the spiritual and intellectual spheres but also to the material, since the leader is responsible for the practical welfare as well as for the growth in faith of those committed to him. Administrative leadership is not restricted to the church, but is also needed in the secular world, for in a factory, a classroom or an office every person needs to find the place which corresponds to his needs and to the will of God.

Both kinds of leadership, the administrative which cares for and the prophetic which transforms, are necessary if the church is to retain a healthy and dynamic balance. If prophetic leadership is lacking the church ossifies in traditional, rigid formality. If administrative leadership is lacking, then all becomes movement, and people who get into difficulties and cannot keep up with the pace are no longer cared for and lose contact with the church. Since local churches today are for the most part organized under one kind of leadership and therefore also under one leader, they tend to a greater or lesser extent to one of these two types of leadership only, and so easily lose their balance. It is therefore very important today not only to develop the full range of gifts in the church, but also to build up the differentiated structure of leadership as it is displayed in the New Testament.

The Charism of Discernment

Ability to distinguish between spirits

The gift of being able to distinguish between spirits (1 Cor. 12:10) is the ability to distinguish from one another divine, human and demonic forces. Jesus possessed this gift to a very marked degree. In Mark 3:11-12 Jesus recognized the presence of demons, although what they said sounded very pious. In Matt. 16:17 he recognized that the confession of Peter had been inspired by God — yet shortly afterwards he had to rebuke Peter sharply, though the response was meant kindly: "But he turned and said to Peter, 'Get behind me, Satan! You are a hindrance to me; for you are not on the side of God, but of men' " (Matt. 16:23). In Acts too it is repeatedly made clear that discernment of spirits is necessary in order to be able to look "behind the scenes", especially when something *looks* spiritual but really has Satan behind it (e.g. Acts 13:10, 16:17f.).

The gift of discernment is frequently found in quiet people who listen a great deal to the voice within. They have a sense of what power it is that stands behind a word, an action or a situation. They cannot explain it any more than a person can explain a prophecy or vision, but their gift can be tested, like prophecy, by seeing whether their words are confirmed or not by succeeding events. The ability to distinguish between spirits is particularly necessary when contributions are made during a time of worship which claim to be inspired directly by the Holy Spirit, e.g. prophecy, teaching, a word of wisdom or of knowledge, or even a vision or the interpretation of a prayer in another language. He who is able to discern the spirits becomes inwardly disturbed when human thoughts are presented as prophecy, when a clever compromise proposal masquerades as a word of wisdom, or when demonic forces insinuate themselves into charismatic utterances. The ability to discern is also needed for putting things right when someone claims to have the gift of faith but in reality only wants to insist on his own, bigoted, human ideas.

The gift of distinguishing between spirits is not given solely for the testing of charismatic utterances. It is also competent to test many other things that are said or done, for it is concerned with the whole question of whether it is God, man or Satan in the background. Thus for example at a church meeting the process of arriving at a decision can be so arranged as to leave room for the gift of discernment to be exercised. Heribert Mühlen describes such a process. "The leader briefly sets out the problem. In the general silence which follows, each person present brings the problem before God and prays in a deep spirit of submission to God's will for insight, knowledge and wisdom. After about 15 or 20 minutes everyone in turn says briefly and concisely what as he prayed to God he found to be the right decision . . . If differences still remain, a further period of silent prayer follows. This time everyone thinks about what he has just heard and prays it through, asking himself whether he ought to change or correct his opinion or perhaps express it differently . . . The more each person is prepared to listen to what was said to the others as they prayed, the more likely it is that the guidance will emanate from the Spirit of God rather than from human intelligence and strength of will. It is indeed a matter of *discerning* what comes from human impulses and what from the impulses of the Holy Spirit."[130]

Whenever we come up against the many questions and uncertainties which beset most of the important decisions of life, and many charismatic contributions in the church, we may pray with special earnestness for the gift of discerning the spirits. If we can wait until God's voice makes itself clearly heard, we shall in general find that charismatic intuition and objective considerations are so closely interwoven that the guidance of the Spirit becomes very evident. It can however sometimes happen that the Holy Spirit will reassure us and others that we must go the way of faith despite all the objective reasons to the contrary, upheld only by the agreement of the church and the sense of joy and inner calm which God will give us.

Part Three

LIVING UNDER THE CONTROL OF THE HOLY SPIRIT

CHAPTER NINE

The Right Place for Charismatic Gifts

It is repeatedly stressed in the New Testament that charismatic gifts must not be isolated from other aspects of the Christian life. They can only be exercised in an edifying way if relationships with the other works of the Spirit are sound. The right place for communication between charismatic gifts, fruit of the Spirit, service and spiritual guidance is the local church. Putting it in up-to-date language we might say that charismatic gifts are healthy only when they are integrated within the life of the church and the many aspects of its spiritual work. Paul seems to have in mind a kind of *dynamic balance* between the various works of the Spirit: the charisms can develop their own dynamic when each charism is balanced against the others, when there is effective mutual support between the gifts and the fruit of the Spirit, when personal charismatic experiences are brought together under the influence and control of the local church, and when balance is maintained between charismatic speech and charismatic action. Where this balance is present and the healthy adjustment of the various spiritual forces and their effects is contributing to peace, then the dynamic of each individual work of the Spirit can develop unhindered. The closer the communication becomes, the more specialized will be the development of individual gifts. In the pages which follow I shall try to describe the way in which the powers of the Holy Spirit can be held together in the church in a dynamic balance, for there will be a healthy development of charisms only when the church is living according to the pattern of the body of Christ.

Integration of charisms within the life of the church

Charisms without the church are unthinkable: "To each is given the manifestation of the Spirit for the common good" (1 Cor. 12:7). Paul speaks about the church in quite concrete terms, so that it is undoubtedly the local church that he means. In 1 Corinthians he begins with the actual experience of the Lord's Supper (1 Cor. 10:16-17) and with the church into which Christians are baptized (1 Cor. 12:13). From the image of the body of Christ various principles for the integration of the charisms within the life of the church may be drawn.

1st Principle: Everybody has something, but nobody has all

Every born again Christian has charismatic gifts. This is stated unmistakably in our text. "In 1 Cor. 12:4-13 Paul uses the word 'all' or 'every' four times (vv. 7,11,13) quite emphatically. It could not be made clearer. Just as we have *all* been baptized, he says in verse 13, so we have *all* received the Spirit, and thus we have *all* received the specific gift of the Spirit which is our charism. In other words every believing Christian is also a charismatic (i.e. gifted by the Spirit)."[131]

Nobody has all: this principle too is clearly laid down by Paul. To one person this charism is given, to another that, to a third yet another. If anyone makes his own special charism into the central charism of the church, the beautiful, harmonious, life-sustaining organism is transformed into the caricature of a body: "If the whole body were an eye, where would be the hearing? If the whole body were an ear, where would be the sense of smell? If all were a single organ, where would the body be?" (1 Cor. 12:17,19). This means that without the *variety* of gifts the church is not capable of life. The secret of her power lies in the working together of the various gifts of grace.

2nd Principle: There are varieties of gifts, and therefore also varieties of task

The Holy Spirit distributes the gifts as he will; first, then, there is the gift, and from it arises the task. The practice in the churches is often reversed: there is a traditional list of offices, functions and tasks, and we seek people to fill them. When someone takes on a task he must try and mobilize his gifts as best he can — or trust that the Holy Spirit will give him an appropriate charism afterwards. In most cases there are many people working in the wrong place. It is obvious that the effectiveness of work organized in this way cannot be high.

The principle of going *from the gift to the task* applies also of course to the individual. The gift which he has should determine the task which he undertakes. ". . . the gift of administration (should be used) in administration. A teacher should employ his gift in teaching, and one who has the gift of stirring speech should use it to stir his hearers" (Rom. 12:7-8, NEB). Although the individual, specific gifts of grace are here mentioned in turn, one at a time, we must guard against an unscriptural schematization. It is certainly clearly stated in the New Testament that nobody has all the charisms, but this does not exclude the possibility that one person may have several charisms. The principle of the variety of gifts and tasks is therefore wide in scope: everyone should try to ascertain what gifts the Holy Spirit has bestowed upon him, and thus be enabled to find the tasks to which he is called.

3rd Principle: The differences exist not for the sake of distinction but for the sake of completeness

This principle really states the obvious, yet how hard we find it to bring our emotions and our understanding of ourselves into line with this insight! The differences are not differences of value but of function: "The eye cannot say to the hand, 'I have no need of you', nor again the head to the feet, 'I have no need of you'. On the contrary, the parts of the body which seem to be weaker are indispensable" (1 Cor. 12:21-22). The differences do not mark any distinction of rank, but are necessary because no one individual can do everything yet the church has need of all.

From this it follows that there is no fundamental or firmly fixed order of importance among the charisms. That charism is always the most important which is most urgently needed at any given time. Thus charisms are not intended for giving a higher status to the person who has them, nor for the formation of splinter groups. When that happens, when struggles for prestige break out or party spirit appears, the church is in very grave danger. Paul has to begin his letter, after all, by dealing with the problem of splinter groups. He almost implores them as he exclaims, "Is Christ divided?" (1 Cor. 1:13).

4th Principle: The better the communication between church members, the better the charisms will be able to develop

The gifts of God are complete: everything which is needed is there. But they can fulfil their function only if the charisms are being integrated within the life of the church, so that those who possess them are working together. If a man has a strong heart but weak legs, he will not be able to undertake long walks. If in a church the prophetic gifts are well developed but the serving gifts are not, only the worship will be rich, but the life of the church as a whole will be poor and will lack the warm security of a nest. If the opposite is true, the church will degenerate into a social institution. It is clear from the example of the church at Corinth how badly a church can fail if the balance between the charisms is lacking. There were many gifts and their variety was impressive, but nevertheless the splinter groups and the arrogance of some individuals about their gifts was crippling the life and missionary effectiveness of the church.

It is instructive to follow how Paul solves the problem of one charism dominating the rest. Ulrich Brockhaus writes: "Although in the life of the Corinthian church there existed powerful tensions and disorders, Paul does not once attempt to exclude particular charisms from the church or even to forbid their exercise during services of worship . . . The reason for this is certainly not that Paul was too peace-loving to be able or willing to enter into such a battle with the charismatics . . . Paul does not exclude these charismatics from the church for the simple reason that he accepts their charism as a charism. He is here confronted with brethren who have not yet learned to put their charism to useful service . . . But their charism is and remains nonetheless a charism, a gift of God. They belong with their gifts to the body of Christ. Hence amputation would be the worst solution of all: it would mean that the service this charism was intended to render would be lost forever."[132]

The balance between fruit of the Spirit and gifts of the Spirit

"Fruit" is a term often used in both Old and New Testaments. Jesus taught that one should judge men by their fruits, and he fell back on examples from nature such as the parable of the unfruitful fig-tree (Luke 13:6-9). Paul thinks along similar lines and coins the expression "fruit of the Spirit". "But the fruit of the Spirit is love, joy, peace, patience, kindness, goodness, faithfulness, gentleness, self-control" (Gal. 5:22-23).

Biologically fruit is the result of a long process of growth, which can be observed continuously developing from the seed onwards through all the stages. There are no leaps; no phase of the development can be omitted or shortened. It is very significant that one of the ways in which the Holy Spirit works should be described as "fruit". It tells us that there is an aspect of the Spirit's work which is marked by continuing growth, which cannot be shortened by sudden events, and whose result is tangible, solid and lasting. The fruit of the Spirit consists of a number of qualities of human character which cannot be quickly learned, but which form themselves slowly in the structure of one's personality; which one cannot receive suddenly like the gifts, but which must be allowed to grow.

Gifts and fruit are very different aspects of the Spirit's work. In their structure they are almost opposites: fruit is the result of a long process of growth, a charism is the result of a free gift of the Spirit, directly given; fruit is a continuing feature, a charism is spontaneous; fruit has more to do with the inner man, a power which forms human character, while a charism has more to do with the outside world, a gift which is employed in word and deed. The fruit of the Spirit becomes more and more part of a person, whereas a charism is more like a tool which one takes in one's hand; in other words, it can also be exercised by a person who is not yet spiritually mature. Charisms are apportioned by the Spirit as he wills; in the growth of the fruit of the Spirit the person himself is involved through his surrender, his devotion and his faithfulness. The fruit builds the vessel and the charism fills the vessel.

From this it is obvious that it is only the fruit of the Spirit, not the charism, which is a sign of the extent to which Christ has been formed in us. Anyone who is unwilling to take upon himself the toil of growing continually in the faith, and hopes instead to shorten the process by means of the charisms, will be greatly disappointed. He will not grow in faith more quickly, but more slowly, since charisms which lack the corresponding fruit of the Spirit serve to edify neither the church nor the individual. It is not through charisms that a man becomes great in the Kingdom of God, but only through the fruit of the Spirit.

What happens when the fruit of the Spirit appears without the gifts? The life of faith becomes wearisome, sterile and joyless. It is easy for a false legalism to develop. A person becomes proud of his own standing in the faith and forgets his task in the church and in the world. Where charisms are lacking, personal faith experiences no further challenges to service and therefore no chance to prove itself and to receive new motivation for growth.

What happens when charisms appear without the fruit of the Spirit? The charisms are used, it is true, but because of spiritual immaturity they are used in a way which leads not so much to edification as to destruction. The vessel which is meant to contain the charism is lacking; there is only a sieve which permits nothing to be held fast and usefully employed. People without the fruit of the Spirit *squander* their charisms in every direction and cause nothing but harm. The situation in the church at Corinth makes it plain what sort of problems arise when charisms are exercised without the corresponding fruit of the Spirit.

Spiritual growth resulting in the fruit of the Spirit is toilsome and strenuous. It takes place only when we make time for God and his word, when we expose ourselves daily in prayer to the working of the Holy Spirit, and when we live in close fellowship within the church so that God is able to reach us through our brothers and sisters. In nature growth is always preceded by death: the seed must die in order to allow the germ to take root in the ground. Jesus has accomplished this death for us; he compared himself with the biological example. The fruit of the Spirit will appear only if we are for ever letting portions of our own interests, our experiences, our contacts, our goals and our inner nature die for Jesus' sake, so that what God wants to grow in us may be enabled to burst forth into life.

If we have developed an awareness of the balance between the fruit of the Spirit and the gifts of the Spirit, both these works of the Holy Spirit will be able to fructify each other and help the charisms to find their proper level. Those who are aware of the effectiveness of charisms in their own lives and who also know the importance of the fruit of the Spirit will be motivated to strive for the fruit of the Spirit, for they will know that without the fruit their own personality is like a sieve which gives the charisms no chance of working in the way God intended when he gave them. Similarly the visible fruit of the Spirit in my life will strengthen my courage in using the charism, in that I know that the necessary spiritual basis for service to others is in the process of being built.

Charisms without fruit are dangerous; fruit without charisms is lacking in power. It is of great importance that the two should be combined in the right proportion. The charismatic who lives without the solid basis of the fruit of the Spirit will rapidly develop into a fanatic, or he will have so many negative experiences with his charism that he gives up using it. The Christian who stands on the foundation of the fruit of the Spirit but lacks the power of the charisms, becomes self-satisfied, loses his missionary, attractive power and stands in danger of ossification. The charismatic movement of our day, with its helpful insights as well as its dangers, displays once again the importance of maintaining a balance between the gifts of the Spirit and the fruits of the Spirit, because only when this is present can the power of the Spirit lead to the edification of the church, to mission and to service.

The balance between the individual's gift and the church's ministry of oversight

In theological discussion this question generally narrows down to the question of *charism* and *office* in the church. We cannot go into that question here, but I start from the conviction that it is not true to the New Testament to pose this set of alternatives. The New Testament deliberately avoids using the normal words for "office", words which connote power and dignity. Now and then the term *oikonomia* is used, which is best translated as "stewardship" or "trusteeship" in the sense of being a steward for God; in other passages *diakonia* is used, and we have already come to see that this term is interchangeable with *charisma*.[133] In view of the close association of these two terms and the reality which underlies it, I would agree with the opinion of Ulrich Brockhaus, who writes on the subject of charism and office: "Paul saw the gradually emerging offices as charisms like the others, as gifts of the Spirit which require supplementation and themselves supplement others, fragmentary and yet necessary in their place, both as varied and as similar as the gifts of all the other members of the church. On the one hand this made it possible for him to give his full support and recognition to these men, to have an almost unlimited openness and breadth of vision in accepting all the new things which confronted him at this level in the churches — so we cannot speak of any contrast here between Spirit and office. On the other hand he made fundamental restrictions about the degree to which individual office-bearers could be set over the whole church."[134]

The charismatic as an individual is set against the background of the church as a whole. It is the church which practises pastoral ministry and exercises church discipline, the church which ratifies the exercise of individual gifts and gives particular functions to the various members on the basis of their gifts. On the other hand the church is not a separate entity, she is not a person in herself, but rather lives through the whole range of charisms which have been given to her members, on the foundation of the word of God and under the guidance of the Holy Spirit. There needs to be just as much of a dynamic balance between the charismatic experience of the individual and the total experience of the church as between the gifts of the Spirit and the fruit of the Spirit.

The church's life is based upon the exercise by every member of his personal charism in his own individual way. If the church tries to formulate a set of rules to bring the charismatics "into line", she will lose her originality altogether. On the other hand the church must take care that individual members do not dominate the times of worship or the field of Christian service, lest the basic principle which Paul sets out in 1 Cor. 14:26 be lost sight of: "When you come together, each one has . . . (something to offer)." In this passage Paul sets the church two important tasks. First she must take care that the multiplicity is not lost: it is important that various charisms should be exercised and that no one of them should be allowed to dominate. But secondly it is important that the same charism should be exercised by several people: that glossolalia should be heard in the form practised by person A, but also in that practised by persons B and C; that not only prophet D with his special message, but also prophets E and F should be allowed to speak; that not just one deacon but several should be carrying out the various services which have to be rendered. The Holy Spirit does not suppress the personal characteristics of the charismatic; in the church therefore not only the full range of charisms but also the full range of human personalities should be enabled to take part. If the individual charismatic is living in this kind of communication with others, he will be able to express his own individuality without fear, for it is being integrated within the sphere of the Holy Spirit's influence and within the total life of the church.

When an individual charismatic speaks or acts spontaneously in the Spirit, it is not really possible for him to tell whether what he has said is truly of the Spirit and whether his action is in accordance with the will of God. That is the task of the church, which tests and confirms the contribution either through those of her members who possess the gift of discerning the spirits, or through the whole company who have met together. This removes a great load of responsibility from the individual charismatic. He can speak and act as he thinks the Spirit is inspiring him, in confidence that the church will either confirm or reject what he has said or done. The experience of rejection may be humanly speaking unpleasant, but it is easier to bear than a wrongful influence or confusion of the church through speech and action which merely claim to be charismatic. Paul says: "Let two or three prophets speak, and let the others weigh what is said . . . the spirits of prophets are subject to prophets" (1 Cor. 14:29,32). If the church is under the guidance of the Holy Spirit she will know when something is wrong. If a person has truly prophetic gifts he will recognize, should he be found to have mingled Spirit-given and human elements and not to have spoken according to the will of God, that it is the prophetic spirit among the others which is judging him. When Christians follow this practice in a spirit of mutual trust, the individuality, variety and spontaneity of the charisms can be preserved without giving rise to any disorder. The dynamic balance between the individual's charismatic experience and the church's responsibility for oversight leads to peace.

The lonely charismatic, and the charismatic group which isolates itself, easily fall victim to extremism, for they will very soon come to regard their own charisms as the really central ones. Because of the one-sidedness of their view they are not in a position to produce a sound judgement to guide their life. For our human life we need all our senses — for our spiritual life we need all the gifts. If we live within the fellowship of the church we can retain our own individuality and yet have a share in the fulness. We become great *in our brothers and sisters*!

A person who becomes completely submerged in a group, without developing his own charism, is like wax. He is dependent on the group and will be left alone for the very reason that he has lost his own selfhood and become dissolved within the group. He can give nothing to the others, and hence he will soon receive nothing either. The dynamic balance between the individual's charism and the church's oversight is thus an indispensable prerequisite for the healthy development of charisms and for the healthy structure of the church.

The balance between charismatic speech and charismatic action

It is a general rule of human experience that speech and action should go together. The man who says great words but fails to back them up by his actions loses the confidence of others. Obviously therefore this balance between speech and action is important too where charisms are concerned. This is made clear in the first letter of Peter: "As each has received a gift, employ it for one another, as good stewards of God's varied grace: whoever speaks, as one who utters oracles of God; whoever renders service, as one who renders it by the strength which God supplies; in order that in everything God may be glorified through Jesus Christ" (1 Pet. 4:10-11). This passage speaks of the two great categories of charismatic gifts, speech and action, as a matter of course.

Even Paul had difficulty in checking the one-sided concentration on speaking which marked the charismatics at Corinth. Here the charisms of the word were clearly dominant; yet even here he alludes to the other kind of charism, especially in 1 Cor. 12:28, where he speaks of healings, helpers and administration. In Rom. 12 the charisms of action are very clearly set out alongside the charisms of the word: Paul includes service, giving, leadership and mercy in the list of charisms. The problem has remained to this day: even in the charismatic movement — but much more so in Pentecostalism — charisms of the word have played the dominant role.

This one-sided emphasis is dangerous, for it makes the service of worship very much into the pivotal point of the church's life. The community life, help for the weak and ill, the administrative gifts of the church, her social activity, questions of life-style and education are given short measure. Moreover witness soon loses its credibility when it is based on words alone, even if the words possess a charismatic quality. Speech without action is like book-keeping without receipts and vouchers. Church life which consists only of the words spoken in services of worship, even when these are spoken with authority, fails as testimony, for in testimony it is the life of the witness that plays the principal rôle, not his words.

When the charisms of the word are given a one-sided emphasis, the word loses its credibility, especially in our own age, which has seen an "inflation" of words brought on by the mass media. The spiritual life becomes theoretical; the favourite notions which are particularly characteristic of a Christian who has his mind chiefly centred on his own charism are exaggerated until they outweigh everything else — for the objective reference to reality is missing. When a one-sided emphasis is given to the charisms of action, the chief thing lacking is any awareness of the spiritual reference points which form the necessary background for charismatic action — for the principles of faith must always be present even in practical work. The action then easily loses the habit of quiet contemplation of God, of praise and worship, of meditation and attentive consideration of the word of God, all of which can be conveyed by a worship service which leaves room for the charisms of the word.

Jesus Himself lived out in a unique way the balance between word and deed. "And the Word became flesh and dwelt among us, full of grace and truth; we have beheld his glory, glory as of the only Son from the Father" (John 1:14). We can follow him only when our own speech and action are in similar accord. A living faith always leads to a faith-inspiring life. The charisms will develop in a healthy manner only if the balance between charismatic speech and charismatic action is retained.

CHAPTER TEN

Misuse of Charismatic Gifts

The charisms are given by the Holy Spirit but exercised by man. They are therefore placed within the sphere of human limitations and exposed to error and sin. It is possible for charisms to be misused through the manner in which people handle the gifts with which they have been entrusted. Eugen Mederlet writes: "When someone speaks incomprehensible words and says, 'That was a prayer in tongues inspired by the Holy Spirit', when someone engages in a particular activity because he is convinced that he had been led to do so by the Holy Spirit, or when, similarly convinced, someone utters a prophecy addressed to somebody else, his word or action may be derived from any combination of divine grace and human error. We may speak of fanaticism when people or groups fail to recognize or acknowledge this element of human distortion in their experiences of God, and when they regard everything, and require others to regard everything, as the pure communication of the Holy Spirit."[135]

Now that we have developed some principles for the healthy exercise of charismatic gifts, let us go on to consider some common abuses, before finally coming to sum up with a description of charismatic practice.

Gifts as a substitute for the assurance of salvation

Assurance of salvation is based upon the promises of the word of God accepted in faith. This is attested for instance in the first letter of John: "And this is the testimony, that God gave us eternal life, and this life is in his Son. He who has the Son has life; he who has not the Son has not life. I write this to you who believe in the name of the Son of God, that you may know that you have eternal life" (1 John 5:11-13). The word of God is the foundation upon which our faith rests. The Holy Spirit confirms this faith in our hearts. "For you did not receive the spirit of slavery to fall back into fear, but you have received the spirit of sonship. When we cry, 'Abba! Father!' it is the Spirit himself bearing witness with our spirit that we are children of God" (Rom. 8:15-16).

This way to the assurance of salvation is not an easy way. When we fall into doubt we are dependent on our faith, on our acceptance of the teaching of the Bible for ourselves: we live in hope. It is understandable therefore that man should strive to find some *sure sign* of his salvation. But there is no short cut to faith. Signs and wonders have the purpose of displaying the power of God, but not of giving people assurance of their salvation — not because God intentionally wants to make the way difficult for us, but because signs and wonders are not in themselves capable of giving us assurance. There are also miracles which have as their source not the power of God but the power of man or of Satan.

The danger that charisms may become a substitute for the assurance of salvation is not to be dismissed. The danger is particularly present where miraculous gifts and emotional charisms occupy the centre of attention, and where glossolalia is made into an unequivocal sign of the reception of the Spirit. It is then no longer faith but miracles which become the guarantee of salvation; it is not the inward assurance of the Holy Spirit that I am a child of God, but the outward sign of a charismatic gift which becomes the ground for my assurance of salvation. Where charisms take the place of faith, Christ is forced out of his central place. The charism serves no longer to glorify Jesus but rather to give confidence to the person who has it. Most abuses in the exercise of charisms have their origin here.

Gifts as a way of avoiding the cross

Charismatic revivals have always stood in danger of placing the victorious church in the foreground and suppressing the idea of the imperfect, suffering church. Thus the classical Pentecostal movement and parts of the charismatic movement today have been dominated by a success-story mentality. There seems to be no experience of lethargy, no weariness, no uncertainty, no illness, but only mighty power, healing and unerring prophecy. Some of the young movements of today seem to have tendencies in this direction also. This trend leads to separation from the traditional churches. Eckhard Schaefer says in a lecture entitled "Charisma and the Cross": "The triumphant church meets in special groups, where people come not to live together but only for a time of prayer; where one cannot say, 'The Lord has put us here and added to our numbers', but where one has to say, 'I come here because I recognize myself again in these brothers.' I do not say this disparagingly. If such a meeting is understood as a kind of dessert following the main course — all right! But when this becomes the main meal itself, I personally must say no, because the cross is to be found in the midst of the church."[136]

Charismatic gifts are not a route to by-pass the cross. On the contrary charisms and cross belong together, so much so that martyrdom can be a charism. This is made clear in the New Testament repeatedly. When Jesus was baptized John testified: "I saw the Spirit descend as a dove from heaven, and it remained on him" (John 1:32). In the same context John says, "Behold, the Lamb of God, who takes away the sin of the world!" (John 1:29). The special equipping with the Holy Spirit which Jesus here experiences is not the prelude to a triumphal march, but the first step on the way to the cross. This becomes clear from the start in that following his baptism Jesus is led into the wilderness.

Jesus is no exception: the Holy Spirit bestows his gifts upon us so that we may be equipped *for taking up our cross daily*. Paul allows us a glimpse into the "normal" life of a Spirit-filled Christian in 2 Cor. 4. "But we have this treasure in earthen vessels, to show that the transcendent power belongs to God and not to us . . . we are always being given up to death for Jesus' sake, so that the life of Jesus may be manifested in our mortal flesh . . . For it is all for your sake, so that as grace extends to more and more people it may increase thanksgiving to the glory of God. So we do not lose heart. Though our outer nature is wasting away, our inner nature is being renewed every day." (2 Cor. 4:7-16).

Charismatic gifts do not lead us on a road which by-passes the cross. God cannot spare us the way of the cross; if he did, we should count his power to our own credit. Another reason why charismatic gifts do not by-pass the cross is that they are given for the benefit of the church and therefore need to exist in solidarity with the imperfection of the church, and with her suffering too. Karl Rahner has written: "The genuineness of a charism, which is of course a commission for the Church and to the Church, and not from the Church outwards, is shown by the humility and patience with which the one sent bears the inevitability of suffering which his charismatic gift entails: by the fact that he builds no church within the Church so as to make it easier for himself, does not allow himself to become embittered, but knows that it is the one Lord who creates within His Church both the power and the resistance to it, the wine of enthusiasm and the water of sobriety, and who has given none of His servants the task of representing Him alone."[137]

Gifts without service

Paul emphasizes that charisms are forms of service (1 Cor. 12:5). Charisms are not given in order that people should *possess* something but in order that they may *do* something. If the charism bestowed by the Holy Spirit is not employed in useful service a series of distortions will result, leading ultimately to abuse of the gift.

A charism is in the first place a potential which begins to be realized only when it is developed and used. Here the same principles apply as with every human ability. If service does not result from the charism, it soon atrophies.

Without service a charism easily becomes a plaything, especially if it is a charism of the word. For it makes an impression on others when prayers are uttered in other languages, when visions are seen or prophecies given, when sick people have hands laid upon them. A certain phase of play may very well occur to start with, arising from the joy over the gift that has been received. But soon it must be turned into responsible service, for unreflective play is full of dangers, even where charisms are concerned. Play means that a person's thoughts are centred upon the charisms and not on the needs of the church.

Where charisms are exercised without service to others, the scene is set for the gift of grace to develop into a status symbol. The charism ceases then to be a tool and becomes an act of self-assertion. A church in which the exercise of gifts is motivated by service knows no fixed divisions of rank: the gift most in need at any moment is the most important. Where charisms are exercised without regard to service, differences of rank appear at once, for the charism has been separated from its real purpose and the balance of charisms in the church has been deeply disturbed. Moreover the chance for the individual to find the place which God intends for him within the church has been thrown away. A proper service structure in the church is not the result of the personal wishes of its individual members, but of their gifts. Charismatic activity without service therefore damages both those who have gifts and the whole church in a lasting way.

Gifts without doctrine

When charisms develop there is a danger that people will substitute personal experience for doctrinal understanding. Charisms arouse enthusiasm; doctrine is more demanding, because it addresses itself more to the mind. The emotionalism of charismatic experience is new, whereas many Christians feel that they have been "preached to death" after many years of going to church. It is certainly true that our services are too rationalistic, too dry and too monotonous, and that they encourage a consumer attitude on the part of the individual church member. On the other hand the charismatic revival will go astray if sound teaching is lacking and if there is a greater emphasis on prophetic messages than on Bible study. Paul himself was familiar with this problem, and that is why he begins his extensive treatment of the subject of charisms in 1 Cor. 12:14 with the words: "Now concerning spiritual gifts, brethren, *I do not want you to be uninformed . . .*" (1 Cor. 12:1).

A healthy balance is needed between charismatic activity and teaching. It is unscriptural to maintain that the charisms of proclamation ended with the closing of the New Testament canon, for the church as a body of Christ still needs even today the application of the word to the present situation which those charisms can contribute. It is equally wrong to go to the other extreme and to give the charismatic word priority over the doctrinal analysis of the Bible. The problem will be least apparent where the charism of *teaching* is present — when doctrine ceases to be a wearisome, intellectual decipherment of the biblical message and becomes a matter of compelling and inspired insight.

Charismatic sensationalism

Even in Corinth those charisms which caused the greatest sensation were the ones most highly regarded, especially glossolalia. This same tendency is to be seen in many circles today: prophecy, revelation, words of wisdom and of knowledge, glossolalia and its interpretation, miracles and healing — these are the gifts which claim the centre of attention. This means that gifts of grace which were intended to be gifts of service have been turned into *miracle gifts*. It is of course true that among the charisms there are many miraculous gifts, but this is only *one* side of the picture. It is not that miracles should be rejected, but only the over-valuing of miracles at the expense of other gifts.

Sensationalism does not contribute to the edification of the church. It diverts the attention away from Jesus Christ and towards the miracle itself. People who look only for sensation usually display a dangerously low degree of growth in the faith. Edward O'Connor mentions people who assess a prayer meeting much too superficially,

> judging solely by the amount of charismatic activity which has taken place. If there are several prophecies and a healing, it is a

> wonderful prayer meeting. If nothing happens except the offering of prayers, even if those prayers are very deep, they are disappointed.[138]

The search for charismatic sensations can take on the features of an addiction. The American critics of the charismatic renewal movement have coined a word for it: "charismania". Here too it is a matter of finding the golden mean. Paul challenges us to strive for the gifts of grace. At the same time he brings before our vision the whole range of charisms, including both the miracle gifts and the gifts of administration, the gifts of the word but the gifts of action as well. Where the range of charisms is seen in its full breadth, and where the gifts are being constantly integrated within the life of the church, it will be impossible for the seeking of gifts to develop into a mania.

Gifts as a means of gaining power over others

The New Testament emphasizes that every born again Christian has charismatic gifts, that every charism is especially important when it is needed, and that no charism is intended to exalt the person who has it over the rest. Nevertheless there is a great temptation to misuse a charism as an instrument for dominating others. Because the majority of Christians are unaware of their own charisms and therefore do not consciously exercise them, the impression arises that those who are conscious of exercising spiritual gifts form an élite. Many charismatics themselves reject this idea, but are cast in the role by others. Others however use their charism either deliberately or unconsciously as evidence of a special authority which qualifies them for leadership. The danger is especially marked in the case of a charism which is sensational in its effects.

O'Connor describes how a charism can be used as a means of gaining power over others. He refers to three types of person. There is the man who is unable to tell whether he is submitting his decisions to the Holy Spirit or whether he is simply unable to make his mind up. Normally such a person is ridiculed and certainly not taken seriously. However the concept of being led by the Spirit offers him the possibility of interpreting his own weakness as strength and shielding himself from criticism. A second type is the person who has an unhealthy ambition to achieve status as a religious leader. When he stands before others as God's representative and begins to stir up their emotions by his rhetoric he experiences a feeling of power. Similar to him but slightly different is the person who fancies himself to be a prophet. He loves to surround himself with an aura of divine mystery and to watch others gathering around him in awe awaiting a divine message from his lips.[139] It is obvious that here the charism has been diverted from its proper task. It is no longer being used to serve others, but as an instrument for gaining power over them.

Gifts as an excuse for forming cliques

The formation of cliques is probably the greatest danger of all where charisms are eagerly sought. Alfred Kuen writes: "After an investigation stretching over a period of ten years, John Kildahl concludes that practically everywhere those who have had a charismatic experience form an 'in-group' in their local churches and cause tension and divisions by their attitude to 'non-charismatics'. In America particularly those groups which do not put the study of the Bible at the centre of their activities have rapidly changed into 'charismatic clubs' in which people seek especially the gifts of prophecy and of speaking in tongues, healing and miracles."[140]

Certainly one cannot lay all the blame for such a development at the door of the charismatic groups, for many local churches have set themselves against the conscious exercise of charisms and are not prepared to allow a charismatic structuring of their church life. Without doubt however there exist on the charismatics' side arrogance, presumption and the tendency to take the line of least resistance, which in most cases means forming a group of their own and avoiding the *cross of normal life in the local church*. The danger is obvious. The church lacks some important charisms, and in the charismatic group there are similar tendencies to one-sidedness, resulting in an excessive emphasis on emotion in the charismatic experiences of the group. The result is that both suffer: the formation of the group is bound to result in a progressive diminution of dynamic life in the church, but also in the development of fanatical excesses in the charismatic group.

CHAPTER ELEVEN

Dynamic Balance in the Body of Christ

Assessments of the present-day charismatic revival vary very widely. Some reject it: while they accept that the charisms in themselves are scriptural, they see so many dangers that they think it would be better to discontinue attempts to encourage a charismatic breakthrough.

Others, for the most part people who are deeply involved in the revival, believe that a new era has begun for the church. They welcome everything which has the appearance of being a charism, but evidently lack the ability to distinguish between spirits.

Yet others attempt a compromise. They count up the dangers which lie in the charismatic revival and reckon them against the positive effects which may be observed. The two sides are roughly balanced, so that it is possible to take up a neutral attitude.

Paul faced similar questions, but he dealt with them in a totally different way. The situation in the church at Corinth was difficult — much more difficult than the church situations usually are which so disturb us today. Nevertheless he recognizes all the charisms which he finds at Corinth as Spirit-given, even when they are being seriously misused. Patiently and painstakingly he seeks to win over his readers to an understanding of healthy structures in the church in which the charisms also can be restored to health of function. He attempts both to awaken understanding of the basic principles, i.e. to tackle the question from a doctrinal standpoint, and also to give some very practical rules of conduct to guide the church on how to proceed.

We must constantly remind ourselves that the problems which Paul had with the Corinthians and the questions which trouble us today are not exclusively associated with the exercise of charisms. Arrogance, one-sidedness and group egoism are problems typical of the spiritual life in all its aspects. Siegfried Liebschner stresses this: sceptics, he says, "must see that such mistakes are symptomatic of dangers which are part of the facts of human nature, and from which nothing spiritually real is immune. It is of course true that disorders are as a rule more obvious in the case of charisms than mistakes in less conspicuous areas of spiritual life such as for example theological thought."[141] So too we may say of the church structures which Paul develops as an answer to the problems posed by the charismatics, that their value as spiritual signposts is not restricted to the correction of charismatic abuses, but is relevant wherever spiritual experiences need to be integrated within the whole life of the church.

How then does Paul solve the problem? He sets out rules of conduct for integrating the charisms within the whole spectrum of the works and powers of the Spirit. This is made concrete and practical by Paul's clear teaching that the integration is possible only within the local church, and for this purpose he develops the image of the body of Christ. These rules of conduct form the principle of dynamic balance. *Everybody has something: nobody has everything!* When inter-communication is functioning well, then everyone is free to develop that which he has — thoroughly one-sided, individual and limited as it is — for the simple reason that he possesses his completeness only in the others.

Dynamic balance is not therefore a principle which limits the charisms, but one which frees them to fulfil their function as gifts and powers of the Holy Spirit intended for the service of others. Dynamic balance is not a "Halt" sign preventing people from consciously developing their gifts, but rather an encouragement to do so. If we are observing the spiritual laws which Paul lays down we may await without anxiety the fulness of the Spirit and of the gifts, because a basis has been established upon which the charisms can be employed in building up the church.

CHAPTER TWELVE
Charismatic Practice

The descriptions of charismatic practice which follow are derived mainly from my personal experience. At important points I have tried to include practical examples from other denominations or areas of experience in the charismatic movement. It is not my aim to give a complete description of all the practical possibilities for the use of charismatic gifts, but to bring together some examples of how they may be used in the hope that this will stimulate others to follow their own ways in the exercise of the gifts.

Charismatic worship

This phrase has become a familiar one, although it poses some problems. For every act of worship is charismatic, or inspired by the Holy Spirit, otherwise it is not worship at all. Usually in our churches the service is planned and prepared beforehand by the minister within the framework of an order of service provided by the church. It is certainly possible for charismatic gifts to play a part in the minister's preparation for the service, but they will only be the minister's own gifts — unless we take into account theological books or hymns which have been inspired by the Holy Spirit, by which on a roundabout route charismatic gifts may enter into the service through the medium of the printed page.

It is however equally possible to have a spontaneous *prayer service*, which has not been prepared beforehand at all, or only in part. This is a service "given" at the moment it takes place, in which charismatic or traditional contributions flow from communal silence into the act of worship. The spontaneous service, which has been reintroduced to the churches by the charismatic movement, will in what follows be called a "charismatic service".

In 1 Cor. 14:26ff. such a service is described: "What then, brethren? When you come together, each one has a hymn, a lesson, a revelation, a tongue, or an interpretation. Let all things be done for edification. If any speak in a tongue, let there be only two or at most three, and each in turn; and let one interpret. But if there is no one to interpret, let each of them keep silence in church and speak to himself and to God. Let two or three prophets speak, and let the others weigh what is said. If a revelation is made to another sitting by, let the first be silent. For you can all prophesy one by one, so that all may learn and all be encouraged." Paul is not describing an exceptional case here, but the normal order of service in the church which gathered at Corinth, that is, the internal meeting of the church. There is good reason for believing that this was the normal course which early Christian meetings took, although in this passage not all the charismatic elements are listed (and probably the service also included some liturgical elements).[142]

Watchman Nee goes a step further and maintains that there are two entirely different types of meeting in the New Testament: the church meeting as described in 1 Cor. 14, and the 'apostolic' meeting in which one person preached and the others listened (Acts 2:14-41, Acts 3:12-26). In criticism of the present-day church he points out that we have turned the 'apostolic' meeting, which was intended for pagans, into (almost) the only kind of sevice we hold. "It is said that all may prophesy. How different from one man preaching and all the others sitting quietly in the pew listening to his sermon! . . . Meetings where activity is one-sided do not come within the scope of the church, for they lack the distinctive feature of all church gatherings.

Today, alas! this style of meeting is the chief feature of the churches. No meeting is attended with such regularity as this one . . . If apostolic meetings take the place of church meetings, then the church members become passive and indolent, always expecting to be helped, instead of seeking, in dependence upon the Spirit, to be helpful to the other members. It is contrary to the New Testament principles of mutual help and mutual edification."[143]

Watchman Nee's strictures do not have to be interpreted as meaning that we should do away with all preaching services, but they make it clear that in our services we no longer take at all seriously the principle of the charismatic church. Charismatic worship has not only biblical testimony on its side, but is the most effective way of breaking down the consumer attitude encouraged by our usual church services.

There are many ways in which spontaneous, charismatic services can be conducted. They can for instance be left completely unstructured, so that they develop of their own accord out of silence; or one can carefully guide them, or prepare parts in advance while allowing other parts to take shape spontaneously.

Dieter Koller describes six different types of charismatic service:[144]

1. *The prayer meeting.* If this is to become charismatic, plenty of silence will be needed between the prayers, and an introduction which encourages people not to pray at random but to pay attention to the *connecting thread.*

2. *Shared quiet time.* In the consideration of a Bible passage personal questions are also raised. Often the group will be seeking the answer to questions raised by the group's members; often too an individual will be seeking the answer to a personal problem through the inspiration of the group. The quiet time is based on the principle that the Holy Spirit will give prophecy, revelation or words of wisdom and knowledge, which will be written down and later shared with the group. This shared quiet time can of course also be practised by just two people.

3. *Guided meditation.* e.g. "The Father's house". "Here we mean the process whereby a congregation gives itself to a spiritual reality by means of a mental image. For instance they will go in spirit along the way which is called Jesus (John 14:6) and which leads by various stages to the Father. The leader announces the successive stages of the journey. The congregation pauses in imagination for a few minutes at each point, and conducts silent or audible converse with Christ: confessions of sin, thanksgivings, songs of joy, intercessions or 'Thomas questions' (cf. John 14:5, 'Lord, we do not know . . .'). The participants then say something of what they have experienced, learned, heard and seen in the Spirit, especially how Jesus has led them finally to the Father."[145]

4. *Service of blessing.* "Anyone who desires a word of blessing with the laying on of hands goes forward, kneels down and is allowed either to name his problem aloud or to confess his desire silently to God. Those who feel impelled to bless him go up behind him as he kneels and speak a word of blessing, laying their hands upon him. The church is not divided into those who give and those who receive."[146]

5. *The creative service*. This can be organised "by choosing a spiritual theme, e.g. 'Jesus in the year 2,000', which in the first part is worked through separately by a painting group, a poetry group, a dance group and a music group, and then in the second part brought together and celebrated in a plenary session."[147]

6. *Around the Lord's Supper.* According to the particular tradition of the church, a charismatic communion service may be celebrated in a variety of forms. It may be completely free, in

which case at a moment suggested by the inner progression of the service the words of institution are read and the Lord's supper distributed; or it may be arranged in such a way that parts of a liturgy are used while other parts of the service are allowed to take shape freely. The introduction to the communion service, or the personal climax at the end, can also take a charismatic form, emerging from a time of silence.

While the suggestions of Dieter Koller demonstrate the creative range of possibilities for organizing a charismatic service, Arnold Bittlinger gives us an order for a prayer service which is more firmly bound to traditional forms of worship:

"1. Exposition of a Bible passage by the minister, or group Bible study.
2. Communal prayer with especial emphasis on intercession.
3. Celebration of the Lord's Supper.
4. A time of silence during which individual contributions can be made.
5. The Lord's Prayer said together.
6. A blessing pronounced by the minister."[148]

From the area of the Catholic movement of Charismatic Renewal Heribert Mühlen writes of prayer services in which the liturgical celebration of the Eucharist includes freely shaped, charismatic elements. "In some groups the prayer meeting is followed once a week, or at less frequent intervals, by the celebration of the Eucharist . . . the transition from the prayer meeting to the Eucharist is formed by the intercessions, which are of course provided for at this point in the usual celebration of the Mass. Because they generally have a very practical content . . . this is for many a motivation to open their mouths for the first time in a prayer meeting . . . The celebrant should not alter the text of the Mass (except where he formulates the prayers for the day in his own words). There is sufficient opportunity for free expressions of faith, especially after the communion . . . towards the end of the service announcements are often made which include calls for help in practical social and human ways . . . Moreover it is amazing how even small children (five and six-year-olds) do not become fidgety in a service which lasts for more than two hours if they too are given opportunity to take part with very simple prayers and intercessions. Separate and specially arranged services for children are then no longer necessary!"[149]

The suggestions for the organization of charismatic services which now follow have come from my own experiences in connection with the *Rufer* work, and are therefore more closely related to free church practice, although when it comes to prayer meetings denominational differences are much less pronounced than is the case with traditional forms of public worship.

1. Free, spontaneous services require a leader. In principle they are led by the Holy Spirit, but he uses individuals for this purpose. Only a very experienced and mature group will be able to function under the direct guidance of the Holy Spirit where there is a full range of individual impulses. Normally someone is needed who possesses the charism of leadership and who always intervenes when the service threatens to lose its inner harmony — when the "thread" is in danger of being broken. Leadership should be as unobtrusive as possible, but it must be able to intervene immediately when this is necessary, e.g. to stop an unscriptural contribution, to call the congregation to silence, to interrupt if a prayer in another language is not followed by an interpretation so as to make sure that the people wait for the interpretation to come, and so on. It must be clear at the beginning of the service who is exercising the leadership.

2. The congregation must know that no one is allowed to be passive in a charismatic service. Everyone has something, and therefore everyone is needed. This does not mean that everyone must necessarily say something; but no one should withdraw from the inward listening, lest any contribution which the Holy Spirit wants to give to a member is lost. It is sometimes possible to see clearly that a gap has been left because someone has lacked the courage to say what he ought to have said. Often this is confessed in the conversation afterwards, and the missing contribution filled in retrospectively.

3. Although in a charismatic service attention is focussed on the inspiration of the Holy Spirit, our humanity is not excluded. A person who normally talks a great deal is also in danger of talking too much at a charismatic service. He must therefore avoid giving uncontrolled expression to the many impulses which come to him, in the mistaken impression perhaps that in a charismatic service every impulse is guaranteed to be inspired by the Holy Spirit. A person who is normally more inclined to be silent than to speak must similarly be careful not to hide behind his quietness and so block the movement of the Spirit. Our human peculiarities and bad habits are naturally more evident and disturbing to others at a charismatic service than at a traditional preaching service, where it is scarcely possible to say anything wrong because one is not allowed to say anything at all.

4. Every free service inspired by the Spirit will have a recognizable connecting thread running through the various thoughts

and charismatic contributions. For "God is not a God of confusion but of peace" (1 Cor. 14:33). The contributions do not stand unrelated side by side, but display a connected development. The Spirit wishes to lead us to a Bible passage, to repentance, to a common insight, to a decision, to praise and worship. This can happen only where people listen to one another, where contributions are made after a period of silence and where care is taken to ensure that each person is not simply expressing his own favourite thoughts.

5. The important thing about a charismatic service is not what we want to say to God, but what God wants to say to us. Care must be taken therefore that the prayer service does not turn into an ordinary prayer meeting, in which it is mostly a matter of our bringing our personal concerns to God. The Holy Spirit wants to direct us. Therefore we need sufficient time to be able to begin each new part in silence, until we realize where God wants to lead us in this service.

6. Paul himself emphasizes the importance of variety. Spoken prayers should not follow one another continuously, nor should there be a whole series of prophecies, nor vision after vision; God intends us to experience the full range of gifts, and a monotonous series of constantly similar contributions often threatens to stifle this. The relaxed atmosphere and originality which a wide variety produces will create a greater degree of attentiveness in the service. It is, moreover, the only guarantee that a healthy balance between the different gifts will be achieved within the service.

7. In addition to a wide range of charismatic gifts, the charismatic service needs the firm leading of the Spirit. Not every gift can be exercised during every service; it is also important to discover the right moment for that which has formed itself in my mind to be uttered. The first sign of the leading of the Spirit may be that a thought or an image, an insight or a prophecy, takes shape in my mind. Charismatic thoughts are often marked by particular clarity and power. When in addition to this I find I have a strong inner compulsion to make my contribution now, I should once again take a deep breath and after this brief hesitation say what is to be said. Whether or not it was charismatic will be shown by how well it has fitted in with the development of the whole service and by what echo it has awakened among the others present, who are equally gifted with the Spirit.

8. Sometimes it may happen that I have a clear thought like this, but that I have already taken such a prominent part in the service that I do not wish to say anything else at this point. If so, I can pray that the thought may come into somebody else's

mind. One will often find that the thought does then pass to another: perhaps it will be expressed in another form more in keeping with the individual style of the person concerned, but it will be the same basic idea which is conveyed. This possibility is also open to the person who is inexperienced and who has insurmountable inhibitions about exercising his charism in the service. If he then hears his thought being expressed by another and confirmed by the congregation, he will next time have more courage to participate directly himself.

9. There are various types of charismatic contribution which must be evaluated by the congregation: "Let two or three prophets speak, and let the others weigh what is said" (1 Cor. 14:29). This instruction of Paul's surely applies equally to those charisms which are closely related to prophecy, such as visions (revelations), the interpretation of prayers in other languages and the word of knowledge. How can this evaluation by the church be in practice carried out? Experience has shown that it is good if a contribution of this sort is followed by a fairly long period of silence. Following this there are various possible ways of making it clear whether the church confirms or rejects the message. Usually it is shown by the contributions which follow, or someone says "Amen" or "Thank you" for the contribution. On the other hand people should feel free to express a negative reaction such as: "That sounded to me as if it came from man rather than God." It is important to have discussed in advance the necessity of testing the validity of charismatic contributions, and for the congregation to know in what ways they can make their views known.

10. It is very helpful if some kind of discussion can be held when the service is over. The most important thoughts from the service can be gone over again, and perhaps they will be supplemented by further contributions which were "suppressed" during the service itself. The group should establish where there were gaps — if any — in the progression of thought. Personal experiences, thanksgiving for some contribution, questions about a prophecy or an interpretation, resolutions made during the service — all can form part of the content of such a discussion. Above all it can help people to learn the art of working together in fellowship as directed by the Spirit; for even in a charismatic service we should learn by our mistakes.

Charismatic services are important for the opportunity they give for the full range of God-given charisms to function. If they begin from silence, they often possess a depth, a beauty and a clarity of thought rarely found in traditional services. Such maturity in exercising gifts in fellowship in the setting of a free service is, however, only slowly achieved. It is of great importance here that spectacular gifts like glossolalia, prophecy and visions should be exercised with modesty and restraint. As given by the Spirit these gifts are not in fact spectacular, but they often become so in our hands. They should add an occasional dab of colour to the charismatic service, but not drench it continuously. We must bear in mind that there are other charisms which have a part to play in the service: worship, singing, teaching, testimony, personal prayer. All these can achieve the intensity and spontaneity of a charism. If a prophecy is uttered, a vision described and interpreted, a prayer in another language spoken and explained or a clarifying word of knowledge made known in a deeply spiritual atmosphere like this, then it will no longer be regarded as sensational. It will be heard as the voice of God addressing the present situation of the church as it assembles, and the church will then quietly consider what it has heard and evaluate it.

Charismatic structuring of the church's ministry

The charismatic movement has in many places brought new life to church *services* while the structure of *service* and ministry has remained the same as ever. The greater part of those attending church regularly is still made up of passive members whose part consists chiefly of listening. A small number are active, but mostly their activity takes the form of doing things to help the minister, and taking over duties which the minister cannot manage for reasons of time. The services rendered are largely governed by tradition: the actual gifts of the church members and the real needs of the present day are often left unconsidered. What is lacking, in other words, is a charismatic structuring of the church's ministry.

There are a few examples of the opposite happening. One of the best known is the Church of the Redeemer at Houston, Texas. Following a personal visit to this church, Cardinal Suenens wrote: "The most striking example known to me of a fully successful integration of institution and charism at the parish level is that of the Episcopalian parish of the Church of the Redeemer in Eastwood, a poor section of Houston, Texas . . . Graham Pulkingham . . . the pastor and four of his friends, animated by a deep charismatic spirituality, succeeded, by a gradual osmosis, in winning over other members of the parish to their vision of renewal. Gradually, in the power of the Spirit, these formed a community which lives a kind of community life described in the Acts of the Apostles, even sharing their possessions. At this moment, there are about thirty persons, men and women, engaged full time in the various ministries of the parish and even beyond, which they sum up under the fivefold division of apostle, prophet, evangelist, shepherd, teacher . . . It is a marvellous example of a Christianity lived in all its social implications, within a climate of deep prayer, personal as well as communal and liturgical."[150] This church started out from the charisms of its members, who allowed themselves to be called to a life of total surrender. From this there developed the new, charismatic structure of ministries in the church.

This is also probably the only way in which a charismatic structure of ministries can arise from a rigid, traditional church structure. Firstly the individual members must become aware of their own charisms, and especially those which cannot be exercised at the charismatic service. I should like to give one or two examples.

People who have prophetic gifts, who have been repeatedly able to give a word of wisdom or who possess the charism of leadership should be those particularly called upon to exercise leadership functions — provided of course that their everyday lives are led by the Spirit and that the fruit of the Spirit is to be seen in them.

If there are several church members who have a particular gift of administration, compassion or healing, then it is clear that the church has a special ministry to those who are weak or ill.

For preaching, Bible study and children's work people are needed who have the gifts of teaching, knowledge and prophecy.

For evangelistic work we need the charisms of meeting, prophecy, teaching, counselling and miracles.

The administration of the church needs the gift of administrative leadership, sharing of possessions and faith.

The general responsibility for the church should lie in the hands of at least two well-tried church members, who may well possess the gifts of prophetic and administrative leadership.

One cannot impose a new charismatic structure of ministry on any church. It must begin gradually. The most important part in the first instance is played by the minister. He is the bearer of the central office in the church, and he has responsibility for practically every sphere. Certainly he is often frustrated because he finds that he is supposed to do everything but is unable to do everything. Usually however he goes about it in the wrong way and sets goals for the church which correspond to his own gifts. An evangelistic minister therefore builds up a church which has no other great emphasis except evangelism; a minister with administrative gifts develops a church with a sense of social responsibility; the typical preacher tries to centre everything around his pulpit and the preaching service. The result is that one wrong kind of structure for the church is only replaced by another, equally wrong.

The first step towards the establishment of a charismatic structure for ministry consists of having a minister who recognizes the situation and is willing in his preaching and in practice to take further steps in the direction of a charismatic structure.

The second step is to find an area of the church's life in which the restructuring is most likely to succeed. Perhaps in the church there are two house groups which have come into being because the two families had large sitting rooms and because the two fathers were fond of talking. Now the two house groups have practically folded up. Perhaps one discovers in the church two couples who are evidently living examples of the charism of marriage. One begins two new house groups centred upon these two families, which because of their life-style already have many contacts in the neighbourhood.

The third step consists of slowly re-organizing the leadership structures of the church. According to the rules of the denomination concerned, there will be varying ways of achieving a situation where those members who have the charism of leadership are given the actual leadership of the church. The same is true of other central ministries in the church, such as planning of the services, preaching, administration, children's and youth work.

The fourth step is perhaps the hardest. In most churches there are some jobs which are traditional, but for which no suitable and appropriately gifted people are available. For instance, the musical side of the church's life may be at a low ebb because of a lack of helpers; or there may be an old people's home which is a constant burden on the church because there is no one really able to minister to the residents. The church should pray earnestly for a while to be given the necessary charisms for the undertaking of such tasks; if there is still no appropriate charism to be found, these areas of responsibility must be given up.

The fifth step consists of building up new structures and taking on new responsibilities in areas where up till now nothing has been done, but for which suitable charisms exist in the church.

These steps are not to be taken as a blueprint. Sometimes the Holy Spirit may work in the opposite order; but somehow the structures have to be altered step by step, if a church is ever to find its way into a charismatic structuring of its ministries.

It is to be hoped that as a result of the movement for charismatic renewal of the church these questions of structure will gradually take on the importance which they deserve, for the charismatic renewal must certainly not be allowed to take place only at the level of worship. We are still only in the very early stages of considering this subject; a more thorough exchange of ideas and experiences is only slowly getting under way. The development of a charismatic structure of ministry is however very important if the charisms are not to remain as a fringe phenomenon on the church's periphery but are to embrace the church at its centre.

Charismatic gifts in everyday life

Though charisms are given primarily to the *church* for its edification, they are nonetheless associated with the whole life of the person who has them. The person who has administrative gifts will not work in that way only within the sphere of the church but also at his place of work and in his family life. Prophecy is not limited to charismatic acts of worship or to preaching: inspired speech is possible in everyday life as well. The charisms find in daily life a wide-ranging field of activity where they are also needed — for in everyday life we need the power and gifts of the Holy Spirit just as much as we do in the church.

In the first letter of Peter we are exhorted to make use of our charisms on the principle of good stewardship, wherever it is needed: "As each has received a gift, employ it for one another, as good stewards of God's varied grace: whoever speaks, as one who utters oracles of God; whoever renders service, as one who renders it by the strength which God supplies; in order that in everything God may be glorified through Jesus Christ" (1 Pet. 4:10-11). In church services today more and more Christians are expecting a place to be provided for charismatic spontaneity. Gradually, too, the idea of a charismatic structure of ministries in the local church will gain weight. There remains the further task of becoming sensitive to the opportunities for charismatic activity in everyday life. In the section which follows I want to outline these possibilities, so that we may become aware of the possibilities for the Holy Spirit's working in our everyday lives.

God's gracious gift of *eternal life* releases our lives from the usual human frame of reference, in which the important things are possessions, power, honour, affluence and pleasure, and gives us new criteria for the assessment of the events which take place in our lives. He who becomes aware that his life is completely governed by worldly terms of reference should pray for this gift, in order that he may find new goals to live for. He who is involved in a strenuous career needs the gift of eternal life if he is not to become enslaved by the rules which his career sets for him, but to remain open to the leading of God. He who is embittered because of some injustice done to him can pray for this gift, that he may learn to look beyond the short-term events of life in this world and take in the "long breath of eternity".

Many people suffer because they lack contact with others. Although they are continually in the presence of other people, no real meeting takes place, still less a contact which might produce spiritual fruit. They need the gift of *meeting*, which will gradually give them the ability to understand the other person in his situation, to enter genuinely into his life, and to look beyond their own problems in order to be able totally to devote themselves to the other. Hence meeting is a gift of grace which we cannot do without, whether it be in the family, the church, the place of work or the neighbourhood in which we live. It is one of the most important qualifications for missionary living.

The gift of *marriage* is, in an age when marriage is undergoing a severe crisis, certainly one of the most important gifts. Marriage as a gift of grace is a sharing of two lives which has become strong enough to support others. Of course God leads two people together in order that they may have mutual joy in one another. But he also leads them together in order that they may bring joy to others. Charismatic marriage is a cell through which the Holy Spirit works in many directions. It is always an unselfish marriage, whose partners are more concerned to serve others than themselves. Those who are partners in such a marriage, or who can observe it in others, will know that it is also a joyful marriage for the partners themselves — not in a superficial way, but because it is a sharing of life together which is constantly receiving from its responsibility for others new stimulation and strength for itself.

The *single life* can likewise only be joyful when the single person draws others into his sphere of responsibility. This is both its special opportunity and the secret of fulfilment. The single life as a gift of grace does not abstain from taking a partner simply in order to cover up personal insecurity or lack of opportunity with a veneer of spirituality; it abstains because of God's call to care for many people, or to fulfil a task which demands independence. This may be some quite normal activity, such as taking up a caring profession; it can also happen in any other circumstance of life.

The gift of *prophecy* finds innumerable opportunities to be used in daily life. I will mention just a few. A mother with prophetic gifts has a better insight into the situation of her children. In bringing them up she can begin at the place where the real problems lie. For the very reason that there is so much uncertainty in the whole realm of education today, it is often only prophetic insight and inspired speech which will be of any help. The teacher too needs this charism, as do all those whose job brings them predominantly in touch with other people. Prophecy also has a most important part to play in an area where we perhaps least expect, namely in economics. The economy is not a matter of indifference to God: it is not his will that people should be out of work and lose their livelihood. Because God has a plan for the whole world including the world of economics, a Christian in a factory can be given prophetic insight into the situation of his firm, whether he is an executive, a member of a works council or a worker on the shop floor. An inspired word spoken in conversation, or in the process of arriving at a decision, will alter the situation decisively and cause good to come.

Even the gift of *revelations* is not restricted to use in the church. In everyday life visions can be experienced in the same quiet way as prayer in another language when it takes place outside a meeting for worship. Suddenly in one's imagination a set of events becomes clearly visible in pictorial form, where previously it was abstract and incomprehensible. Children often literally see such things, as is illustrated by the following story which I have on reliable authority. A child who was playing in the street ran out and was run over by a tractor. The great wheels of the vehicle rolled straight over the child's chest. Yet the child stood up again as if nothing had happened. The tyremarks were still visible on his clothes. Everyone was absolutely amazed. The child could not understand at all why the adults were so excited and exclaimed: "Why, didn't you see the men who lifted up the wheel as it went over me?" Behind the visible events the child in his vision saw the invisible and yet real intervention of the angels of God.

The gift of *counselling* reminds us too readily, because of the connotations of the word, of the pastor's or psychotherapist's consulting room. *Paraklesis*, which means literally calling someone alongside to help, is however a charism which has almost as many applications in daily life as prophecy. Charismatic "paracletes" are people whom others trust, whose advice they instinctively seek when they have problems, in whom it is easy to confide because they radiate confidence. Those in particular whose profession brings them into much contact with other people will need this charism at every step. It is also a quite remarkable source of help in relationships between parents and children. A person who is trusted in this way will often have an unusual number of opportunities for evangelism, for when people have confidence in a person they will be more likely to have confidence in his faith.

The *word of wisdom* has a very special relevance to our day. Fewer and fewer problems are being resolved by one person's decision taken in isolation. Decision-making is more often the result of consultation and discussion within a group. Group decisions are based upon a more thorough knowledge of the facts, and they are therefore often more appropriate than decisions taken by an individual. But the way there is wearisome: it takes much time and causes strain on the nerves. Executives in industry and in public administration, and leaders in the church as well, complain that nowadays they spend all their time in hurrying from one committee to another so that they no longer have opportunity for private reflection and work. The word of wisdom shortens the decision-making process, not by using dictatorial methods nor by exercising hidden influence, but by throwing light on the situation. What characterizes the word of wisdom is the ability to make the facts of the situation understood and to formulate a possible course of action which is instinctively recognized as the right one. The agreement of the group is based on the common insight which has been given to it. Certainly many Christians will have surprising experiences if they begin to ask for a word of wisdom for the quite normal and everyday problems which they face.

The *word of knowledge* has the function of making God understood to men. It results in enlightenment for the listener, a sudden understanding or "disclosure" experience. To put it in popular parlance, the "penny drops". Peter's sermon at Pentecost is a perfect example of this gift, which makes the nature and activity of God comprehensible to men in a particular situation. In everyday life there are many opportunities for the word of knowledge — really in every conversation about spiritual matters, and in answering the many questions raised by children and colleagues at work.

The gift of *teaching* provides a striking parallel to the word of knowledge, but in contrast to that gift it is concerned less with giving the answer to a particular question than with helping others to understand the basic principles of the faith. The charism of teaching can be used quite specifically in daily life in the work of a school teacher for instance. Let us imagine a conversation in the classroom about the relationships between the members of the class. The teacher speaks of understanding, concern for others, and of helping one another. If he has the teaching charism, he will be able not only to awaken by the deft use of his normal teaching skills an understanding of the problems of community life, but also to say something about the spiritual foundations of our relationships with our fellow men. This charism is of special value in religious education, but it is also of help in giving religious instruction to children at home and in conversations between those who are growing up.

Paul makes it clear that the gift of *glossolalia* has its special place right in the midst of everyday life. It is there limited of course to quiet, personal use. Prayer in other languages, in the form of the Holy Spirit praying an inaudible prayer within me, can accompany me throughout the day. In situations of tension, of difficulties, of sudden decisions, of contact with new people, praying in other languages can deepen my relationship with God. It requires less concentration and can nonetheless hit the nail on the head, for the Spirit who prays through me knows what are the important issues of each moment. Of course prayer in other languages must not displace prayer with the mind, for that would mean that my spiritual consciousness was being suppressed, but it can be complementary to it. He who practises this charism will forever be finding that after praying in this way a thought will suddenly come to him, or an insight be given, which is of considerable help in the situation although he has not prayed consciously about it. This represents a form of *interpretation* of glossolalia in everyday life.

The main use of *singing in the Spirit* will be within the service of worship. Many people however are fond of singing while they work or when they are in difficult situations, where it gives them an emotional balance. Here singing in the Spirit also has a place. It does not simply calm a person down like an ordinary song, but leads him to a deeper relationship with Jesus. A feeling of oppression can be changed into joy, lack of courage into hope, ill humour into praise. I remember once a tiring car journey home after a weekend which had been crammed with meetings. We were so tired that we had to keep relieving one another at the wheel, at short intervals. Then one of us began to sing in another language, and the others joined in. The tension gave way to an atmosphere of spontaneous joy. The tiredness remained, but we were able to give back to God the many questions which had been raised in the course of the weekend, and only then did we find new strength.

Prophetic leadership is needed by, for example, the leader of a research team. It is bad when research is controlled by the regulations of administrators, for bureaucratic organization is not conducive to the freedom of the creative spirit. It is of the utmost importance that people who are involved in any kind of creative activity should do it on the basis of a spiritual gift. In this way divine impulses can help to give shape to creative thought and action. This is as true for the politician as for the architect, or again for the manager of an advertising agency who helps to form the taste and consumer habits of a great mass of customers. All attempts at reform require this creative impulse of the Holy Spirit if they are to serve people in a way which is in accordance with God's will. Basically they will serve other people only when they are actually serving God, because God has a better overall view of how things are developing than any man, and his impulses will be more likely to fit the real circumstances than any impulse of man.

The gift of *service* obviously has a particular relevance to everyday life, especially at this present day when it seems possible to care for man's material welfare only by means of a progressive expansion of the administrative machine. The problems of administration claim a great deal of time and energy. Inappropriate action or excessive emotional involvement provide fuel for constant conflict. Charismatic helping may be recognized by its ability to defuse at once a situation charged with conflict by going right to the heart of the matter. *Diakonia* can ensure peace in the factory; it can transform a bad atmosphere simply by doing enough about the essentials. The gift of service is often combined with natural authority. It then becomes quite normal for colleagues at work when they are faced with a difficult situation to go to the Christian who has this charism and ask his advice. They do this because they know that if anyone can solve the problem, he can. The gift of service can be particularly evident when there is a road accident. The man with this gift does not give way to panic: he quickly gains an overall view of the situation and is able to take the necessary steps without any great fuss. He looks after the person who has been injured, makes others responsible for controlling the traffic, sends someone to the telephone, tries to find a doctor, and at the same time calms down the other people who are present. Charismatic service need not always however involve taking over leadership. In a similar situation it could, for example, be much more important to go over to a frightened child and take it in one's arms, so as to prevent the child from receiving a harmful shock.

The gift of *sharing possessions* has a very central role to play today. Ability to share has become one of the most important virtues in our world, with its almost unimaginable differences between the poor and the rich nations. Many Christians have realized that it is not enough for us to have government aid programmes, but that the life-style of the individual is being called in question. We find it hard to make decisions and to be living examples in this sphere — making it all the more necessary to have the charism of sharing.

Despite all the social help given by the state there is still much need, especially in those areas which cannot be adequately dealt with by financial support. Who is in special need of the charism of *compassion*? In the first place, all Christians who work in specialized nursing professions — nurses, teachers of the handicapped, doctors, and those who care for an old person. There is however much need also outside the protective environment of our hospitals, special schools and old people's homes. The gift of compassion is therefore very important outside the caring professions as well. Many families have handicapped children, and many factories employ disabled people. Besides these there are emotional problems which are virtually impossible to cure. Here too a kind of nursing is necessary: the readiness again and again to help and advise, or to take over simple activities which the ill or weak person cannot cope with. Anyone who looks after an emotionally disordered person knows that it is impossible without the compassion which comes from the power of the Holy Spirit.

In everyday life the gift of *faith* will not be the impressive type of faith which moves mountains, for it is usually concerned with minor problems. But this is just where it is so important that the gift of faith can recognize the place where God is going to do a miracle or cause a change to come about; in other words, when we should go forward, and when we must adapt ourselves to circumstances as they are. Faith knows that at a certain point everyday things will change, to the glory of God. It knows at a certain moment that what looks like a hopeless situation is not really hopeless. Where the charism of faith appears hope is engendered. This gift is the oxygen which produces an atmosphere in which work can go forward continuously, joyfully and even sometimes without taking thought. This gift is equally useful to the mother of a large family, the minister who goes to a difficult parish, or the social worker who is placed in a slum area.

What has the gift of *miracles* to do with everyday life? Augustine draws a distinction between great miracles and small ones. The small miracles are for him the ones which are sensational in their effect, because they are the exception. The great miracles are those which are renewed every day and upon which our lives depend: the miracle of life, the miracle of growth in nature, the daily miracle of light and heat, or the miracle of reproduction. In dealing with the gift of miracles it is particularly necessary for us to learn to notice the unsensational, daily miracles of God which are great for the very reason that they are constantly with us. It frequently happens that we are nearly involved in an accident. The emergency stop saves us — a second later and there would have been a disaster, and there was no time to pray. In this situation we see the working of God's power. We do not perhaps experience a "classical" exorcism of demons. But we live in a world in which the activity of demonic powers opposed to God is on the increase. We take it for granted in this situation that we are able to pray. In reality it is a miracle of the Holy Spirit. We have never witnessed the raising of the dead. But perhaps for special reasons we have been for a while under such pressure in our work, and at the same time involved in helping with some service for the Lord, that humanly speaking we are heading for a breakdown. If we can be happy and relaxed under the pressure of this double responsibility, it is a miracle of the Holy Spirit. Perhaps there is someone who has not yet had this experience and is in a situation where he urgently needs the power of God in this way. He should pray for the gift of miracles. For this gift is not a special gift restricted to certain great men of God, but a perfectly normal part of the Christian's equipment for his everyday life.

The gift of *healing* is closely linked with the responsibility of the church. Nevertheless it can be repeatedly experienced in everyday life as well. Members of a family can pray for one another and when someone falls sick administer the laying on of hands. Prayer for one who is ill should become a quite normal and expected form of mutual help. This is true even of children. A four year old boy knew that whenever he was ill his parents would lay hands on him with prayer. One day when his mother had an attack of migraine and had to go and lie down he went quite naturally to the mother's bedside, laid his hands on her and prayed that she might be healed. The mother recovered at once. The child of course thought that the healing was magical, as was only natural at his age. His parents talked it over with him and tried to explain the meaning of healing through prayer. Silent prayers for healing are likewise important in everyday life. An exhausted mother can in her imagination lay hands on her noisy children and bless them. This silent prayer of blessing also has a place where there are tensions at work: it can be used by the nursery teacher who has an unruly group of children to look after, or by a driver who sees that the driver of the car in front of him is obviously on edge, and is able by this means to bring that man into the sphere of God's influence. As in the church context, the gift may be applied not only to physical illness but also to nervous disorders and social tensions.

The gift of *martyrdom* is not confined to the act of giving up one's life for Jesus' sake, but applies to every kind of suffering for the faith. This situation frequently arises in everyday life. Let me illustrate this with an example. Suppose someone finds that others are plotting against him at work. First of all he must look at the situation objectively. If it is his own fault that this is happening, he should change his ways. If he is really suffering for the sake of the faith, he should still try to defend himself in an objective manner. There are however some situations where the only way to alter the state of affairs would be to respond by counter-intrigue. If straight talking fails and there is nothing for it but a relentless struggle for power, the situation is ripe for martyrdom. This is the time to ask God for the charism of ability to suffer. The reaction must not be a bitter one, but loving. This cannot be achieved without the gift of the Holy Spirit, because our own strength would not suffice.

Administrative leadership as a charism takes on special importance in everyday life where someone is responsible for a group of people — for instance a manager at work, or a bus driver who has charge of the school bus. He should regard his responsibility as a spiritual task. The gift of administrative leadership will help him to give appropriate instructions to those under him, for the decisions which are in accordance with the will of God also correspond to the real needs of men. The government minister who has the gift of administrative leadership will develop a natural authority which will keep every civil servant in his right place. The housewife will care for her family in such a way that both her husband and each child will have the necessary room to express themselves. Without the charism leadership must be fought for, but as a charism it becomes a natural function of one's personality.

The gift of *discernment of spirits* is outstandingly important in everyday life. For we allow ourselves more frequently to be guided in our decisions by the events going on around us than to be led by a prophetic word or a venture of faith. We often let ourselves be influenced by circumstances because we know from experience that God can speak through them. But then we must always face the question: are the circumstances which influence me signs of the divine will, or are they barriers erected by forces opposed to God, which must be broken through? Is this opportunity which suddenly presents itself to me God-given or is it a temptation? It is at this point in our daily lives that the gift of discerning the spirits has a part to play. The first thing to do, of course, is to look into the objective facts. Often these facts will already point in a certain direction. There remains however an element of uncertainty, for the facts can be misleading and it could be that although a person is humanly speaking not fitted for a certain responsibility, God will give him the abilities he needs. Or the contrary may be true: he may be humanly speaking well suited to perform this task, but God knows a better way for him. Faced with such uncertainty we need the gift of discerning the spirits, which behind the events can see the power which brought them about, whether it is divine, human or a force opposed to God.

CHAPTER THIRTEEN

Becoming Aware of Gifts and Developing Them

Regeneration and reception of the Spirit go together, and the reception of charisms is part of receiving the Spirit. The charisms are therefore given to us when we say "yes" to God and so give the Spirit the opportunity to make his home within us. From this point onwards we may enjoy charismatic experiences. If that does not happen we shall remain unaware of our gift. Perhaps we do not expect ever to find charismatic powers at work in our lives. This means that we have never even prayed for a gift: perhaps we are afraid of the gifts of grace because we do not wish to pray in other languages or because we do not feel capable of uttering prophecy or laying hands on the sick.

Many Christians nonetheless have a desire that their gift should be awakened and developed. How can this happen? Jesus answers this question in the parable of the friend at midnight (Luke 11:5-13). A man suddenly has a visitor and has no bread in the house. Although it is midnight already, he goes to his friend and asks him for bread. The first reaction of the friend in this situation is not very friendly. He begins by refusing, and will not help until the one who is making the request begins to get on his nerves. Jesus himself tells us what it is to which the parable refers: "If you then who are evil know how to give good gifts to your children, how much more will the heavenly Father give the Holy Spirit to those who ask him!" (Luke 11:13). This story is a parable of contrast. God is not to be compared with the unfriendly friend. God is quite different: the context emphasizes how gladly God gives: "For everyone who asks receives, and he who seeks finds, and to him who knocks it will be opened" (Luke 11:10).

God gives gladly but he waits for us to ask. The passage therefore emphasizes also our own activity. Looking at it from this point of view one could put it this way: only he who asks will receive, only he who seeks finds, and only he who knocks will have the door opened to him. Why does God expect us to ask? Why does he not give before we ask, seeing that he knows our needs better than we ourselves know them? We shall soon find the answer if we consider what would probably happen if God automatically gave us everything we need. Imagine an earthly father treating his children in such a way. He would find little joy in them. His children would soon take his gifts for granted; they would become ungrateful and always be wanting more. By waiting for us to ask, God is leading us to recognize our own needs. It is important for us to recognize what we need, in order that we may be prepared for the free gift of God.

When I ask for a charism I fulfil the first condition for the awakening of my spiritual gifts. The prayer must however proceed from the right motives if God is to grant what we ask. Some Christians pray out of self-seeking motives. They want special gifts in order that they may have a higher standing in the church. This will lead them to seek especially those charisms which attract attention, such as healing, miracles or glossolalia. Gifts of service, sharing possessions, compassion and martyrdom are less in demand. Others may want particular charisms to help them get on in their professional life. If they possessed the charism of leadership they would be promoted more rapidly in their profession. God cannot grant such requests. Charisms are given in order that God may do his work through them, that the church may be edified and that Jesus Christ, and with him the Father, may be glorified. God wants them to be used in the service of others. Even the parable of the friend at midnight illustrates that. He needs the bread in order to feed his visitor, not himself. That is what makes him so bold as to disturb his friend at midnight.

The proper motive in asking for charisms is, in the first place, the realization that one's own talents are insufficient. A mother notices that because of too many demands on her time she has become hard towards her children: she should pray for the gift of compassion. A minister who knows that he cannot say to his church what they really need to hear can pray for the gift of prophecy. A person who often finds himself in difficult situations where he is involved in controversy can pray for the word of wisdom. One can even pray for several gifts, so long as the prayer arises from a recognition of one's own limitations and not from the desire to be a spiritual superman and to play a special role in the church. Self-awareness means humility, and humility means courage to face up to reality. Part of a realistic assessment of a situation is the recognition of my own limitations. But it is exactly at this point that I can reckon with the fact that God can extend my limits, because his possibilities are unlimited. Humility sees things in a natural way and does not underestimate a person's human capabilities either. It rejoices in them, yet at the same time looks for God to give more.

For many Christians their charism is already visible in embryo form. In this case it is important to become aware of these "embryo" gifts so that they may be practised and used. How are we to recognize these charismatic beginnings? First one should ask oneself the question: where has God set his seal on my ministry up till now? Perhaps it will have been repeatedly in the same area. One person may recall that he had often prayed for the sick and that many of them have become better. Another may discover that people with whom he has shared his possessions have been able to do a great deal with it. He should pray that his gift will be strengthened and deepened.

Another way of recognizing my charisms is to ask myself in what areas I am particularly involved. There are some people who become very impatient when time and energy is wasted due to a lack of organization and oversight. They should pray for the gift of service. Another sees with exceptional clarity the need of people who are in difficult situations. He needs the gift of counselling. Often someone will begin to pray for a gift because of a specific difficulty with which he is unable to cope. That is a thoroughly good motivation for asking for charisms. Some people are not clear about where their own needs lie and do not know the limitations of their own personality. They should simply pray that God will give them the gifts they need. They can also ask a person who has the gift of prophecy to pray with them about it. Perhaps he will be able to promise a particular gift. But here too the process must not be seen as something automatic: sometimes the time is not yet ripe and God requires us to wait.

We must not make these suggestions into a blueprint. The Holy Spirit has many and various means of making himself known. I may be in a desperate situation and be able to find no way out of it. Here I can simply pray that God will change the circumstances, or that he will give me the gifts which will enable me to do what is necessary for him to be glorified. I may see a task before me, which I am convinced God has committed to me. Here I may ask for the charisms I need in order to perform that task. If God gives me the necessary gift, I shall be all the more confident that he has commissioned me; if I do not receive the appropriate gifts, I must pray again about what God wants me to do.

The basic condition for becoming aware of and awakening spiritual gifts is the confidence that God will give what is right. This implies also a readiness to accept the distinctions which he makes. Some people are given striking gifts, which also carry with them special dangers. Others God expects to work in quieter ways. Many Christians receive one well-defined charism; others receive several. Nor does God tie himself slavishly to his distribution of gifts: in an emergency he may give temporary gifts, which the person concerned does not normally possess and which he will not receive again; in other cases some gifts seem to be buried for a while until suddenly they reappear. Some people refuse certain gifts, thinking to themselves perhaps, "Lord, give me what you will, but please not the gift of glossolalia. That would be too embarrassing." Or they may think, "Of course I will accept my gift, but it must be something which expresses itself in a way that is in keeping with my position in the church." God's answer to such reservations on man's part is often to give nothing at all. For he allows no one to usurp his sovereign authority to give or withhold what he will.

Although charisms can be recognized by a variety of signs and awakened in a variety of ways, there are several passages in the New Testament which suggest a connection between the awakening of charisms and the laying on of hands. Thus in 1 Tim. 4:14 Paul says to his disciple Timothy: "Do not neglect the gift you have, which was given you by prophetic utterance when the council of elders laid their hands upon you." The practice of the laying on of hands must be safeguarded from two misunderstandings. Firstly, it is not a rigid institution implying that charisms can be received or awakened *only* through the laying on of hands. Secondly, it is not a ritual act, but simply a prayer for blessing made by Christians who have received a special commission to do it. The power does not lie in the laying on of hands, but in the prayer. The outward gesture of the laying on of hands does however help the one who is seeking the blessing. It is a visible sign of the love of God, a symbol of the hand of God outstretched to give. The personal approach of the one who blesses to the one who is blessed makes it clear that the charism is an integral part of the church's life: it is not something which results simply from a two-way relationship between the individual and God, but something which is included within the responsibility of the church.

The prayer of blessing for the reception of charisms properly belongs at the beginning of the Christian life, and is best combined with water baptism. Since however baptism is often administered before a person has consciously said "yes" to God and before he has been born again, and since there is anyway in many cases no expectation of receiving charisms, there are many Christians who are unaware of their gifts of grace and have had no definitely charismatic experiences. Such people are therefore unable to develop their gifts within the church and to take their own place within a charismatic structure of ministries. We must never forget therefore that the experiences of becoming aware of and awakening charisms which are characteristic of our own day are only provisional experiences, and that it is our task — a task which still lies before us — to restore the expectation and experience of receiving or stirring up charisms to the place where, according to the New Testament, it belongs — at the point of conversion, regeneration and water baptism.

Epilogue: Looking Ahead

"Stewards of the grace of God" — under this title we have tried to describe the various levels at which the gifts of the Holy Spirit operate and at which they are experienced today. The charismatic movement of today has drawn our attention again to God's free gift of the charisms and made us ask questions about their significance. At the same time we have considered some problems, distortions and abuses which remind us of the difficulties of exercising the charisms in a sound and healthy way. We are called to stewardship: that implies that we are not to belittle what God has put into our hands, but to use his gifts in the way shown to us in the New Testament, to trade with the "pound' which he has given us.

Paul most solemnly declares that charismatic gifts are not an isolated activity of the Holy Spirit, that they must be integrated first and foremost within the life of the local church. Only then shall we see a healthy development of these gifts. But the other levels at which they must be integrated are also important if we are to avoid the danger of one-sidedness, distortions and abuses. The uninhibited exercise of charisms is easy, but integration is difficult. It is a life long task for every Christian. We should not be surprised therefore to find so many examples of gifts being distorted, and so few churches in which consciously charismatic experiences have been integrated and in which they have affected the organizational structure of the church.

The absolute necessity of integrating the gifts within the life of the local church explains the wording of the (German) sub-title of this book: "From the charismatic movement to charismatic renewal of the church". In the light of the New Testament a charismatic movement cannot rightly exist, for charisms are tools for service in the church and through the church to the world, and they cannot constitute a special movement. Nevertheless the churches bear a great deal of the blame for the fact thaat there is a charismatic movement, since they frequently keep outside their doors those who have had consciously charismatic experiences. My initial assumption is that the charismatic movement at its heart is a first kindling brought about by the

Holy Spirit with the purpose of restoring the charisms to their rightful place in the life of the churches. This first kindling must not however be allowed to turn into a permanent institution, and there are great dangers if it does. The charismatic movement must therefore become a charismatic renewal of the churches.

I call upon the churches to welcome the "charismatics", so that it may become clear that all Christians are charismatics and have the responsibility to exercise their gifts consciously and with self-control. The church has sufficient resources of strength to enable it to cope with the new emotional life and the full range and variety of the charisms. The church will however be able to cope only if she continues in diligent study of the word of God, so that she may be able to recognize how the charisms should be integrated within the whole life of the church, and at what point mistakes in their development turn into abuses.

I call upon "charismatics" to act consistently and return to their churches, giving up their special groups and cliques. If they do not, the gifts which the Holy Spirit has bestowed upon them will be turned into weapons which divide. This reconciliation will be possible only if they give up the false way of the *triumphalist* church and bear the cross of life within the local church community. If someone is not able successfully to parry the opposition from the side of the church in love, neither will he be able to exercise his own gift in love.

"The end of all things is at hand; therefore keep sane and sober for your prayers. Above all hold unfailing your love for one another, since love covers a multitude of sins. Practise hospitality ungrudgingly to one another. As each has received a gift, employ it for one another, as good stewards of God's varied grace: whoever speaks, as one who utters oracles of God; whoever renders service, as one who renders it by the strength which God supplies; in order that in everything God may be glorified through Jesus Christ. To him belong glory and dominion for ever and ever. Amen." (1 Peter 4:7-11).

Notes

Introduction
(pages 9-14)

1. O. A. Dilschneider: Die Notwendigkeit neuer Antworten auf neue Fragen, in *Erfahrung und Theologie des Heiligen Geistes,* ed. Heitmann/Mühlen, Hamburg & Munich 1974, pp.151ff.
2. H. Mühlen: *Die Erneuerung des christlichen Glaubens,* Munich 1974, pp.45f.
3. Quoted in *Jesus-Generation — auch in Europa?,* ed. W. Kroll, Wuppertal 1972, 2nd. ed., p.119.
4. Quoted in Mederlet/McDonnell, *Charismatische Erneuerung der katholischen Kirche,* Schloss Craheim 1972, p.38f.
5. Quoted in *"Charismatische Erneuerung der Kirche",* Feb. 1975.
6. Quoted in Gassmann (et. al.), *Neue transkonfessionelle Bewegungen,* Frankfurt a. Main, 1976, p.187.
7. From a typescript.
8. *Die Gemeinde,* No. 34/1976.
9. *Die Gemeinde,* No. 46/1976.
10. The *Gemeinschaften* (lit. "fellowships") are groups of conservative evangelical believers having their roots in Pietism, which retain a loyalty to the official national Protestant Church of Germany while having their own additional times and places of meeting and organization.
11. Quoted in *Wer bestimmt, was charismatisch ist?,* R. Brockhaus aktuell, Heft 2, p.36.
12. E. Lubahn, *Schwarmgeist,* Wuppertal 1976, pp.33f.
13. Broadbent/Hubmer, *Heute noch in Zungen reden?,* Bad Liebenzell 1975, p.104.
14. O. Riecker, *Ruf aus Indonesien,* Neuhausen 1971, p.185.

Chapter One
(pages 17-22)

15. B. Schlink: *Er zeigt der Wege Sinn,* Darmstadt 1969, pp.205ff.
16. D. Bennett: *Nine O'Clock in the Morning,* Coverdale, p.36f.
17. A. Bittlinger: *Die charismatische Erneuerung der Kirchen* (in Mühlen, op. cit. p.19).
18. W. Becker: *Die Charismen in der evangelischen Kirche heute* (in R. F. Edel (ed.): *Kirche und Charisma,* Marburg 1966, p.163).
19. L. J. Suenens: *A New Pentecost?,* Collins Fountain edition, pp.72-74.
20. Ibid. pp.221, 224.
21. O. Riecker, op. cit. pp.105f.
22. *Jesus People Report,* Wuppertal, 1972, p.39.
23. Ibid., p.61.

Chapter Two
(pages 23-28)

24. E. Schweizer: *Gemeinde nach dem neuen Testament,* Zürich 1949.

25. E. Giese: *Und flicken die Netze*, Marburg 1976, p.244.
26. R. F. Edel, op. cit. pp. 78ff.
27. A. Bittlinger: *Gemeinde ist anders*, Stuttgart 1966.
28. E. Hinson: *2000 Jahre Zungenreden*, Kassel 1968.
29. G. Ruhbach: *Das Charismaverständnis des Neuen Testaments*, art. in *Monatschrift für Pastoraltheologie*, p.409/1964.
30. Cf. M. T. Kelsey: *Tongue Speaking*, Hodder & Stoughton 1968, p.51.
31. K. Ecke: *Fortsetzung der Reformation*, Memmingen 1965, p.37.
32. H. Bruns: *Ein Reformator nach der Reformation*, Marburg 1937, p.127.
33. H. Mühlen: *Die Erneuerung des christlichen Glaubens*, Munich 1974, p.252.
34. G. Kruger: *Lebensformen christlicher Gemeinschaften*, Heidelburg 1969, pp.48f.
35. E. Hinson, op. cit., p.63.
36. E. Geldbach: *Christliche Versammlung und Heilsgeschichte bei John Nelson Darby*, Wuppertal 1971, p.109.
37. E. Scheve: *Dem Herrn hintennach sehen*, Berlin 1908, pp.209f.

Chapter Three
(pages 29-41)

38. W. Hollenweger: *The Pentecostals*, London 1972, p.21.
39. K. Hutten: *Seher, Grübler, Enthusiasten*, Stuttgart 1968, 11th edn., p.506.
40. S. Grossmann (ed.): *Der Aufbruch*, Kassel 1974, p.43.
41. Quoted by W. Hollenweger, op. cit., p.23.
42. Cf. E. Giese, op. cit.
43. Quoted by W. Hollenweger, op. cit., p.206.
44. K. Hutten, op. cit., p.517.
45. Quoted by W. Hollenweger, op. cit., p.216.
46. S. Grossmann, op. cit., p.44.
47. W. Hollenweger: *Die Pfingstkirchen*, p.105.
48. R. F. Edel (Hrsg.): *Das Leben aus dem Geist*, Band 1, Marburg 1969, p.45f.
49. L. Eisenlöffel: *Ein Feuer*, pp.50-51, quoted by W. Hollenweger, op. cit., p.179.
50. Dennis and Rita Bennett: *The Holy Spirit and You*, Kingsway 1974 edn., pp.62f.
51. M. Carothers: *Prison to Praise*, Hodder and Stoughton 1972
52. J. Paul: *Die Taufe in ihrem Vollsinn*, Mülheim/Ruhr 1930, p.93.
53. Quoted by Hollenweger, op. cit., p.181.
54. A. Bittlinger: *Die charismatische Erneuerung der Kirchen*, p.22.
55. H. Schneider: *Die Bedeutung der Geistestaufe in der charimatischen der katholischen Kirche*, Schloss Craheim 1974, p.16.
56. H. Schneider, ib. p.26.
57. K. Hutten, op. cit., pp.538ff.
58. Quoted ibid. p.540.
59. Quoted ibid. p.539, note 31.
60. Ibid. p.541.
61. W. Hollenweger (ed.): *Die Pfingstkirchen*, Stuttgart 1971, pp.378ff.
62. Ibid. p.385.
63. W. Hollenweger: *Charismatische und pfingstliche Bewegungen als Frage an die Kirchen heute*, in H. Meyer, op. cit., pp.55ff.

Chapter Four
(pages 42-58)

64. A. Kuen: *Die charismatische Bewegung*, Wuppertal 1976, p.14.
65. E. O'Connor: *Spontaner Glaube*, Freiburg i.B. 1974, p.248 (*The Pentecostal Movement in the Catholic Church*, Notre Dame, Indiana, 1971).
66. Cf. A. Kuen, op. cit., p.17.
67. E. O'Connor, op. cit., p.252.
68. Heitmann/Mühlen, op. cit.
69. Quoted by L. J. Suenens, op. cit., p.94.
70. Quoted by C. Marshall: *Something More*, Hodder paperback 1977, p.276.
71. Gassmann, op. cit., p.197.
72. *Materialdienst der Evangelischen Zentralstelle für Weltanschauungsfragen*, 1976, p.11.
73. *Die Gemeinde*, no.46/1976.
74. Quoted by W. Hollenweger: *Enthusiastisches Christentum*, p.239.
75. Katholisch-charismatische Gemeinde-Erneuerung, D-4790 Haxterhöhe 2, Paderborn Informationsstelle für Charismatische Gemeinde-Erneuerung in der Evangelischen Kirche, Seeburgstrasse 1, D-8131 Berg am Starnberger See 3.
76. H. Mühlen: *A Charismatic Theology*, London/New York 1978, p.347.
77. H. Mühlen, op. cit., p.350f.
78. H. Mühlen: *Die Erneuerung des christlichen Glaubens*, pp.46f.
79. Quoted by E. Giese, op. cit. p.231.

Chapter Five
(pages 59-69)

80. G. Rohrmoser: *Die metaphysische Situation der Zeit*, Stuttgart 1975, p.7.
81. H. Gruhl: *Ein Planet wird geplündert*, Frankfurt am Main 1975, p.343.
82. J. v. Scheidt: *Innenwelt-Verschmutzung*, Munich/Zürich 1973.
83. H. Gruhl, op. cit., p.342.
84. *Der Spiegel*, no. 8/1972, p.116.
85. V. Frankl: *Der Mensch auf der Suche nach Sinn*, Freiburg i.B. 1975, p.11.
86. H. Lübbe: *Unsere stille Kulturrevolution*, Zürich 1976, pp.73f.
87. E. Benz: *Der Heilige Geist in Amerika*, Düsseldorf/Cologne 1970, p.208.
88. Ibid., p.210.
89. A. Rosenberg: *Flugblätter für Freunde*, no. 14, 1961, p.6.
90. W. v. Lojewski: *Jesus People*, Munich 1972, pp.108f.
91. E. Benz, op. cit., pp.215f.

Chapter Six
(pages 73-82)

92. H. Buchner: *Handbuch philosophischer Grundbegriffe*, Munich 1973, p.537f.
93. Quotations are from the Revised Standard Version, 2nd edn., unless otherwise stated.
94. H.-J. Kraus: *Reich Gottes: Reich der Freiheit*, Neukirchen-Vluyn 1975, p.319.

Chapter Seven
(pages 83-92)

95. H. Küng: *The Church*, London Search Press 1971, p.188.

96. S. Liebschner: *Mut zur vom Geist gestalteten Gemeinde*, in *Wer bestimmt, was charismatisch ist?*, p.25.
97. G. Hasenhüttl: *Charisma — Ordnungsprinzip der Kirche*, Freiburg i.B. 1969, p.112.
98. J. Moltmann: *The Church in the Power of the Spirit*, SCM Press 1977, p.295.
99. W. de Boor: *Die Frage nach dem Heiligen Geist*, Wuppertal 1974, p.29.
100. H. Mühlen: *Die Erneuerung des christlichen Glaubens*, p.235.
101. G. Hasenhüttl, op. cit., p.115.
102. Ibid., p.115f.
103. Broadbent/Hubmer: *Heute noch in Zungen reden*, p.104.
104. *Denn er hatte seinem Gott vertraut*, Christusbruderschaft Selbitz (not dated), p.112.

Chapter Eight
(pages 93-130)

105. G. Hasenhüttl, op. cit., pp.131ff.
106. U. Brockhaus: *Charisma und Amt*, Wuppertal 1972.
107. In the following description of the various charisms I have made use of parts of my book *Wirkungen — Gott im Alltag*, Schloss Craheim 1969, now out of print.
108. Cf. U. Brockhaus, op. cit., p.136f.
109. G. Hörster: *Gnadengaben im Neuen Testament* in *Wer bestimmt, was charismatisch ist?*, p.8.
110. G. Hasenhüttl, op. cit., p.191.
111. B. Schlink: *Ruled by the Spirit*, Lakeland 1970, p.46f.
112. G. Murray: *Euripides und seine Zeit*, Darmstadt 1957, p.50.
113. H. Horton: *The Gifts of the Spirit*, Assemblies of God Publishing House,
114. H. Horton: *The Gifts of the Spirit*, Assemblies of God Publishing House, 1960 edn., p.48.
115. A. Bittlinger: *Der frühchristliche Gottesdienst*, p.30.
116. G. Hörster, op. cit., p.9.
117. M. T. Kelsey: *Tongue Speaking*, Hodder and Stoughton 1968, p.216f.
118. Broadbent/Hubmer, op. cit., p.33.
119. L. Christenson: *The Charismatic Renewal among Lutherans*, Minneapolis, Lutheran Church Renewal Services, 1976.
120. C. ten Boom: *Jesus ist Sieger*, Wuppertal 1967, p.28 (*Defeated Enemies*, London 1968).
121. A. Bittlinger: *Im Kraftfeld des Heiligen Geistes*, Marburg 1968, 2nd. edn., p.120.
122. G. Hörster, op. cit., p.16.
123. G. Hasenhüttl, op. cit., p.150.
124. J. Brosch: *Charismen und Ämter in der Urkirche*, Bonn 1951, p.56.
125. Ibid, p.50.
126. Ibid, p.57.
127. R. Brown: *Beten und Heilen*, Kassel 1975, p.92f.
128. H. Mühlen: *A Charismatic Theology*, London and New York 1978, p.162.
129. W. Becker: *Krankenheilung als Dienst der Ältesten*, in Donsbach/Becker etc.: *Wir üben Gemeinde* (I), Kassel 1975, p.87.
130. H. Mühlen, op. cit., p.190f.

Chapter Nine
(pages 131-142)

131. U. Brockhaus: *Charisma und Dienst*, in *Die Gemeinde* no. 35/1975.
132. Ibid., no. 36/1975.
133. Cf. A. Bittlinger: *Im Kraftfeld des Heiligen Geistes*, p.131.
134. U. Brockhaus: *Charisma und Amt*, p.237.

Chapter Ten
(pages 143-149)

135. S. Grossmann (ed.): *Der Aufbruch*, p.124.
136. E. Schaefer: *Charisma und Kreuz*, manuscript p.7.
137. K. Rahner: *Das Dynamische in der Kirche*, Freiburg i.B. 1958, p.69.
138. E. O'Connor, op. cit. p.201.
139. Ibid, p.197f.
140. A. Kuen, op. cit., p.44.

Chapter Eleven
(pages 150-151)

141. S. Liebschner, op. cit., p.30.

Chapter Twelve
(pages 152-171)

142. Cf. U. Brockhaus, op. cit., p.148 and note 37.
143. Watchman Nee: *The Normal Christian Life*. I have been unable to find this passage in the (abridged) English version of the book, but it appears on p.239f. of the original: *Concerning our Missions* (London and Shanghai 1939) and in the German version (Hanover 1968). See *The Normal Christian Life* Colorado Springs, International Students Press, 1969, pp.119f.
144. D. Koller: *Charismatischer Gottesdienst* in Donsbach/Becker, op. cit., p.63ff.
145. Ibid., p.69.
146. Ibid., p.71.
147. Ibid., p.71f.
148. A. Bittlinger: *Der frühchristliche Gottesdienst*, p.21f.
149. H. Mühlen: *Die Erneuerung des christlichen Glaubens*, pp.219ff.
150. L. Suenens, op. cit., p.150.

Bibliography

(This bibliography does not claim to be exhaustive. It indicates the books which I have found useful. In order to provide a maximum of information for the interested reader I have divided it up into a considerable number of sections, although it has not always been easy to draw the dividing lines between them. I think however that this procedure is justified by the resulting overall view.)

NB. This bibliography is the one which appeared in the German original (1977).

1. Literature on the subject of charisms and the Holy Spirit

1.1 Technical works of theology

Brockhaus, Ulrich: *Charisma und Amt.* The Pauline teaching on charisms against the background of functions of the early Christian church. Wuppertal, 1972.

Brosch, Joseph: *Charismen und Ämter in der Urkirche*, Bonn, 1951.

Edel, Reiner-Friedemann: *Heinrich Thiersch als ökumenische Gestalt*. A contribution on the ecumenical concerns of the Catholic Apostolic Churches. Marburg, 1962.

Hasenhüttl, Gotthold: *Charisma*. Principles of church order. Freiburg i.B., 1969.

Heitmann, Claus & Mühlen, Heribert (ed): *Erfahrung und Theologie des Heiligen Geistes*, Hamburg & Munich, 1974.

Hinson, E. Glenn; Stagg, Frank & Oates, Wayne E.: *Tongue Speaking in Biblical, Historical and Psychological Perspective*, New York (Abingdon Press).

Hollenweger, Walter J. (ed): *Die Pfingstkirchen*. Vol VII of the series *Die Kirchen der Welt*, edited by Hans Heinrich Harms, Hanfried Krüger, Günter Wagner & Hans-Heinrich Wolf, Stuttgart, 1971.

Hollenweger, Walter J.: *The Pentecostals*, London, 1972.

Meyer, Harding (ed): *Wiederentdeckung des Heiligen Geistes*. The Holy Spirit in charismatic experience and in theological thought. Frankfurt a.M., 1974.

Moltmann, Jürgen: *The Church in the Power of the Spirit*, London & New York, 1977.

Mühlen, Heribert: *Morgen wird Einheit sein*. The coming Council of all Christians as an aim for the separated churches. Paderborn, 1974.

Rahner, Karl: *The Dynamic Element in the Church*, London, 1964.

Rahner, Karl: *Theologie aus Erfahrung des Geistes. Schriften zur Theologie*, vol. XII, Zürich, Einsiedeln & Cologne, 1975.

Ritter, Adolf Martin & Leich, Gottfried: *Wer is die Kirche?* Offices and the local church in the New Testament, church history and today. Göttingen, 1968.
tory and today. Göttingen, 1968.

Schweizer, Eduard: *Church Order in the New Testament*, London, 1961.

1.2 Theology for the general reader

1.2.1 Protestant

Benz, Ernst: *Der Heilige Geist in Amerika*, Düsseldorf & Cologne, 1970.

Bibra, Otto Siegfried von & Paehl, Erwin: *Religion und Wirklichkeit*. The biblical message of the triune God. Gladbeck, 1976.

Gassmann, Günther & others (ed): *Neue transkonfessionelle Bewegungen*. Documents of the evangelical, action-centred and charismatic movement. Ökumenische Dokumentation III, Frankfurt a.M., 1976.

Giese, Ernst: *Und flicken die Netze*, documents of the history of revivals in the 20th century. Marburg, 1976.

Rüegg, Robert: *Zur Kritik an den Geistesgaben*. Schiers, 1972.

Rüegg, Robert: *Bücherrundschau über Geistesgaben und Gemeindedienste*. Schiers, 1976.

Schmidt, Hans P., Hollenweger, Walter J. & Bürkle, Horst: *Der Geist und die Geister*. Three articles on the multiplicity of religious expression in our time. Constance, 1976.

Weber, Hans-Ruedi: *Kirche im Kampf um den Frieden*. Clergy and laity in early Christianity and today. Wuppertal, 1968.

1.2.2 Roman Catholic

Lubsczyk, Hans: *Aufbauen oder niederreissen*. An Old Testament scholar on the church today. Munich, 1969.

Schamoni, Wilhelm: *Die Gaben des Heiligen Geistes*, Paderborn, 1960, 4th. edn.

1.2.3 Russian Orthodox

Jungclaussen, Emmanuel (ed): *Aufrichtige Erzählungen eines russischen Pilgers*, Freiburg i.B., 1974.

1.2.4 Free Church and Evangelical

Barclay, William: *Promise of the Spirit*, London, 1960.

Bärend, Hartmut: *Anleitung zum Bibelstudium*. The Holy Spirit and His fruits. Wuppertal, 1977.

Betz, Ulrich & Rumler, Gerd (ed): *Wer bestimmt, was "charismatisch" ist?* In search of criteria for the evaluation of recent spiritual revivals — R. Brockhaus aktuell, Heft 2, Wuppertal.

de Boor, Werner: *Die Frage nach dem Heiligen Geist*. Holy Spirit, fruit of the Spirit, gifts of the Spirit. Wuppertal, 1974.

Brown, Roland: *Beten und Heilen*. Praying for the sick. Kassel, 1975.

Ertis, Otto A.: *Die Erneuerung der Gemeinde aus dem Geist*, Kassel, 1960.

Fromm, Lothar (ed): *Das Zeugnis des Heiligen Geistes*, Basle, 1968.

Klaiber, Walter: *Zwischen Schwärmerei und Erstarrung*. The Holy Spirit's work in our church. Stuttgart, 1976.

Krajewski, Ekkehard: *Geistesgaben*. A Bible study on 1 Cor. 12-14. Kassel, 1963.

Kuen, Alfred: *Die charismatische Bewegung*. An attempt at evaluation. Wuppertal, 1976.

Laubach, Fritz: *Krankheit und Heilung in biblischer Sicht*, Wuppertal, 1976.

Lubahn, Erich: *Schwarmgeist und Heiliger Geist*. An attempt at a biblical interpretation. Wuppertal, 1976.

Mallau, Hans: *Wenn du glauben könntest*. On the healing of the sick through the prayer of faith. Wuppertal, 1975.

Pache, René: *Person and Work of the Holy Spirit*, Chicago, 1954.

Plowman, Edward E.: *The Jesus movement in America*, Pyramid, 1971.

Riecker, Otto (ed): *Ruf aus Indonesien*. Talks by Petrus Oktavianus, Detmar Scheunemann and Volkhard Scheunemann. Neuhausen, 1971.

Schäfer, Kurt: *Kraft, die verwandelt*. On the nature and work of the Holy Spirit. Stuttgart, 1976, 2nd. edn.

Schneider, Johannes: *Die Gemeinde nach dem Neuen Testament*. Kassel, 1955, 3rd. edn.

Schnepel, Erich: *Wirkungen des Geistes*, Marburg, 1974.

Torrey, Reuben Archer: *The Holy Spirit*, New York, 1927.

Tozer, A. W.: *When He is Come*, Harrisburg, 1968.
Watson, David: *One in the Spirit*, London, 1973.

1.2.5 Pentecostal and Neo-Pentecostal

Bard, B. T.: *Apostelsgeschichte*, Erzhausen, 1966.
Basham, Don: *Face up with a miracle*, Whitaker House, 1971.
Basham, Don: *Ministering the Baptism in the Holy Spirit*, Monroeville, 1971.
Bennett, Dennis: *Nine o'clock in the morning*, Coverdale.
Bennett, Dennis & Rita: *The Holy Spirit and You*, Kingsway, 1974.
Boyd, Frank M.: *The Spirit works today*, Springfield, Mo.
Carothers, Merlin: *Prison to Praise*, Hodder, 1972.
Carothers, Merlin: *Power in Praise*. Sequel to *Prison to Praise*. Logos, 1972.
Carothers, Merlin: *Praise Works*, Logos, 1973.
Carothers, Merlin: *Answers to Praise*, Logos, 1973.
Cho, Yonggi: *Successful Living*, 1976.
Gee, Donald: *Spiritual gifts in the work of the ministry today*, Springfield, Mo.
Gee, Donald: *Now that you've been baptized in the Spirit*, Springfield, Mo.
Gee, Donald: *Concerning spiritual gifts*, Springfield, Mo.
Gee, Donald: *A new discovery*, Springfield, Mo. (original title: *Pentecost*).
Harris, Ralph W.: *Spoken by the Spirit*, Springfield, Mo., 1973.
Horton, Harold: *The Gifts of the Spirit*, Assemblies of God, 1960, 6th edn.
Pethrus, Lewi: *The wind bloweth where it listeth*, Bethany Fell., 1968.
Shakarian, Demos, and John & Elizabeth Sherrill: *The Happiest People on Earth*, Hodder and Stoughton, 1975.
Steiner, Leonhard: *Mit folgenden Zeichen*. A portrait of the Pentecostal movement. Basle, 1954.
Theis, Erich: *Wie Er*, Erzhausen, 1976, 4th edn.
Wead, Douglas R.: *Hear His Voice*, Carol Stream, Ill., 1976.
Wilkerson, David: *The Cross and the Switchblade*, Hodder & Stoughton, 1967.

1.2.6 Charismatic renewal movement

Bennett, George: *Miracle at Crowhurst*, Evesham, 1970.
Bittlinger, Arnold: *Charisma und Amt*, Stuttgart, 1967.
Bittlinger, Arnold: *Der frühchristliche Gottesdienst und seine*

Wiederbelebung innerhalb der reformatorischen Kirchen der Gegenwart, Marburg, 1964.

Bittlinger, Arnold: *Gifts and Graces*, London, 1967.

Bittlinger, Arnold: *Liebe und Charisma*. Reflections on 1 Cor. 13. Hannover.

Bittlinger, Arnold: . . .*und sie beten in anderen Sprachen*. The charismatic movement and glossolalia. Schloss Craheim, 1972.

Christenson, Larry: *The Charismatic Movement among Lutherans*, Bethany Press.

Christenson, Larry: *A Message to the Charismatic Movement*, Bethany Press.

Christusbruderschaft (ed): *Denn er hatte seinem Gott vertraut*. In memory of Walter Hümmer. Selbitz.

Die Bedeutung der Gnadengaben für die Gemeinde Jesu Christi, with contributions by A. Bittlinger, L. Christenson, H. Doebert, W. Hümmer, A. Richter, and an introduction by K. Hutten. Marburg, 1964.

Edel, Reiner-Friedemann (ed): *Kirche und Charisma*. The gifts of the Holy Spirit in the New Testament, in church history and today. Marburg, 1966.

Grossmann, Siegfried (ed): *Der Aufbruch*. Charismatic Renewal in the Catholic Church. Kassel, 1974.

Grossmann, Siegfried: *Wirkungen*. God in everyday life. Schloss Craheim, 1969, 2nd. edn.

Hall, Robert E.: *There is More*, Plainfield, N.J., 1972.

Harper, Michael: *Prophecy. A Gift for the Body of Christ*, London, 1964.

Kelsey, Morton T.: *Tongue Speaking*, Hodder & Stoughton, 1968.

MacNutt, Francis: *Healing*, Ave Maria, 1974. The fundamental book about healing through prayer.

Marshall, Catherine: *Something More*, Hodder paperback 1977.

Marshall, Catherine: *Beyond Ourselves*, Hodder.

Mederlet OFM, Eugen & McDonnell OSB, Kilian: *Charismatische Erneuerung der katholischen Kirche*, Schloss Craheim, 1972.

Mühlen, Heribert (in co-operation with Arnold Bittlinger, Erhard Griese and Manfred Kiessig): *Einübung in die christliche Grunderfahrung*. Vol. I: teaching and promise; Vol. II: prayer and expectation. Mainz, 1976.

O'Connor, Edward D.: *The Pentecostal Movement in the Catholic Church*, Ave Maria, 1971.

Schlink, Mother Basilea: *Ruled by the Spirit*, London, 1970.

Schneider SJ, Herbert: *Die Bedeutung der Geistestaufe in der charismatischen Erneuerung der katholischen Kirche*, Schloss Craheim, 1974.
Suenens, Léon Joseph: *A new Pentecost?*, Fountain, 1977.

1.2.7 Critical of the Charismatic Movement

Broadbent, W. G. & Hubmer, Fritz: *Heute noch in Zungen reden?*, Bad Liebenzell, 1975.
Gottwald, Wilhelm: *Biblisches Zungenreden heute?*, Bad Liebenzell, 1973.
Hubmer, Fritz: *Zungenreden, Weissagung — umkämpfte Geistesgaben*, Denkendorf, 1972.
Ising, Hartmut & Markmann, Otto: *Gnadengaben? Die Rufer-Bewegung und das neue Zungenreden aus den USA*, Berlin.
Ising, Richard: *Kräftige Irrtümer. Eine Stellungnahme zum Thema "Schwärmer einst und jetzt"*, Berlin.
Schwengeler, Bruno: *Verschobene Proportionen*, Heerbrugg.

2. General theological literature

2.1 Technical works of theology

Ecke, Karl: *Fortsetzung der Reformation*. Kaspar von Schwenckfeld's vision of an apostolic reformation. Memmingen, 1965.
Geldbach, Erich: *Christliche Versammlung und Heilsgeschichte bei John Nelson Darby*, Wuppertal, 1971.
Goppelt, Leonhard: *Die apostolische und nachapostolische Zeit*, in *Die Kirche in ihrer Geschichte*, ed. K. D. Schmidt & E. Wolf, Göttingen, 1966, 2nd. edn.
Hershberger, Guy F.: *Das Täufertum, Erbe und Verpflichtung*, Die Kirchen der Welt, Reihe B, Band II, Stuttgart, 1963.
Kraus, Hans-Joachim: *Reich Gottes: Reich der Freiheit*. Basic principles of systematic theology. Neukirchen-Vluyn, 1975.
Krüger, Günter: *Lebensformen christlicher Gemeinschaften*. An educational analysis. Heidelberg, 1969.
Küng, Hans: *The Church*, London, 1969.
Pflüger, Peter-Michael (ed): *Das Mysterium und die Mystik*. Contributions towards a theology of the Christian experience of God. Würzburg, 1974.

2.2. Theology for the general reader

Aichelin, Helmut: *Religion — Thema von morgen*. Description

and evaluation of a surprising phenomenon. Stuttgart, 1972.
Becker, Wilhard: *Keine Rolltreppe zum Himmel*. Life under trial and testing. Kassel.
Becker, Wilhard: *Nicht plappern wie die Heiden*, Schloss Craheim, 1971, 4th edn.
Bibra, Otto Siegfried von: *Der Name Jesus*, Wuppertal, 1976, 8th edn.
Busch, Dietrich & Grossmann, Siegfried (ed): *Die Wiederentdeckung des Menschen*. Biology, psychology, educational theory and theology in discussion about the image of man. Wuppertal & Kassel, 1976.
Donsbach, Helmut, Becker, Wilhard, etc.: *Wir üben Gemeinde* (I), Kassel, 1975.
Edel, Reiner-Friedemann (ed): *Das Leben aus dem Geist*. Vol. I: *Evangelische Zeugnisse über das geistliche Leben*, Marburg, 1969. Vol. II: *Katholische Zeugnisse über das geistliche Leben*, Marburg, 1965.
Geppert, Hans J.: *Wir Gotteskinder*. On the Jesus People movement. Gütersloh & Würzburg, 1972.
Grossmann, Siegfried: *Christen in der Welt von morgen*, Schloss Craheim, 1969.
Grossmann, Siegfried: *Christen nehmen Stellung "Ideologisierung der Schule". Was können Eltern und Lehrer tun?*, Kassel, 1974.
Grossmann, Siegfried (ed): *Christsein 70. Junge Bewegungen berichten*, Schloss Craheim, 1970.
Grossmann, Siegfried (ed): *Christsein 73. Junge Bewegungen berichten*, Kassel, 1972.
Grossmann, Siegfried & Walter, Karl Heinz (ed): *Der chemische Traum*. Drugs as a challenge to the churches. Schloss Craheim.
Grossmann, Siegfried: *Die Rufer*, Hannover, 1966.
Grossmann, Siegfried: *Mitteilung des Lebens*. The gospel as news in the modern world. Schloss Craheim, 1972.
Haack, Friedrich-W.: *Von Gott und der Welt verlassen*. The religious underground in our world. Düsseldorf & Vienna, 1974.
Heiler, Friedrich: *Ecclesia caritatis*. Ecumenical sermons for the Christian year. Marburg, 1964.
Hermanns, Jan Rainer: *Kennst Du Jesus?* Sociological report on the Jesus People in Germany. Munich, 1972.
Hirzel, Stephan: *Heimliche Kirche*. Chronicles of the heretics at the time of the Reformation. Hamburg.
Hollenweger, Walter J.: *Glaube, Geist und Geister. Professor Unrat zwischen Bangkok und Birmingham*. Frankfurt a.M.,

1975.
Hutten, Kurt: *Seher, Grübler, Enthusiasten*. Sects and special religious fellowships of the present day. Stuttgart, 1968, 11th edn.
Jesus People Report, Wuppertal, 1972.
Klempnauer, Günther: *Christentum ist Brandstiftung*. The Jesus People under fire. Wuppertal, 1972.
Kroll, Wilfried (ed): *Jesus-Generation — auch in Europa?* The Jesus revolution from Finland to Morocco. Wuppertal, 1972, 2nd. edn.
Kroll, Wilfried (ed): *Jesus kommt!* Report of religious revival among young people throughout the world. Wuppertal, 1971.
Küng, Hans: *On being a Christian*, Collins, 1977.
Lojewski, Wolf von: *Jesus people oder die Religion der Kinder* , Munich, 1972.
Luther, Ralf: *Neutestamentliches Wörterbuch*. An introduction to the language and meaning of the early Christian writings. Hamburg, 1962, 16th edn.
Nee, Watchman: *Release of the Spirit*, Indianapolis, 1965.
Nee, Watchman: *The Normal Christian Life*, Colorado Springs, 1969. (See note 143.)
Präger, Lydia (ed): *Frei für Gott und die Menschen*. The book of the brother- and sisterhoods. Stuttgart, 1964, 2nd. edn.
Sanders, J. Oswald: *The best that I can be*, OMF, 1968.
Scharpff, Paulus: *History of Evangelism*, Eerdmans.
Scheve, Eduard: *Dem Herrn hintennach sehen*. Memoirs. Berlin, 1908.
Strolz, Walter (ed): *Mystische Erfahrung*. The limits of human experience. Freiburg i.B., 1976.
Weckerling, Rudolf (ed): *Jenseits vom Nullpunkt?* Christianity in West Germany. Stuttgart, 1972.
Wilder Smith, A. E.: *Ergriffen? Ergreife!* The dialectic of fellowship and its consequences according to the epistle to the Philippians, Neuhausen, 1976.

3. Secular literature

Frankl, Viktor E.: *Der Mensch auf der Suche nach Sinn*. Towards a rehumanizing of psychotherapy. Freiburg i.B., 1975, 4th edn.
Gruhl, Herbert: *Ein Planet wird geplündert*. The balance of terror in world politics. Frankfurt a.M., 1975.

Lübbe, Hermann: *Unsere stille Kulturrevolution*, Zürich, 1976.
Riemann, Fritz: *Grundformen der Angst*. A study in depth psychology. Munich and Basle, 1975, 10th edn.
Riesman, David: *The Lonely Crowd*, New Haven, Conn., 1961.
Rohrmoser, Günter: *Die metaphysische Situation der Zeit*. Towards the reform of religious consciousness. Stuttgart, 1975.
Scheidt, Jürgen vom: *Innenweltverschmutzung*. Hidden aggression: symptoms, causes and therapy.
Toffler, Alvin: *Future Shock*, New York, 1970.

FURTHER READING

(None of these titles appears in the original German bibliography.)

Basham, Don: *A Handbook on Holy Spirit Baptism*, Monroeville, Pa.
Bridge, D./Phypers, D.: *Spiritual Gifts and the Church*, London, 1973
Bruner, F. D.: *A Theology of the Holy Spirit*, Grand Rapids, 1970
Brumback, C.: *What Meaneth This?*, Springfield, Mo., 1947
Christenson, Larry: *A Charismatic Approach to Social Action*, London, 1975
Dunn, J. D. G.: *Baptism in the Holy Spirit*, London, 1970
Gunstone, John: *The Charismatic Prayer Group*, London
Harper, Michael: *Power for the Body of Christ*, London, 1964
None Can Guess, London, 1971
As at the Beginning, London, 1965
This is the Day, London, 1979
Let My People Grow, London, 1977
Pulkingham, Graham: *Gathered for Power*, London, 1973
They Left Their Nets, London, 1974
Rea, J. (with duPlessis and others): *Layman's Commentary on the Holy Spirit*, Plainfield, N.J.
Smail, Tom: *Reflected Glory*, London, 1975
Urquhart, Colin: *When the Spirit Comes*, London, 1974
Watson, David: *One in the Spirit*, London, 1973
Wallis, Arthur: *Pray in the Spirit*, Eastbourne, 1970
Wallis, Arthur: *Into Battle*, Eastbourne, 1973

CONTENTS

Page

PREFACE

The East Midlands area includes the counties of Derbyshire, Leicestershire, Lincolnshire and Rutland, with parts of Northamptonshire and Yorkshire, but lacks clearly defined geographical or geological boundaries. The greater part lies within the drainage basin of the River Trent. It includes the southern part of the Peak District, Charnwood and the Jurassic Uplands, including Lincoln Edge.

The excursions illustrate the great diversity of the geology that can be studied within short distances of the main population areas of Nottingham, Leicester and Derby. They can be undertaken on foot or by car and vary in length from two hours to an entire day.

The guide has been split into three sections; the Precambrian, the Carboniferous and the Permo-Triassic through to the Jurassic. Each section introduces the geological history and the main rock types represented in the area. Each excursion has one or more clearly defined objectives, a logistics section listing the appropriate Ordnance Survey (OS) and British Geological Survey (BGS) maps, and where appropriate, a section describing the geological background of the excursion area. Geological terms highlighted in bold in the text are explained in a glossary.

Every effort has been made to ensure that all the information in the guide is accurate. The East Midlands Geological Society and the Geologists' Association would like to receive any information regarding changes to footpaths, other rights of way, or on damage and destruction of geological exposures. As far as possible the excursion routes follow public rights of way, but the details of routes given in this guide do not imply a right of way. Some of the localities are on private land and permission for access must be obtained before visiting the site. It is becoming increasingly difficult to find permanent exposures of rocks and we have a responsibility to maintain those that are available. Over-collecting and excessive hammering can quickly destroy an exposure and bury it in a scree of discarded debris. The majority of geological features can be clearly seen without hammering which damages the value of the site for future visitors. Hammering not only destroys the landscape but also destroys relations with landowners and farmers. Some of the sites are Nature Reserves and particular care is needed to conserve the flora and fauna as well as our geological heritage.

Participants should observe the country code and The Code for Geological Field Work issued by the Geologists' Association as follows:

Obey the Country Code and observe local byelaws. Remember to shut gates and leave no litter.

Always seek permission before entering onto private land.

Do not interfere with machinery.

Do not litter fields or roads with rock fragments that could cause injury to livestock or be a hazard to vehicles or pedestrians.

Avoid undue disturbance to wildlife. Plants and animals may inadvertently be displaced or destroyed by careless actions.
Do not take risks on insecure cliffs or rock faces. Take care not to dislodge rock; others may be below.
Observe and record the rocks; do not hammer indiscriminately, if at all.
Do not remove *in situ* fossils or minerals; only collect from scree, fallen blocks or waste tips. Never remove any rocks from walls.
For quarry visits:
Obtain permission before your visit.
Report both your arrival and departure.
Safety hats are obligatory and should be worn at all times; stout boots are recommended.
Keep away from machinery.
Be sure that blast warnings are understood.
Beware of rock falls; quarry faces are highly dangerous and may collapse without warning. Keep away from the foot and the top of faces.
Keep clear of sludge lagoons.
Copies of the full Code for Geological Field Work can be obtained from The Geologists' Association, Burlington House, Piccadilly, London WlV 9AG.

It is the responsibility of the users of this guide to ensure their own safety and that of third parties. Quarries and deep-sided exposures are dangerous. Safety helmets should be worn and are obligatory in working quarries. Always be aware of traffic when examining roadside exposures, even on quiet lanes.

Peter Gutteridge would like to thank everyone who has helped in the compilation of this guide and the authors for their contributions and patience. He would particularly like to thank Albert Horton who assembled the authors' contributions into a unified whole and edited the first version of this field guide, Les Hall for preparing an early version of the text from the authors' contributions and Andrew Rigby for advice on publication.

The guide is a joint production following close co-operation between the East Midlands Geological Society and the Geologists' Association. The costs are shared (the GA acknowledges a grant from the Curry Fund towards its costs) and, as a consequence, the guide appears as part of the G.A. Fieldguide Series.

Most of the original sketches have been re-drawn by cartographers Colin Stuart and Janet Baker.

The contributions by N. Aitkenhead, A. Brandon, J. N. Carney, J. I. Chisholm and A. S. Howard are published with the permission of the Director, British Geological Survey (NERC).

LIST OF FIGURES

PART 1: THE PRECAMBRIAN GEOLOGY AND GEOLOGICAL HISTORY OF THE EAST MIDLANDS

Trevor D. Ford, Geology Department, University of Leicester

Stratigraphy

Charnwood Forest consists of outcrops of the Charnian Supergroup of late Precambrian (Proterozoic) and possible early Cambrian age. The strata are weakly metamorphosed (**greenschist facies**) volcanic and sedimentary rocks, the latter mainly **volcaniclastic** in origin, with several intrusive masses chiefly of **diorite** (Figure 1). These rocks are exposed in a large number of small inliers, which are in effect partially exhumed mountain tops protruding through a blanket of Triassic mudstones, with a veneer of **Pleistocene** "drift". As no single exposure of the Charnian sequence shows more than about 30m of strata, working out a stratigraphy is rather like fitting together a jigsaw with half the pieces missing.

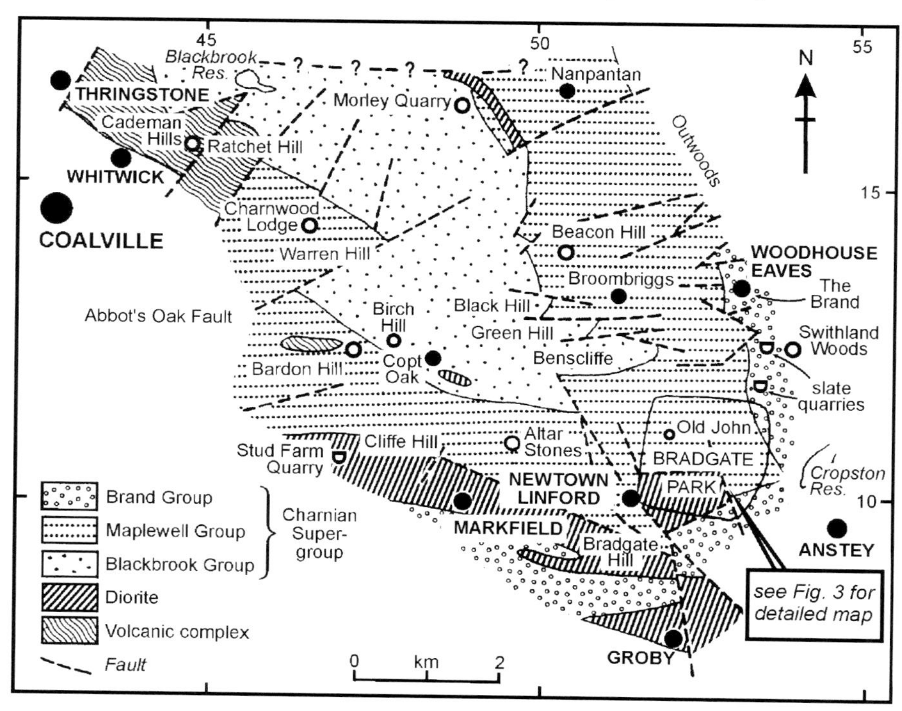

Figure 1. Simplified geological map of the Precambrian rocks of Charnwood Forest

The bulk of the 3500m of the Charnian succession is made of volcaniclastic sedimentary rocks, i.e. fine and coarse **tuffs** mostly deposited in water, in **turbidite** or **greywacke** fashion (Figure 2). These have interspersed local coarse **agglomerates** and slump **breccias** that provide mapping horizons. **Epiclastic** (i.e. non-volcanic) sandstones and **pelites** follow in the topmost division, the Brand Group.

The Blackbrook Group is the lowest division of the tri-partite subdivision of the Charnian Supergroup and reaches 1330m in thickness. It consists mainly of fine-grained slaty, tuffaceous sediments (pelites) with local coarse **lapilli** tuffs, greywackes and slumped horizons.

GROUPS	FORMATIONS	MEMBERS	Watt's Terms
BRAND (Brand Series)	SWITHLAND GREYWACKE (Pelites 260m)	Undivided	(Swithland Slates)
	BRAND HILLS (Quartzite, pelite & conglomerate 0-95m)	STABLE PIT QUARTZITE	(Trachose Grit & quartzite)
		HANGING ROCKS CONGLOMERATE	(Hanging Rocks Conglomerate)
		SWITHLAND CAMP CONGLOMERATE	
MAPLEWELL (Maplewell Series)	BRADGATE (Tuffs & slump breccias 649m)	HALLGATE (640m)	(Woodhouse & Bradgate Beds)
		SLIDING STONE SLUMP BRECCIA (9m)	
	BEACON HILL TUFF (Coarse & fine tuff & breccias 1119m)	OLD JOHN (430m)	(Beacon Beds)
		SANDHILLS LODGE (27m)	
		BEACON TUFFS (740m)	
		BENSCLIFFE AGGLOMERATE (22m)	(Felsitic Agglomerate)
BLACK-BROOK (Blackbrook Series)	BLACKBROOK Tuffaceous pelites (610m)	Undivided	(Blackbrook Beds)
	IVES HEAD Tuffs & greywackes (820m)	SOUTH QUARRY SLUMP BRECCIA (32m)	
		LUBCLOUD GREYWACKES (550m)	
		MORLEY LANE TUFFS (238m)	

Figure 2. The main stratigraphic divisions of the Charnian Supergroup.

The Maplewell Group has more distinctive lithologies, totalling 1768m. At the base a coarse volcanic breccia has clasts of pinkish **felsite** with diffuse boundaries suggestive of **devitrification**. Thick water-lain tuffaceous sediments follow, best seen in Bradgate Park and on Beacon Hill. These give way to a coarse breccia with numerous enclosed blocks of fine-grained tuff: some of these are highly contorted by **slumping**. The youngest unit in this Group is the Hallgate Member, mostly fine-grained volcaniclastic sediments well-known for the impressions of the Charnian **trace fossil** fauna.

Contemporary with the Maplewell Group in northwest Charnwood are several varieties of **porphyritic dacites** and **andesites**. These have been interpreted as a complex of lavas, **ignimbrites** and shallow intrusions. It is generally thought that they were erupted from volcanoes in northwest Charnwood though these cannot be identified, as contacts with the sedimentary sequence are not clearly exposed. It is thought that the emplacement mechanism was a series of dacite domes erupting explosively before collapsing into a substantial **caldera**.

The Brand Group marks a change from volcaniclastic to epiclastic sediments, with conglomerates and sandstones giving way to the thick Swithland Slates with trace fossils of possible early Cambrian affinity. The conglomerates contain a few **quartzite** pebbles, but none of distinctly pre-Charnian origin. Some 355m thickness is exposed. However, a few clasts apparently derived from a diorite (markfieldite) intrusion (see below) have been found indicating a period of erosion of the former cover of these intrusions before the Brand Group was deposited.

Palaeontology

Following the discovery of an impression thought to be that of a primitive Cnidarian or sea-pen in 1957, a variety of comparable impression trace fossils have been found at several localities. These include medusoids (jellyfish) such as *Cyclomedusa*, sea pens including the solitary *Charnia masoni*, *Charniodiscus concentricus* and the compound *Bradgatia linfordensis*, and a primitive arthropod *Pseudovendia charnwoodensis* all occurring in the Hallgate Member. Other probable jellyfish have been found in the Ives Head Formation low down in the Charnian sequence. Burrows of *Teichichnus* type occur in the highest unit, the Swithland Formation, and are best seen in gravestones in local churchyards. Elsewhere these burrows are only known from Cambrian rocks suggesting that most, if not all, the Swithland Formation is Cambrian in age.

Intrusions

As the nearest source of hard rock to London, Charnwood Forest has three major quarries working at present. One is in the volcanic complex of Bardon Hill, which may be partly intrusive, whilst the other two are in major diorite intrusions emplaced within the Charnian sequence. In the north, around Shepshed, a dark rather mafic diorite is quarried for aggregate by ARC, whilst in the southwest an elongated mass is quarried by Tarmac Roadstone plc near Markfield. This southern diorite is possibly a **laccolith**, some 12km long around Markfield and Groby. It is characteristically green-spotted with altered hornblende in a pinkish **granophyric** groundmass of orthoclase and quartz, and locally known as markfieldite. The age relationships are uncertain, as field exposures do not make it clear whether the diorites were intruded before or after the Brand Group.

Pre-Charnian Basement

No evidence of what the Charnian rests on has yet come to light. The Morley quarry borehole near Shepshed terminated in dacitic lavas very like those in the exposed Charnian. No clasts of any distinctively pre-Charnian rocks have been found in the volcanic breccias. In view of the palaeogeographic setting it is likely that the Charnian rests on primitive ocean crust of basaltic nature though this has not yet been proved.

Structure

The structure of Charnwood Forest is an asymmetric **anticline** trending NW-SE and **plunging** gently southeast. Thus, the outcrops are disposed in a U-shaped pattern open to the northwest and generally thought to be cut off by a major E-W **fault** concealed beneath the Trias immediately north of Charnwood. Minor folds are superimposed on the main anticline and several faults can be inferred from detailed mapping. The rocks are all pervaded by a near vertical **slaty cleavage** roughly parallel to the fold axis, though considerably diverging from it in the northwest. Cleavage is best developed in the pelite grade rocks. In coarse-grained sediments cleavage is more widely spaced and at right angles to bedding. Alternating fine and coarse beds show a rippled cleavage effect. Both folding and cleavage appear to have resulted from NE-SW compression in earliest Cambrian times as undoubted Cambrian rocks as at Nuneaton are not so intensely cleaved. However, some recent research has suggested that the cleavage is **Caledonian** in age, i.e. late Silurian.

The Age of the Charnian

Apart from the general view that the Charnian Supergroup is very late Precambrian, placing a reliable figure on these rocks is still uncertain, as no unequivocal date has yet been obtained by applying isotope methods to Charnian rocks. The date of 603±2 Ma has been obtained on a diorite intrusion at Nuneaton identical to that at Markfield. Another date determination for the diorite is 552±50 Ma (later re-calculated as 540±57): it approximates to the Precambrian/Cambrian boundary and is probably too young owing to the effect of fluids permeating the rock and from which epidote crystallized. The Bardon Hill extrusive rock yielded a K-Ar date of 684±29 Ma, but this is possibly too old. On the basis of a new determination of 559±2 Ma for the Beacon Hill Tuff (Compston *et al.* 2002) it seems likely that most of the Charnian is around 550-600 Ma old, an age which is consistent with the world-wide occurrences of the Charnian fossil fauna in very late Proterozoic rocks.

Some doubt arises concerning the age of the Brand Group because the field evidence does not clearly show whether it is cut by the diorite intrusion or not. Pebbles of diorite like that at Markfield have been found in the Brand Group basal conglomerate suggesting that the diorite intrusion had been emplaced before the Brand Group was deposited. The Swithland Slates have yielded trace fossils of

Teichichnus type, best seen in gravestones but rarely in the Swithland Slate quarries. This trace fossil species is confined to lower Cambrian rocks elsewhere. These lines of argument indicate a date for at least part of the Brand Group in the Lower Cambrian.

Palaeogeographic Setting

The thick volcaniclastic sequence, the dacitic nature of the volcanic rocks and the geochemistry of the diorite intrusions suggest that Charnwood was part of an **island arc** associated with a **subduction zone** on the northwest margin of the ancient southern continent of Gondwana in late Precambrian times. However, little is known of the nature of that continent in the rest of England and the position of the subduction zone cannot be inferred at present. Palaeomagnetic evidence indicates that Charnwood lay about 60° south of the equator at that time.

Post-Charnian History

The post-Charnian history of Charnwood Forest is not easy to decipher. The emplacement of the nearby Mountsorrel **granite** in Silurian times suggests that there may have been a considerable cover of Cambrian and possibly other Lower **Palaeozoic** rocks, which was subsequently stripped off by erosion. By Carboniferous times the Charnwood massif was part of a Midland landmass separating the Pennine and southern coal basins: both Lower and Upper Carboniferous divisions thin out as they approach Charnwood. In Triassic times the Precambrian rocks formed mountains that were gradually being eroded. The detritus, now part of the Mercia Mudstone Group, filled the hollows and slowly covered the mountains. It is likely that there was a cover of Jurassic and Cretaceous strata but these have been eroded away. Charnian rocks were again eroded during the Pleistocene and are the source of many distinctive glacial erratics in the till sheets of the South Midlands.

Excursions

Three excursions in and around Charnwood are suggested to demonstrate the main features of the late Precambrian geology. The localities are shown by Figures 1, 3 and 8. Charnwood Forest lies in northwest Leicestershire largely between the A511 and A6 roads. It is crossed by the M1 and there is access at junctions 22 and 23. A network of minor roads passes close to most localities and there is ample parking. The terrain is moderate to rough rising to a maximum altitude of 279m at Bardon Hill. Several public open spaces are available to the geologist, but NO HAMMERING is allowed.

Charnwood is covered by Ordnance Survey 1:50,000 Landranger maps 128, 129 and 140. The geology is mostly on British Geological Survey 1:50,000 sheet 155 (Coalville) with small areas on the adjacent sheets 141 (Loughborough) and 156 (Leicester).

EXCURSION 1. THE LATE PRECAMBRIAN ROCKS OF BRADGATE PARK, CHARNWOOD FOREST, LEICESTERSHIRE

Trevor D. Ford, Geology Department, University of Leicester

Objectives

The excursion is planned to give an overview of the complex series of outcrops of the late Precambrian rocks of Charnwood Forest, together with associated extrusive and intrusive rocks.

Logistics

The following walk around Bradgate Park (Figure 3) shows most of the stratigraphic sequence and rock types, as indicated in Figure 1. Park at the Hunt's Hill car park at the northwest corner of Bradgate Park (SK 523117). The route provides a circuit of the Park on a stratigraphic basis with a walking distance of about 4.5km. Allow at least a half-day, but detailed study necessitates a full day. Alternatively the Park may be entered at Hallgate (SK 542114) where the excursion can be started at Locality 8; or entered at Newtown Linford (SK 523098) and start the excursion at Locality 14. Car parks are available at both of these alternative starts. Although there is public access to Bradgate Park, parties intending to follow this excursion are requested to write to The Ranger, Bradgate Park Estate Office, County Hall, Glenfield, Leicester LE3 8RE well beforehand.

Locality Details

Locality 1: Leave the car park and immediately inside Hunt's Hill Wood on the right of the path is a small quarry in medium-grained bedded **tuffs** of the Beacon Tuffs Member, which **dip** at 28° towards the Park. Continue on the path towards the Park gate and at the crest bear left into the wood for some 75m.

Locality 2: The upstanding crags are of coarse tuffs of the Sandhills Lodge Member. Rather like the older Benscliffe Agglomerate Member these also have pink lapilli of **rhyolitic** material. Poorly developed bedding together with poor sorting suggests that the tuffs were deposited from a submarine ashflow.

The toilet block by the Park gate is built of Charnian rocks including many blocks of porphyritic dacite from northwest Charnwood Forest around the Gentleman's entrance. The roof slabs are slates from the Swithland Greywacke Formation.

Locality 3: On entering the Park make for Old John Tower. The northern slopes below the Tower rise to a series of small scarps of fine and coarse tuffs with lenticular bedding dipping at 50° or more to the southeast. The steepening of dip

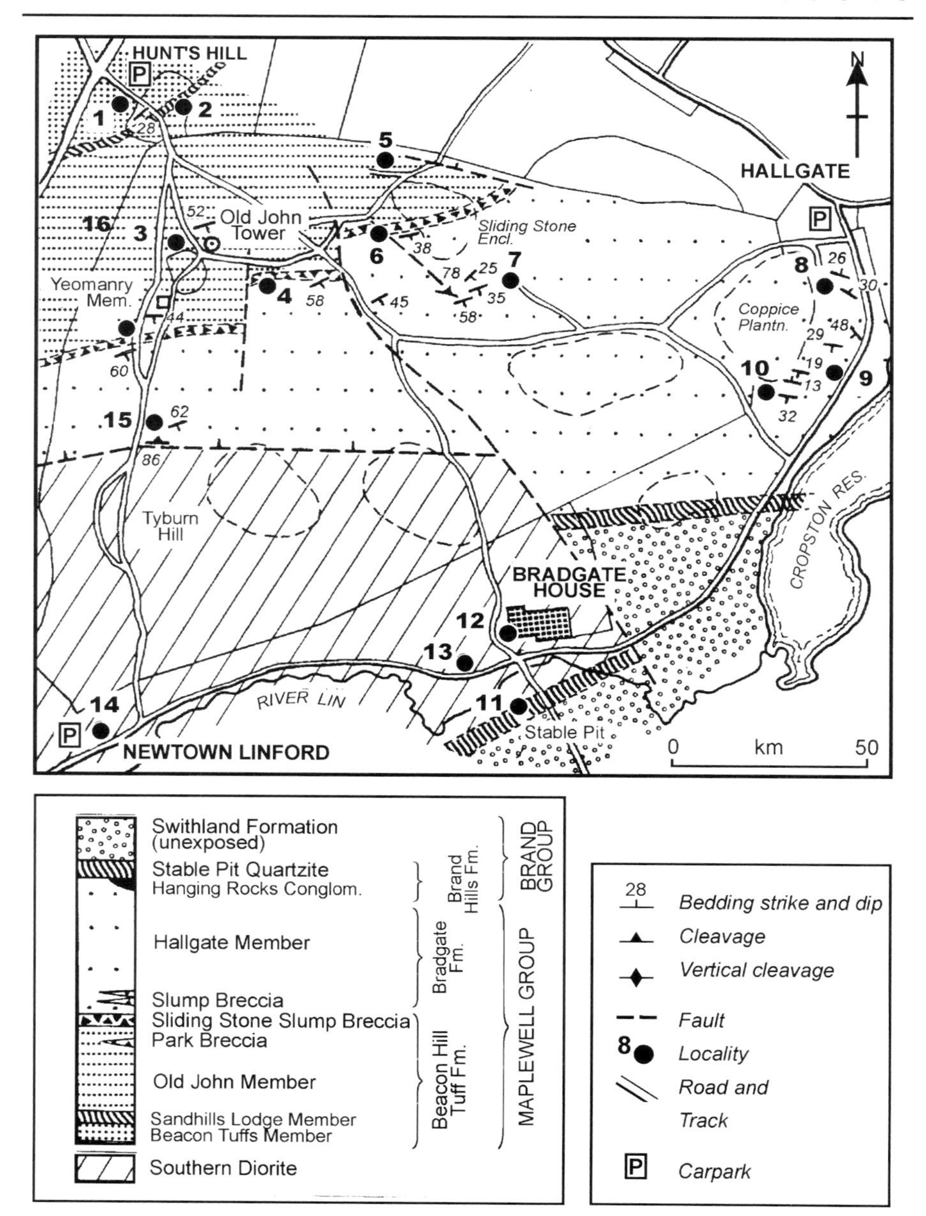

Figure 3. Geological sketch map of the Precambrian rocks in Bradgate Park.

Figure 4. (above) Slumps in the Old John Member, near Old John Tower, Bradgate Park, (Locality 3).

Figure 5. (below) The Sliding Stone Slump Breccia at Locality 6.

from Hunt's Hill Wood raises the possibility of an unexposed minor fold. A bed 20-30cm thick in the second scarp shows considerable distortion by slumping (Figure 4). Around the Tower the crags are of alternating fine and coarse tuffs showing variable cleavage orientation, vertical in the fine-grained beds but normal to bedding in coarse tuffs: this is clearly shown in the right-hand extremity of the outcrop.

Locality 4: Leaving Old John tower by the path downhill to the east a line of low crags lies just to the right of the broad path. These are in the Sliding Stone Slump Breccia Member at the base of the Bradgate Formation. The volcanic breccia encloses clasts up to 1m diameter of contorted fine-grained tuffaceous sediment. Sedimentary studies suggest that these beds of partly consolidated volcanic detritus slumped down a gentle southeast-dipping subaqueous slope. At the foot of the ridge bear left past the nearby dew pond to the prominent tree-crowned Sliding Stone Crag (Locality 6) and continue some 50m north to Locality 5.

Locality 5: 50m north of the Sliding Stone, 4m from the Park wall and well-hidden in the bracken, a low crag is in bedded tuffs of the Old John Member which show a peculiar type of discontinuous bedding known as a pull-apart breccia. Return to the Sliding Stone Crag.

Locality 6: The lowest face of the Sliding Stone Crag is a fine example of a coarse volcanic breccia with numerous large (up to 1m) fine-grained clasts torn up from the underlying sediments by a mass-flow process (Figure 5). On the shady northern face one of these clasts appears to have rolled up demonstrating its plasticity. Climb to the right to a jagged crag where a **joint** face in the overlying bedded tuffs shows vertical sections of peculiar V-shaped depressions of unknown origin.

Locality 7: Continue uphill past the jagged crags and cross the plateau southeast of the Sliding Stone to an extensive crag showing bedding planes with dips of up to 58° to the south. Cleavage dips steeply northwards. The beds here are typical of the Hallgate Member tuffs, whose outcrop extends from Locality 6 almost to Cropston Reservoir; this width of outcrop coupled with the steep dip indicates the great thickness of this unit, possibly accentuated by unexposed strike faults. The inter-relationships of bedding, joints and cleavage are well displayed here. The low ground ahead is floored by less resistant Trias and drift.

Locality 8: Walk downhill passing Dale Spinney on the right to near the Hallgate entrance to the Park, and turn south along the crags immediately east of The Coppice Plantation wall. The variable dip directions indicate the presence of gently folded Hallgate Member tuffs. The minor folds are superimposed on the axial region of the main Charnwood anticline.

Locality 9: Follow the hill spur down from The Coppice almost to the main Park roadway. Some 5m from the road and partly hidden in the bracken are small outcrops of conglomerate (SK 542110). Rounded water-worn pebbles of porphyritic andesite as well as quartzites in a sandy matrix of quartz, **feldspar** and lithic fragments suggest that this may be the base of the epiclastic Brand Group, though the field relationships to the folded Hallgate Member fine-grained tuffs in the crags

Figure 6. The basal conglomerate of the Brand Group (Locality 9). The specimen is 10cm wide.

above are not easy to interpret. It may be that the conglomerate here occupies a channel eroded into the Hallgate Member (Figure 6).

Locality 10: Adjacent to the south corner of The Coppice a small slate quarry shows a shallow synclinal arrangement of fine-grained tuffs of the Hallgate Member cut by nearly vertical cleavage. Bedding is shown by the gently inclined ledges across the face. The beds show some examples of graded bedding.

Locality 11: Follow the main Park roadway southwest for about a kilometre, passing the Visitor Centre en route. Opposite the Bradgate House ruins, cross the bridge to the left to reach Stable Pit Quarry about 100m to the south. The prominent crag on the right is the Stable Pit Quartzite in the lower part of the Brand Group. Its left-hand wall is a slickensided fault and along it is a metre-wide sheared microdiorite dyke, presumed to be an offshoot of the main Markfield diorite intrusion.

Locality 12: Cross to the ruins of Bradgate House, home of Lady Jane Grey. The low crags immediately adjacent to the southwest corner are in diorite. Once known as markfieldite, this is medium-grained with pink feldspar and green hornblende dominant; a micrographic matrix and various alteration products are visible in thin section. The outcrop shows occasional quartz-coated **slickensided** joints. No contacts of this intrusion with country rock are visible (except the possible dyke at Locality 11) and it may have faulted boundaries. The house itself is built of bricks

Figure 7. Alternating coarse and fine grained tuffs in the Hallgate Member at the Memorial Crags (Locality 15). Note the cleavage refraction in coarse and fine beds.

made from local **boulder clay** complete with flints, whilst the quoins are of soft Triassic sandstone, possibly from the Dane Hills in Leicester or from Hollington in Staffordshire. A few replacement blocks are of Lincolnshire Limestone.

Locality 13: Take the Park road westwards for some 250m and look across the brook to the left (south) where a low cliff exposes the Triassic Mercia Mudstone Group. Though now a meander on the River Lin's course, it may once have been a **marl**-pit for brick making.

Locality 14: The Park road continues towards the Newtown Linford entrance gate through a gorge locally known as Little Matlock, or even more fancifully as Little Switzerland! The gorge is cut into the diorite and may be an exhumed Triassic **wadi**, a glacial diversion channel or a combination of the two.

Locality 15: Just before reaching the Newtown Linford gate take the path to the right up the side of the gorge and continue northwards across the diorite outcrop towards the Yeomanry Memorial. On the flat area around and to the right of the Tyburn Hill copse the low crags change from diorite to slaty tuffs with about 100m gap in exposures. This gap may mark the position of a fault or an intrusive boundary, but no field evidence can be found to decide which type of contact it is.

Locality 16: The prominent Memorial Crags, about 100m south of the Leicester Yeomanry Memorial, show a section of the Sliding Stone Slump Breccia in the uphill scarp face. It is overlain by alternating pelitic and coarse tuffs of the Hallgate Member, with classic **refracted cleavage** (Figure 7). The wide south-facing dip slope of the crags is a bedding plane high in this crag's sequence that has several impressions of Charnian fossils, including medusoids, *Charnia* spp. and the compound *Bradgatia*. **These must not be hammered or in any way defaced**. About 100m to the north the low crags by the Memorial itself are in light-coloured fine-grained tuffs of the Old John Member.

The excursion is completed with a 0.5km walk north past Old John Tower back to the Hunt's Hill gate and car park.

EXCURSION 2: THE LATE PRECAMBRIAN ROCKS OF NORTH CHARNWOOD

Trevor D. Ford, Geology Department, University of Leicester

Objectives

This Excursion examines those parts of the Charnian sequence that are not well covered by the Bradgate Park Excursion; it should be taken by road transport and covers about 10km (Figures 1 and 8).

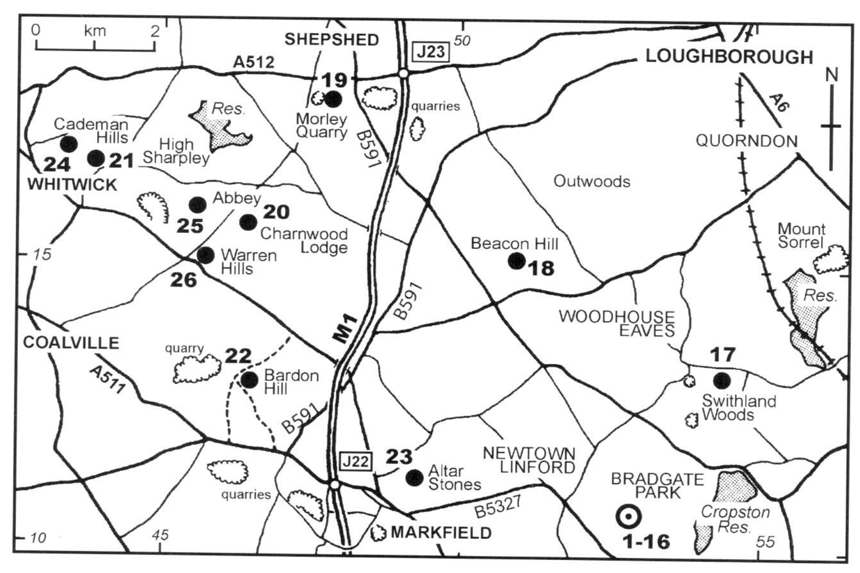

Figure 8. Road map of Charnwood Forest showing the localities visited by excursions 1, 2 and 3.

Locality Details

Locality 17: Swithland Woods. Park at the lower end of the car park at the north end of the Woods (SK 538130). Take the path by the information board and about 100m east is a long disused quarry in the Swithland Greywacke Formation (SK 539122), now regarded as of probable Cambrian age. The quarry is much obscured by vegetation and is best viewed from the roadside. It contains over 30m of water and is securely fenced off and must be viewed from outside the fence. There are plenty of waste slate fragments lying about and these vary from a fine-grained pelite to a coarse greywacke siltstone. Bedding is very difficult to determine in the quarry faces that are largely defined by the vertical cleavage striking NW-SE. A very overgrown Triassic wadi filled with Mercia Mudstone and derived slate breccia is present in the southeastern quarry face, best seen from the wall along the road in mid-winter when there is little vegetation.

From the car park follow the main path southwards and 900m further take a track to the right into the wood where there is a second, larger and deeper slate quarry, again fenced off for security. This is also approachable from the southern car park at SK 537117.

The Swithland Slates provided the Romans with roofing slabs. In the 18th and 19th centuries the slates were widely used for roofing, gravestones, gateposts, mileposts, and for various household utensils and working surfaces. It does not split as thinly as Welsh slate and when the railways brought in bulk supplies from Wales the Swithland slate industry died.

Slate from both quarries, as well as from quarries in the nearby Brand grounds and from Groby, was used in the 18th and 19th centuries for gravestones in many local churchyards. Surfaces cleaned of their lichens and wetted show sedimentary structures including thin graded beds of fine sand with loaded bases and sometimes there are sections of the early Cambrian trace fossil burrow *Teichichnus*. Good examples may be found in Ratby churchyard.

Locality 18: Beacon Hill (SK 510148). Travel north through Woodhouse Eaves and turn left at the T-junction. At the top of the hill turn right into Beacon Hill car park. Beacon Hill is capped with traces of a Bronze Age hill fort. It is the second highest point in Charnwood Forest at 248m above sea-level. If you look due east the next ground at this altitude is in the Ural Mountains of Russia! The summit crags are in the Beacon Hill Tuff Formation, mostly very fine-grained, water-lain tuffs with some coarser beds. Rather more siliceous than elsewhere they tend to have white-weathered surfaces though freshly broken surfaces are greenish. Examination of clean joint surfaces shows that the tuffs have ultra-fine lamination alternating with thin coarser beds giving a rippled effect. Some small-scale slumping and lensing of beds is present. The beds dip fairly steeply eastwards, but a traverse of the low crags reveals that the direction and amount of dip varies across a plunging syncline, which is not easy to recognize. The axis is close to the direction table.

Locality 19: Morley Quarry (SK 476179). From Beacon Hill take the B591 northwest to the A512. Turn left for 1km and left again towards Coalville. After about 200m turn left again along Morley Lane to park near the Shepshed Cricket Club ground. The uphill path to the right leads to the long-disused Morley Quarry, now a Nature Reserve in the care of Charnwood Borough Council, with public access. The quarry faces are in the oldest exposed unit of the Charnian Supergroup, massive fine-grained water-lain sediments, the Morley Lane Tuffs Member of the Blackbrook Group, which dip north easterly at about 35°. Cleavage is well developed and the quarry faces have been stabilized with rock-bolts.

A British Geological Survey borehole was sited here in the core of the

Charnian anticline and penetrated the strata beneath the lowest exposed beds of the Charnian. It proved 541m of Blackbrook type pelitic tuffs and 294m of dacitic volcanic rocks without reaching any distinctive base to the Charnian Supergroup.

Continue southwest towards Coalville for about 4km and turn sharp left immediately after the farm and lodge (SK 457155); go through a gate and park by the next gate at the end of the drive. Buses should be parked by the lodge. Prior permission for visits is necessary from the Leicestershire & Rutland Trust for Nature Conservation, 1 West St., Leicester, LE1 6UU (phone 0116-2533904).

Locality 20: Charnwood Lodge. A prominent crag on the left just inside the second gate is an outcrop of the Charnwood Lodge Agglomerate, a coarse **facies** of the Beacon Hill Tuff Formation formerly known as the "Bomb Rocks" (SK 464158). Nearby this unit passes into strata with a much higher proportion of tuff and there is considerable variation in thickness. The blocks, mostly of **porphyritic** dacite and up to 1 m in diameter, are of the same lithology as the nearby Whitwick volcanic complex. The blocks are slightly rounded and are enclosed in a matrix of coarse tuff (Figure 9). Once regarded as bombs explosively ejected from a nearby but unidentified vent, opinions are now divided as to whether they are blocks rounded by attrition within the vent, by rolling down the sides of the volcano, or boulders rounded on the beach of a volcanic island. Bedding traces appear to be wrapped around the blocks. The relationship with the rest of the Beacon Hill Tuff Formation is uncertain; it is unclear whether the "Bomb Rocks" were deposited contemporaneously with the tuffs or whether the latter were banked against the pile

Figure 9. Blocks of porphyry in coarse ash at the "Bomb Rocks" in Charnwood Lodge grounds (Locality 20).

of blocks.

About 400m northeast of the "Bomb Rocks" there are low crags of the Benscliffe Agglomerate Member, a coarse volcanic breccia with pinkish clasts of felsite.

Leaving Charnwood Lodge drive turn left on to Abbey Road and climb to the Warren Hills (described by Carney Excursion 3, Locality 26). Descend and turn right to Whitwick. At the bottom of the hill in Whitwick turn right on Vicarage St., and at the end turn right at the T-junction, then left after 350m to a small car park some 250m further on at the east end the heavily wooded Cademan Hills.

Locality 21: High Cademan (SK 442169). Take the footpath through the picnic area for about 100m to the heavily wooded summit crags which are composed of massive Grimley Andesite, formerly described as porphyritic dacite or, earlier, as "porphyroid". On the eastern flank there are unbedded volcanic breccias whilst to the west breccia and massive rock appear to be interbedded. The breccias are included in the Cademan Volcanic Breccia Member. There appears to be an intimate association of the breccia with the Grimley Andesite and the **auto-brecciation** may be due to quenching on approaching the surface with subsequent reworking. Contacts with surrounding rocks are not exposed nor are primary eruptive structures visible so that it is uncertain whether the porphyries are extrusive igneous rocks or shallow intrusions. Fresh faces show small **phenocrysts** of quartz and feldspar in a dark matrix. Close vertical jointing parallels cleavage in the Charnian tuffs.

Return to Whitwick and turn southeast for about 3km before turning right on Greenhill Road towards the Agar Nook estate on the eastern limits of Coalville. Drive down Greenhill Road and take the second turning on the left (Kenmore Crescent) in the housing estate. After about 200m a public footpath to Bardon Hill starts between the houses on the left (SK 457141). A view into the quarry may be obtained after about 500m but the summit is on the far side of the quarry and not easily accessible from here. Access points for the summit are from a lay-by on the A511 (SK 462118) or by a chapel at SK 469117. The last two paths meet near Old Rise Rocks, crags in the Hallgate Member, before going on to Bardon Hill. These paths meet near the summit of Bardon Hill after a walk of about 1.6km.

Locality 22: Bardon Hill (SK 461132). Bardon Hill is the highest point in Charnwood Forest and in Leicestershire at 279m O.D. From the footpath one can view the large working quarry on the western side. The quarry is in a complex sequence of volcanic rocks, comprising much altered lavas, which range in composition from porphyritic dacite to andesite. The upper surfaces of the lavas show auto-brecciation. Microscopic examination shows that the core of the complex consists of lavas overlain by fused volcanic breccias. The complex appears to represent a series of small explosive vents within a collapsed caldera. The unconformable and irregular base of the Trias is clearly displayed in the faces.

Continue through Copt Oak or along the A511 and A50 to Markfield. Leave the A50 by the slip road, turn right across the bridge into Markfield village; turn right again on to the cul-de-sac end of the old A50 and 300m ahead is a parking area

by the Altar Stones.

Locality 23: Altar Stones (SK 483109). This is a public access area owned by Leicestershire County Council. From the vantage point on the summit it is possible to get an idea of the local extent of the Markfield diorite intrusion. To the left (SSE) is the old Hill Hole quarry, now flooded and fenced off for safety, though one can view it from Hill Lane (SK 485104). To the right, across the M1 is Cliffe Hill quarry partly flooded and screened by landscaped waste heaps; beyond to the northwest is the newer Stud Farm quarry. The diorite intrusion is some 13km long from Bradgate Park in the southeast to the Stud Farm quarry in the northwest. It varies from about 0.5 to 2km wide and lies parallel to the **strike** of the adjacent Charnian sediments and is thus thought to be a laccolith though no feeder has been detected. In Cliffe Hill quarry the Hallgate Member has been metamorphosed and spotted **hornfels** is present close to chilled diorite. The boundaries of the intrusion are largely hidden by Triassic mudstones and Pleistocene till; indeed the M1 crosses it along a concealed Triassic wadi. The Hallgate Member has yielded poorly preserved medusoids of the Charnian fauna.

The diorite is locally known as markfieldite. Fresh surfaces show a coarse crystalline texture with mottled pink and green colouring due to feldspar and hornblende. Thin sections show a matrix of quartzo-feldspathic micrographic intergrowth.

The Altar Stones crags provide good exposures of the Sliding Stone Slump Breccia with rather smaller and fewer fine-grained clasts than the type outcrops in Bradgate Park. There are also low outcrops of the overlying medium- to coarse-grained tuffs.

EXCURSION 3. PRECAMBRIAN GEOLOGY AND SCENERY OF NORTHWEST CHARNWOOD

J N Carney, British Geological Survey, Keyworth, Nottingham

Objectives

To examine Precambrian rocks of the Charnian Supergroup, including the Bradgate Tuff Formation and Charnwood Lodge Formation, which are divisions of the Maplewell Group. The variety of volcaniclastic rock types exposed includes spectacular volcanic breccias whose content of large rock fragments indicates accumulation close to the original volcanic centres.

Logistics

The localities lie within a relatively small area of pleasant woodland and heathland scenery just east of Thringstone and Whitwick (Figures 1 and 8). All are accessed by good footpaths, although a more thorough examination of the rocky exposures will require some gentle scrambling. Most of the localities are only a short distance from widened verges where cars may be parked. Good parking and toilet facilities are provided at Mount Saint Bernard Abbey, which occupies a convenient central location from which the area may be explored.

Locality Details

Locality 24: Calvary Rock. This is situated within a public recreation area in a woodland setting close to the eastern outskirts of Thringstone. Limited verge side parking is available at the entrance to the locality, by the crags on the south side of Turolough Road (SK 43311723), about 120m east of the junction with Car Hill Road.

Enter the locality by the corner of the stonewall and after a few metres climb to a rocky ridge using the track bearing right. The crags comprise part of the Charnwood Lodge Formation (Cademan Volcanic Breccia Member), and consist of a type of very coarse-grained, poorly sorted, unbedded volcanic block-breccia, which locally is over 400m thick. This lithology is identical to the "Bomb Rocks" of Charnwood Lodge (see Locality 20). The blocks stand out best on weathered surfaces, parallel to the northwesterly strike of the Charnian cleavage. They are **andesitic** in composition, with several per cent of pale cream or white plagioclase **feldspar phenocrysts** in a fine-grained altered matrix. The blocks are seldom in contact with each other, and are instead separated by the coarse-grained, crystal-enriched matrix of the breccia; they show no tendency to be aligned or sorted according to their size, which varies from a few centimetres to almost 40cm across. The larger blocks commonly have rectangular to diamond-shaped cross sections, suggesting their derivation by the collapse and disintegration of a previously well-jointed rock. Most blocks have rounded-off corners, however, and thus suffered limited abrasion during accumulation of the deposit. Note that in volcaniclastic

Figure 10. Calvary Rock, a coarse grained volcanic breccia.

terminology, true volcanic bombs, formed by the passage through air and final impact of tatters of molten lava, characteristically have irregular outlines and contorted shapes, which are not seen here. Therefore, these rocks are classified as volcanic breccia (aggregations of large blocks) rather than **agglomerate** (aggregations of volcanic bombs).

Continue for about 50m along the top of the ridge before descending to the broad track farther east. Follow this for about 100m up a gentle slope past a row of large trees. Beyond the last tree descend the grassy slope to the east to view excellent weathered faces showing volcanic breccia with blocks up to 0.8m across. Returning up the same slope, bear left and follow the track along the top for about 70m to the base of the next craggy knoll which is on the right (southwest) side of the track. Some variation is seen here, in that the volcanic breccia contains sporadic, very large (over 1m-size) rectangular fragments distinguished by their smoother appearance on the weathered surface of the crag (Figure 10).

From here the track can be followed southeastwards, past further exposures of volcanic breccia alternating with massive andesite, as far as High Cademan that overlooks Swannymote Road. Alternatively, from the start of this excursion a walk of a few hundred metres eastwards along Turolough Road brings one to Grace Dieu Wood which can be entered by a track through the wall to the left. There, a series of large crags show further spectacular exposures of volcanic breccia.

Locality 25: Mount Saint Bernard Abbey. Enter the car park by the entrance leading south off Oaks Road (SK 45881638). Much of the Abbey and its grounds are open to the public, but when examining the exposures please bear in mind that this is primarily a place of contemplation and worship, where no hammering of the rocks should be carried out. It is also recommended that large geological parties should first obtain the permission of the Abbey before visiting. The exposures represent an isolated development of massive to bedded, fine- to medium-grained volcaniclastic rocks whose stratigraphical position within the Charnwood Lodge Formation is uncertain.

After leaving the car park, but before viewing the first exposures, have a look at the frontage of the Abbey. It is made out of local stone, which includes spectacular blocks of porphyritic **dacite** and dacite breccia, showing a dark grey, almost black, fine-grained matrix enclosing large (over 1cm in places) euhedral plagioclase (white) and quartz (greenish-grey and glassy) phenocrysts. The dark matrix indicates that this is the 'Peldar Tor' variety of porphyritic dacite, in the old terminology, which is mined at the nearby Whitwick Quarry and at Bardon Quarry. This lithology has since been renamed as the Peldar Dacite Breccia, and is a major component of the Whitwick Volcanic Complex.

The shrine dedicated to the Virgin Mary, to the right of the Abbey, is composed of a massive, medium-grained volcaniclastic rock of uncertain origin, with a dark grey-green, crystal-rich matrix enclosing shadowy andesitic clasts. The rock is exposed at the base of the crag below the statue where the strike is west-northwest. The Charnian cleavage dips about 85° northwards. Closer to the Abbey, the massive rock grades rapidly upwards into a well-bedded volcaniclastic sediment consisting of alternating green and cream-coloured layers up to several centimetres thick. White plagioclase crystals are concentrated in certain layers, which also show normal grading from coarse volcaniclastic sandstone bases to siltstone tops. These beds dip at 60° to the southwest, which is also the **younging direction** indicated by the normal grading.

Pass the sign indicating 'Calvary', and go up the gently inclined double footpath. At the top, keep right along a winding path above the previous locality to view the volcaniclastic rocks lower down in this succession. Gain the top of Calvary by taking the path to the left of the enclosed shrine marked '1836-1936'. The summit is composed of massive, coarse-grained and crystal-rich volcaniclastic sandstone. Just down from the crucifix, spectacular black-coloured slabs of Peldar Dacite Breccia are visible in the wall. At the next junction turn left and view crags, which show once more the transition from massive to bedded volcaniclastic rock. Continue along the path leading back towards the Abbey. To the left, forming the backdrop to a small crescent-shaped lawn, the crags expose a grey; medium-grained volcaniclastic rock enclosing irregular masses of a white-**weathering** finer-grained lithology, which may represent detached sedimentary rafts. This is the stratigraphically highest member of the rock sequence seen at Mount Saint Bernard Abbey.

From the far end of the car park, a track leads for about 500m to a viewpoint situated at the southeastern end of Whitwick Quarry. The Whitwick Volcanic Complex exposed here comprises possible high-level subvolcanic intrusive rocks. Looking towards the northwestern part of the quarry, the massive quarry faces to the left (southwest) are in Peldar Dacite Breccia. To the right, near the northeast corner of the quarry, is a pronounced vertical fracture system which marks the passage between greenish-grey Grimley Andesite (left of the fracture system), pale grey sheared volcaniclastic sediments (forming the main part of the fracture zone) and the Sharpley Porphyritic Dacite. The latter forms the pale grey northeast quarry faces to the right of the fracture zone; it can be viewed more closely around Ratchet Hill, just above this part of the quarry. The outline of a deep Trias-filled valley, which has been eroded along the contact between the Peldar and Grimley bodies, can be seen at the far northwest end of the quarry. It is revealed by the decline in elevation of the Precambrian-Triassic **unconformity**, the course of which is shown by the occasional patches of red and green Triassic mudstone that have escaped removal during quarrying operations.

Locality 26: Warren Hills. This public recreation area, part of the Charnwood Lodge SSSI, can be entered via a signposted track leading southeastwards off Abbey Road (SK 45701533). Limited verge side parking is available.

Lithologies constituting the upper part of the Charnwood Lodge Formation can be viewed at the easternmost of the three craggy knolls that appear on the skyline. They consist of massive, coarse-grained tuff and lapilli tuff with relatively minor proportions of volcanic breccia, the latter with andesitic to dacitic blocks up to several centimetres in size enclosed by a crystal-rich matrix. To see the transition from the Charnwood Lodge Formation into the overlying Bradgate Park Formation, however, follow the grassy path from the signpost southeastwards to the col between the two westernmost knolls. The eastern part of the left-hand knoll consists of a massive rock with a rough, uneven surface texture. This coarse-grained volcaniclastic sandstone or tuff represents the topmost bed of the Charnwood Lodge Formation. It contains small (~4cm) clasts of angular, greenish-grey fine-grained volcaniclastic mudstone or siltstone, which are typically smooth-textured in contrast to the lumpy appearance of the host. To the southwest of the knoll these sedimentary clasts are larger and have irregular, contorted shapes indicating that they represent a semi-consolidated bed that was ripped up and incorporated during deposition of the host rock. The sedimentary rafts form a horizon striking about 150°, parallel to the strike of the Charnian rocks in this area. It is possible that the synsedimentary disturbance represented by this horizon also gave rise to the Sliding Stone Slump Breccia, exposed farther east on the opposite side of the Charnian anticline (Locality 6). The Charnian cleavage seen here **strikes** at about 120°; it is typically more finely developed within the sedimentary clasts than in the coarser-grained host rock.

This first knoll offers fine panoramic views of the Leicestershire countryside. To the south lies the dome-shaped Bardon Hill, with the quarry face visible below the radio mast; it is composed of intrusive rocks of the Bardon Hill Complex which have been displaced laterally by about 1.5km southwestwards, relative to the Warren Hills sequence, by the intervening Abbot's Oak Fault (Figure 1). To the northwest can be seen Whitwick Quarry, with the tower of Mount Saint Bernard Monastery above the trees farther east. To the southwest the Charnian rocks of Warren Hills pass beneath Triassic strata. The latter conceal the Thringstone Reverse Fault along which the Charnian Supergroup was uplifted, relative to Carboniferous Coal Measures strata, during the end-Carboniferous (**Variscan**) deformation. Thus the downthrown southwest side of the fault brings in the synclinal basin of the Leicestershire Coalfield.

The second knoll, about 90m to the west, exposes beds at the base of the Bradgate Tuff Formation. The eastern part consists of black-weathering, well-bedded to laminated volcaniclastic mudstones intercalated with massive, medium-grained volcaniclastic sandstones, many of the latter showing normal grading from coarse-grained bases to medium-grained or silty tops. The grading indicates the younging direction of the sequence is to the southwest. This is also the dip direction of the beds, proving that in this area the Charnian succession is structurally the right way up. It is noted that some of the thinner mudstone beds follow wavy courses and become folded and/or abruptly truncated laterally, features indicating movements within the body of sediment before consolidation. Farther to the southwest, the stratigraphically highest bed consists of massive to vaguely stratified medium-grained and crystal-rich volcaniclastic sandstone. This is also seen in the woods lower down the slope to the west, and it persists almost to the base of the slope (SK 45621512), where mudstone beds, commonly with wavy and disrupted laminae, become increasingly intercalated in the sandstone sequence.

The Warren Hills ridge can be followed to the southeast, where there are further exposures of coarse-grained volcaniclastic rock and sediment-raft breccia.

PART 2: THE CARBONIFEROUS GEOLOGICAL HISTORY OF THE EAST MIDLANDS

Colin Bagshaw, Associate Lecturer, Open University

The period of time between the formation of the rocks of Charnwood and the end of the Devonian period is not represented by any known exposures in the East Midlands area. Palaeozoic sediments that outcrop in the West Midlands, and in scat-

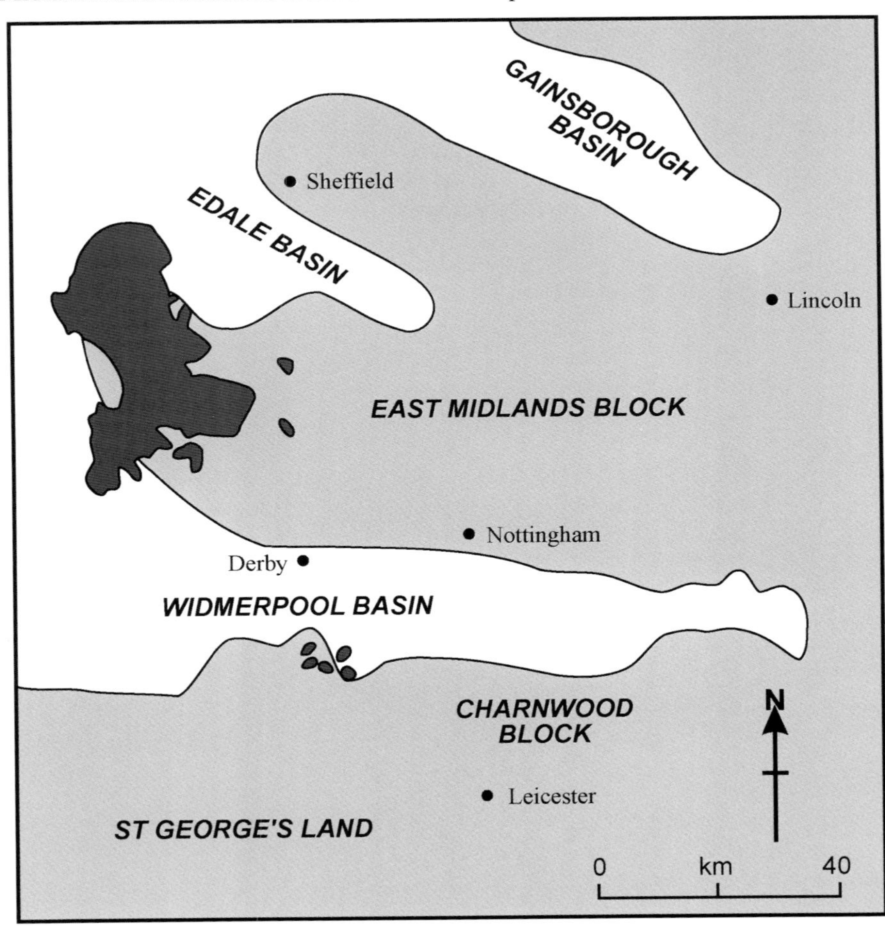

Figure 11. Palaeogeography of the East Midlands and Charnwood Blocks during the Dinantian. (After Anderton et al. 1979). Dark grey areas indicate present outcrops.

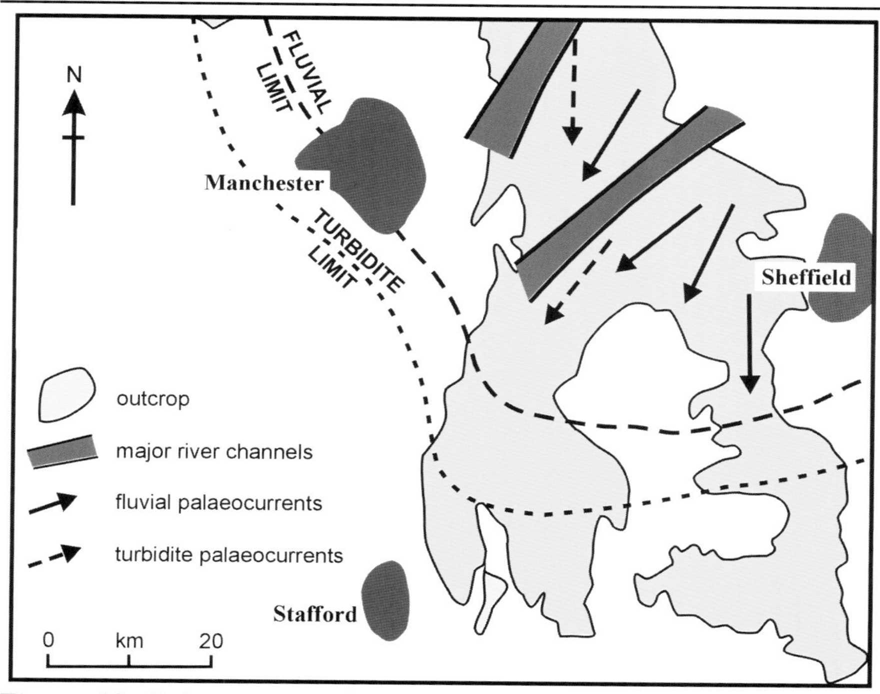

Figure 12. Palaeogeography of the East Midlands area during the Namurian, showing the geographical limits of the northern delta and its associated fluvial and turbidite deposits (After Anderton et al. 1979).

tered exposures and at depth in the East Midlands, are covered by the rocks of Carboniferous age described in this part of the Guide.

Prior to the **Caledonian Orogeny** in late Silurian and early Devonian times the area formed part of a marine platform on the northern edge of a continent. The orogeny was initiated by the collision of this continent with another to the north that resulted in the development of high fold mountains in northern Britain with foothills in the English Midlands. During the Devonian Period the erosion of these foothills supplied sediment to the Anglo-Welsh basin to the south, which resulted in an area of low, but not flat, relief in central and northern England.

During the early part of the Carboniferous Period a marine **transgression** progressed northward from southern England across this eroded surface. Britain was situated in equatorial latitudes at this time, and the tropical climate and clear shallow seas contributed to the deposition of limestones that now form the dominant feature of the White Peak area of Derbyshire. The period of time during which the limestones were deposited is referred to as the **Dinantian** Epoch. In the area of our Wirksworth and Ashover excursions the exposed sequence of these Lower

Carboniferous limestones is divided into three formations. The oldest of these is the Bee Low (Hoptonwood) Limestone, belonging to the **Asbian** Stage, which is noted for its massive beds of very pure calcium carbonate for which it has been mined in the Middleton Moor area for many years. Above this is the Monsal Dale (Matlock) Limestone followed by the Eyam (Cawdor) Limestone, which are both assigned to the **Brigantian** Stage. These are the object of the quarrying activity for roadstone and aggregates which is so evident around Wirksworth and Cromford.

The three formations described above do not make up the whole of the Dinantian limestones of Derbyshire. Together they total about 200m in thickness. Borehole evidence from the north of the county and seismic surveys indicate that there could be up to half as much again beneath the Bee Low Limestone Formation. These rocks and their unconformable contact with those underlying them are not exposed.

The above limestone sequence is not always complete. Interruptions in the deposition of the sediment were caused by their emergence above sea-level from time to time. This led to the formation of **palaeosols** and **palaeokarst** surfaces. There are therefore **unconformities** within the sequence, the most notable of which is developed on top of the Bee Low Limestone (Hoptonwood) Formation described in the Wirksworth excursion.

Another feature of the area is the occurrence of a number of volcanic rocks of basaltic composition within the limestones. Lava flows are present in the area north of Cromford but none is to be found in our excursions. However, associated basaltic tuffs are encountered, notably at Ashover. In many places these have deteriorated by weathering to greenish coloured clays called **clay wayboards**.

A detailed study of the Dinantian limestones throughout Britain reveals a wide variation in their textures and fossil content due to differing environments of formation. They may, for example, indicate shallow water shelf conditions. Others were formed in deeper water basins and yet others suggest reef developments. Hence it is possible to construct a **palaeogeographical** map of the Lower Carboniferous sea floor (Figure 11). This shows considerable variations in depth across the area. In the East Midlands much of the area of the present day outcrop was one of a shallow marine shelf referred to as the **Derbyshire Massif**. This received very little in the way of **siliciclastic** sediment and was therefore a clear water area ideal for sustaining a varied shallow water fauna. Around the margins of this were deeper water basins or gulfs in which large quantities of **argillaceous** sediment and dead organisms accumulated in relatively low energy environments at depth. These basins therefore are represented by sequences of dark grey, argillaceous rocks with muddy limestones. An example of this is the Widmerpool Gulf or Basin, which marks the southern limit of the Derbyshire shelf area and underlies the localities described in the Ecclesbourne Valley excursion.

Along the margins of the shelf areas are many so-called reef developments formed by the combined efforts of algae and reef building animals such as **bryozoans**, **brachiopods** and rare corals. These reefs are often lacking in obvious bedding planes and form large mounds such as High Tor at Matlock Bath and at the National Stone Centre featuring in the Wirksworth excursion.

The top of the Dinantian limestones on the Massif forms a sharp contact with a contrasting series of sediments deposited in the **Namurian** Epoch. In early Namurian times a great **delta** began to make its way southwestwards across what is now the Pennine region (Figure 12). Initially the onset of deltaic conditions was preceded by the deposition of a fine-grained mud referred to locally as the Edale Shales. This shale covered the uppermost limestones of the shelf forming a sharp contact. Unfortunately this junction is rarely exposed as the shale easily breaks down to form a thick soil cover. In the basins such as the Widmerpool Gulf, argillaceous sedimentation continued without a break from Dinantian to Namurian times.

Following the deposition of the Edale Shales, thick spreads of coarse sand were transported into the area. The first of these was responsible for the Ashover Grit which today forms prominent scarp slopes in many parts of Derbyshire and which are seen on the Wirksworth, Ashover and Ecclesbourne Valley excursions. The lower part of the Ashover Grit tends to be medium-grained and massively bedded (unlaminated), and was probably deposited by **turbidity currents** on the sloping, unstable sea floor in front of the delta. It was this part of the sequence, with no planes of weakness, which was the main source of rock from which millstones were once manufactured. The Namurian was previously termed the Millstone Grit Series. In contrast the higher part of the Ashover Grit is coarser grained and **cross-bedded**, and was probably deposited by large rivers. Fossils of Carboniferous plants and trees that were washed along and deposited by these rivers are to be found in a few localities.

During the Namurian from time to time world sea-levels rose. This allowed free-swimming organisms, particularly **goniatites** and scallop-like **bivalves,** to enter the area. Their remains are usually preserved in black mudstone and shale that form beds known as **marine bands**. During deep burial their fossilised shells became flattened by the weight of thousands of metres of overlying rock. They are now usually found in this flattened state, although occasionally they are preserved in their original form in limestone concretions known as **bullions**.

After several episodes of alternating gritstone, mudstone and shale deposition during the Namurian, the area became colonised by vast forested swamps that led to the Coal Measures of the **Westphalian** Epoch. The marine band containing the goniatite *Gastrioceras subcrenatum* marks the base of the Westphalian. In the Chesterfield area this is called the Pot Clay Marine Band. Above this were deposited several hundred metres of sediments of Coal Measures of which only a small percentage is actually coal. The sequence was deposited as a series of cycles called **cyclothems** over an area that was slowly subsiding.

Theoretically each cycle began with a marine transgression depositing a thin stratum of mud or shale containing marine fossils (goniatites, bivalves and the brachiopod *Lingula*). The sediments then gradually coarsen upwards as depths of water decreased and conditions changed from marine to brackish to fresh water deltaic and finally to swamps upon which vegetation could become established. Such vegetation consisted of ancient club mosses, ferns and seed bearing plants. (Present day horsetails and gingkoes evolved from these). The soils on which these plants grew now exist as **fireclay** or **ganister** (sand) in which fossil roots are often abundant.

As generations of these plants died, they decayed in the absence of oxygen in swamps to form vast thicknesses of peat. Eventually each peat horizon was inundated by the next marine transgression as subsidence of the area continued and the whole cycle of deposition was then repeated. In this way numerous seams of peat were buried to great depth and by a series of complex chemical reactions they were converted to coal. These cyclothems are seldom complete, but examples of the rock types involved and their control on scenery is described in the Holymoorside, near Chesterfield, excursion.

Towards the close of the Carboniferous Period another period of mountain building began, this time affecting southern Britain. This was the **Variscan Orogeny** the main effects of which are seen in the intense folding of rocks in Southwest England and South Wales. The Midlands area was affected and experienced approximately east-west compressional forces which formed the main structural element of the Derbyshire Dome and associated features to the east. The folds at Ashover and Crich are good examples of other Variscan structures.

In addition to the folding, contemporaneous faults and joints developed in the more brittle strata, particularly the limestones. It was in these fractures that minerals were deposited during post-Carboniferous times from hot solutions rising from depth. These **hydrothermal** minerals include fluorite, barytes, calcite and a little quartz along with galena and sphalerite, the last two having been worked since Roman times for lead and zinc respectively. Mining activity occurred particularly in the eastern part of the Derbyshire limestone outcrop and old mineral waste tips are evident throughout this area. The ore minerals were taken from the mine workings to smelters for processing and the remains of one of these is described in the Holymoorside excursion (Locality 8).

EXCURSION 4. THE CARBONIFEROUS LIMESTONE AROUND WIRKSWORTH

Trevor D. Ford, Geology Dept., University of Leicester

Objectives

The Wirksworth area provides an opportunity to study the varied sedimentology and facies changes in the Carboniferous Limestone (Asbian and Brigantian). The unconformable cover of Millstone Grit (Namurian) strata, the effects of faulting, mineral veins and mining relics combine to make a highly instructive excursion.

Logistics

Access is by turning off the A6 trunk road at Cromford, southwards on the B5036 towards Wirksworth. Alternatively leave the A6 at Duffield on to the B5023 to Wirksworth and via B5036 towards Cromford. On the crest at Steeple Grange a public footpath, the High Peak Trail, follows the track of the old Cromford and High Peak Railway.

The excursion has been planned as a walk of about 4km though cars or coach can be used by moving up at intervals to keep abreast of the traverse. Start in the top level of the Black Rocks car park (SK 291557) (Figure 13) reached by a lane branching off the hill coming up from Cromford or by a lane branching right immediately before the old railway bridge at the top of the hill coming from Wirksworth and taking the first turn left (beware low bridge). Most of the excursion is on public access footpaths between a complex of old quarries. These form part of the National Stone Centre where permission for parties should be obtained beforehand (01629-824833). Some of the quarry faces are unstable and appropriate safety measures must be taken.

The Steeple Grange area (sometimes known as Bole Hill) between Wirksworth and Cromford is at the southeastern extremity of the Carboniferous Limestone outcrop of the Peak District.

The Wirksworth area is covered by O.S. 1:50,000 sheets 119 and 128, by O.S. 1:25,000 Outdoor Leisure Map 24 and by 1:10,000 sheets SK25NE & SE. It is in the southwestern corner of British Geological Survey 1:50,000 sheet 112 (Chesterfield and Matlock). The special British Geological Survey 1:25,000 sheet for Matlock shows the Wirksworth area in greater detail and has an outline geological history in its margins.

Stratigraphy

The Carboniferous Limestone is here subdivided into Stages and Formations:

Two volcanic horizons, the Lower and Upper Matlock Lavas, are interleaved within the Monsal Dale Limestone Formation.

Excursion 4: Carboniferous Limestone, Wirksworth

Stage	Local Name	Formation
Namurian	Edale Shale	
Brigantian	Cawdor Shale	Longstone Mudstone
	Cawdor Limestone	Eyam Limestone
	Matlock Limestone	Monsal Dale Limestone
Asbian	Hoptonwood Limestone	Bee Low Limestone
Holkerian	Griffe Grange Beds	Woo Dale Limestone

The lowest exposed beds in the Wirksworth **Dinantian** sequence are the Bee Low Limestones of Asbian age, locally known as the Hoptonwood Limestone Formation. These massive, high purity **calcarenites** have been quarried around Middleton Moor for many years and mined for the last 35 years. The Bee Low Limestone Formation is followed in the north of the area by the Matlock Lower Lava, that comprises up to 20m of basaltic lava and tuff. This volcanic horizon thins out southwards and is present as a tuff some 15m thick at Middleton where it lies above the roof of the Middleton Limestone Mine. The tuff dies out beneath the National Stone Centre and was noted only as a "great clay" in the lead mines beneath Steeple Grange.

The Brigantian Stage is represented by the Monsal Dale and Eyam Limestones (formerly known in the Matlock-Wirksworth area as the Matlock and Cawdor Limestones respectively). The Monsal Dale Limestone Formation is somewhat less massive than the Hoptonwood beds and has an increasing amount of **chert** nodules. About 100m thick, they are mainly shelly **crinoidal** calcarenites, deposited in a shallow lagoonal environment. The sequence shows evidence of frequent emergence with **palaeosols** and **palaeokarst** surfaces. The limestones are worked in the Middlepeak Quarries (SK 2854) chiefly for roadstone and aggregate. To the south, in the contiguous Dale Quarry (SK 286543), there is a facies change to deeper water mudstones as the southern margin of the Derbyshire Massif is approached. The Matlock Upper Lava is within the Monsal Dale Limestones to the north of Cromford but thins out to zero by the time it reaches the Steeple Grange area.

The Eyam Limestone Formation (also known locally as the Coal Hills Formation) is around 50m thick and comprises thin to medium-bedded calcarenites, generally cherty and with shale partings. Crinoid debris and gigantoproductid brachiopods are abundant. The Eyam Limestone Formation includes a series of fine-grained **carbonate mud mounds** or "reefs", flanked by coarse inter-mound detrital

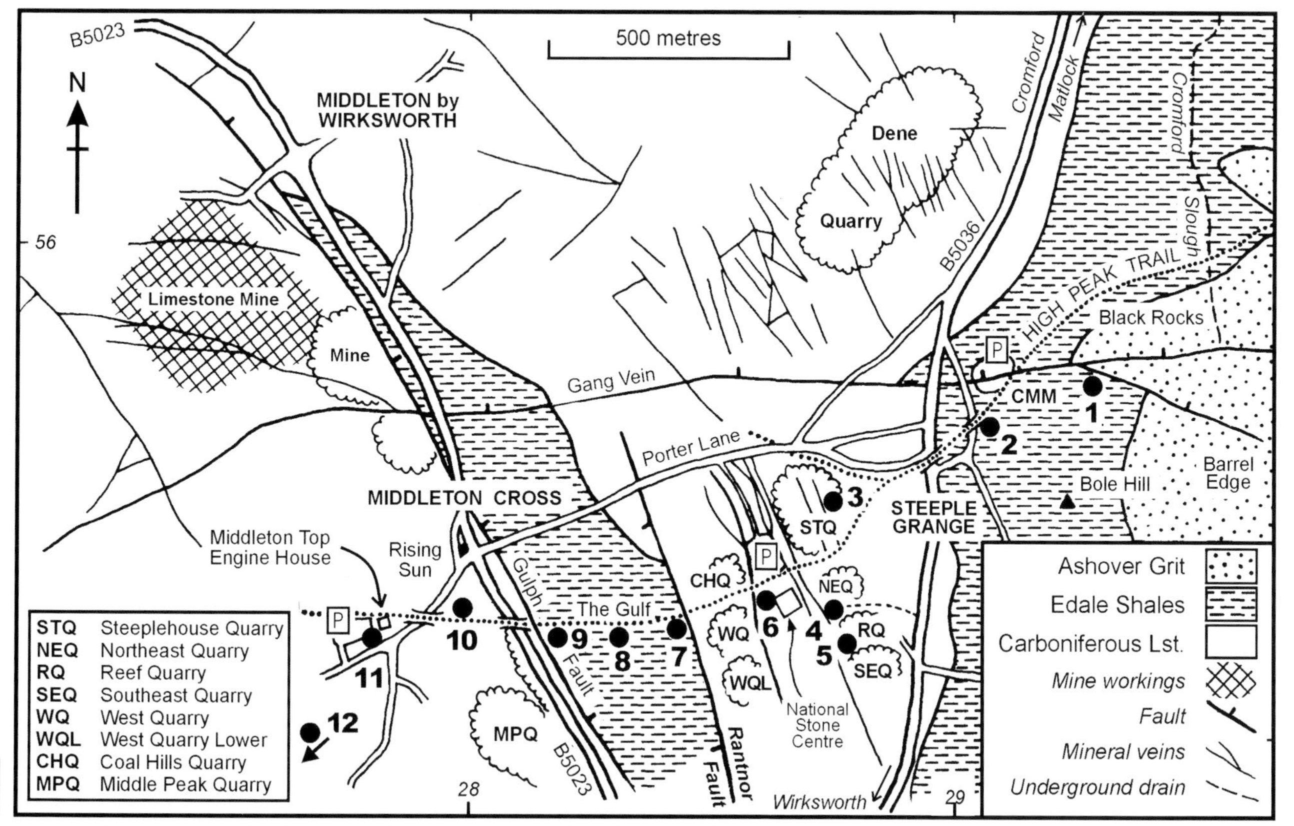

Figure 13. Geological sketch map of the Steeple Grange and Gulf area, Wirksworth.

calcarenites, well displayed around the National Stone Centre. The carbonate mud mounds are calcite mudstones bound by filamentous algae with a degree of sediment trapping by **fenestellid** bryozoans. Irregular **stromatactis** cavities are common. In the mound limestones there are abundant specialized "reef" brachiopods together with bivalves, **gastropods**, rare **cephalopods** and **trilobites**. Low sea-level phases occasionally resulted in emergence and erosion of the mound crests, with development of palaeosol textures in the highest parts of the mounds. A possible Dinantian cave occurs in one mound. The Eyam Limestone Formation rests unconformably on the Monsal Dale Limestones and cuts down to rest on the Bee Low Formation in the road cutting at Wirksworth.

The top of the Dinantian limestone sequence is a sharp contact, rarely visible, with the overlying Edale Shales of Namurian age (Pendleian to Kinderscoutian). These represent distal deltaic mud fed from a river system that appears to have come into the area from the east. The Edale Shales are followed by the lowest of the Millstone Grit deltaic sandstones, the Ashover Grit of Marsdenian age, well exposed around Black Rocks and Barrel Edge east of Steeple Grange.

Dolomitization

Secondary dolomitization has affected all parts of the limestone sequence in a wide area west of Wirksworth. This was once regarded by some writers as due to the effects of brine percolation from the Permian **Zechstein** Sea's former extent over the South Pennine area. However, it is now thought to be due to an early phase of the ore mineralization, since many of the veins were emplaced within dolomitized limestones, and the mineralization is regarded as largely pre-Permian. The dolomitization has resulted in calcite being replaced by dolomite with the consequent loss of sedimentary textures and fossils.

Structure

The dominant structure crossing the Steeple Grange area is the east-west anticline mainly affecting the Dinantian limestones. **Plunging** gently eastwards it is less well developed in the succeeding Millstone Grit. The Edale Shales thin over the crest showing that the anticline had probably started to grow by early Namurian times. The anticlinal axis is not clearly definable but appears to be close to the line of the Gang Vein (Figure 13). The anticline lies at right angles to the later Pennine axis and is transected by the NW-SE Gulf Fault system (Gulph in local mining lore) with its associated **graben** floored by Namurian shale. The anticline is poorly developed west of the Gulf Fault.

Minerals and Mining

The Wirksworth area is at the southern end of the South Pennine Orefield. It is crossed by two major east-west veins or rakes. Gang Vein (also known as Dovegang or Godbehere Vein) lies more or less along the anticlinal axis, whilst Yokecliffe Rake lies 1.5km to the south. Both show some evidence of **wrench fault-**

ing, with only limited vertical displacement. The area is crossed by a swarm of smaller NW-SE and NE-SW veins, locally called **scrins**. Some of the NW-SE veins are along the Gulf and Ranter Faults bounding the Gulf, whilst others lie parallel without evident displacements. The veins contain galena, minor sphalerite and a little pyrite, together with much baryte, calcite and some fluorite. Mineral mining is no longer economic around Wirksworth, though there are many relics of former lead mining.

Lead ore was worked in Roman times with operations centred on their settlement *Lutudarum*; its location is uncertain but it is generally believed to be somewhere near Wirksworth. By the 17th century the mines had gone deep enough to be plagued with water and the first subsurface drainage level or sough was engineered by Cornelius Vermuyden (of draining the Fens fame) starting in 1631. Several short soughs near Cromford and under Wirksworth Gulph were driven before two deep levels were driven. Cromford Sough started in 1673 and Meerbrook Sough was driven from 1772 to 1864. The latter still discharges some 16 million gallons per day and part is taken for public water supplies. The result of all this mining activity is that there is a network of lead mine workings and soughs under much of the Steeple Grange area.

Geomorphology

The Steeple Grange Hill area lies on the watershed between the Ecclesbourne valley draining southwards from Wirksworth and the Via Gellia valley that joins the Derwent at Cromford. **Karstic** features are poorly developed on the limestone. The only caves are occasional solution cavities found in lead mines. Surface drainage is largely by percolation into the limestone, mainly along mineral veins and faults. The Millstone Grit escarpment has several landslip features. The area was not glaciated in the **Devensian** and glacial features have not survived from early glaciations. **Periglacial** action in the Devensian resulted in the limestone being covered with up to a metre of **loessic** subsoil in places.

Locality Details

Locality 1: From the far (north) end of the car park take the footpath to the old lead mine waste heap by the side of Black Rocks (SK 293557). The slope that has been crossed, marks the outcrop of the Edale Shales. The Cromford Moor Mine shaft was sunk through these here and the waste heap provides samples of silty, micaceous shale as well as of limestone and the typical vein minerals galena, sphalerite, fluorite, baryte and calcite.

Looking westwards towards Middleton one is looking along the crest of the anticline, and across the Gulph graben to the Middleton-Wirksworth fault scarp. The course of the Gang Vein is marked by a line of grassed-over waste hillocks (Figure 13). Looking to the northwest is the working Dene Quarry (SR 288563) with northerly dips on one flank of the anticline whilst to the southwest in the distance Middlepeak Quarries (SK 2854) show southerly dips on the other flank. Turning round one can look up to the Millstone Grit escarpment of Barrel Edge and see the obvious displacement relative to Black Rocks, much lower on the north: how much displacement is due to faulting and how much to landslipping is not clear. Neither the underlying shale nor limestone outcrops show evidence of such a large fault displacement and the adjacent hillsides show rough ground typical of landslips. The medium to coarse-grained sandstones of the Ashover Grit have sparsely scattered pebbles up to 1cm in diameter in well-cemented bands. The main face shows a massive parallel-bedded unit with an angular discordance. A cross-bedded channel infill is visible at a higher level.

Whilst at this locality it is worth considering the underground drainage problems faced by the lead miners. A series of underground tunnels or soughs were driven beneath the area to drain off unwanted water. Vermuyden's Sough of 1631 is roughly beneath Dene Quarry and reached the Gang Vein at no great depth under

Figure 14. 'Petrodus' dermal tubercles, Steeplehouse Quarry. Field of view = 7cm.

the waste hillocks straight ahead. The Cromford Sough was driven at greater depth starting in 1672. Its course followed the shale/limestone contact down dip to the east and met the vein well back under Barrel Edge before turning west along the Gang Vein some 200m beneath Black Rocks. Arkwright used the outfall from Cromford Sough to provide waterpower for his mill in the 1770's.

Return to the High Peak Trail and turn left (south) noting the remains of an engine house on the Cromford Moor Mines. The High Peak Trail follows the former Cromford & High Peak Railway opened in 1830 as an extension of the Cromford canal.

Locality 2: About 300m along the trail pause at the first bend (SK 291556). The back gardens of the houses on the left are in a hollow, which was once a quarry for mudstones of the Edale Shales used in brick making.

The bridge across the B5036 road marks the approximate position of the shale/limestone boundary. A few metres ahead the buildings on the left were once a railway station, known as Steeple Grange Wharf since it was built by a canal company.

Locality 3: At Steeple Grange Wharf, a branch railway once led to the Middleton limestone quarry and its track is now used by an enthusiasts' mini-railway. Between the Trail and the latter a narrow path forks right through the undergrowth into Steeplehouse or Smart's Quarry (the name is a corruption of "steep hill") (SK 288554). The quarry is part of the complex owned by the National Stone Centre. It is in the highest beds of the Dinantian sequence, the Eyam Limestone Formation. The quarry exposes crinoid/brachiopod calcarenites, which were once extracted for use as decorative facing panels, overlain by beds with much nodular chert, both dipping gently eastwards. *Gigantoproductus* shells can be seen on joint faces in the right-hand (north) quarry wall. Abundant crinoid remains can be found in the far right corner of the quarry. The bedding surfaces of large slabs in the vicinity of the step in the middle of the quarry floor contain numerous dermal tubercles of the primitive shark-like fish *Petrodus patelliformis* (ribbed conical phosphatic objects about 5-8mm in diameter, Figure 14). Minute teeth called *Anachronistes fordi* have also been found here and may belong to another type of shark. Since fish remains are rare in the Carboniferous Limestone, and many thousands occur here through about a metre of beds it seems possible that a shoal of fish suffered mass mortality and their hard parts were scattered by currents.

Two thin mineral veins cross the quarry and traces of old workings may be found on both quarry walls.

Return to the High Peak Trail and turn right (southwest). Drivers can bring their cars along Porter Lane and down to the National Stone Centre car park. Park above the arch and walk through to the Centre, noting the remains of an old limekiln on the left. The shop sells a variety of geological specimens and the Centre currently contains an exhibition illustrating the story of the use of stone. Refreshments are also available here. From the Centre join the footpath leading eastwards to Locality 4.

Locality 4: Walkers should continue southwest along the High Peak Trail and take the second footpath sloping down on the left, which leads to the National Stone Centre, but before the Centre itself turn full left along the path between the quarries to the public viewpoint to look into Northeast Quarry (formerly Upper Coal Hills quarry) (SK 288523).

The quarry is in the Eyam Limestone Formation: the lowest beds in the centre of the face are some 2m of coarse calcarenites with **calcirudite** bands containing many water-worn fragments of *Gigantoproductus* shells. All sizes from around 10cm downwards may be found and demonstrate progressive comminution of shell

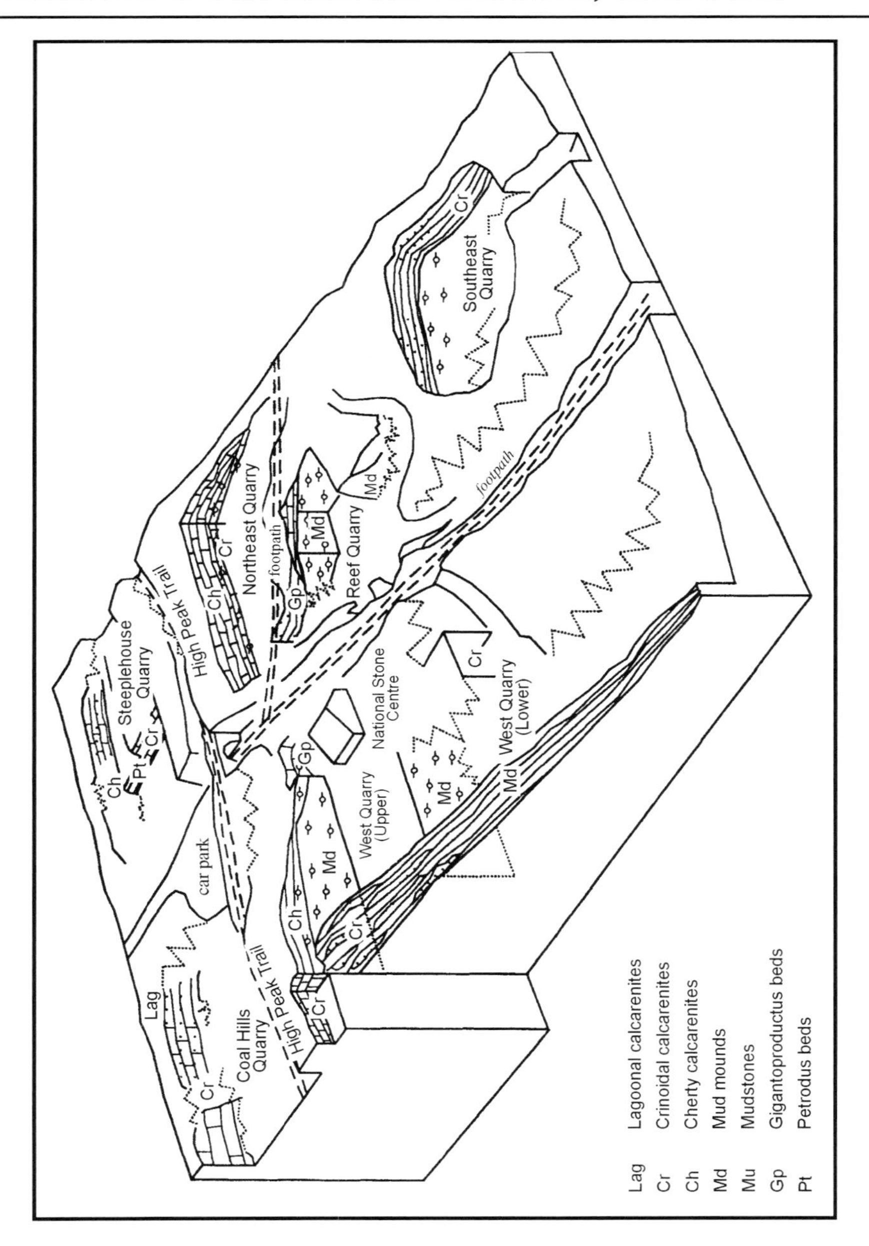

Figure 15. Block diagram of the quarries around the National Stone Centre. Modified after a drawing by Gordon Walkden.

Figure 16. The western margin of the carbonate mud mound with overlying beds rich in gigantoproductids and crinoid debris.

debris typical of a shallow lagoon. If a block of this limestone is cracked open the fresh face yields a sulphurous oily smell, the residue of a possible former accumulation of hydrocarbons. Some 3m up the quarry face these beds give way to a metre or so of fine-grained dark **calcilutites**, evidence of temporarily reduced current strengths. The contact between these two beds shows **ball and pillow** structures, more familiar in **greywacke** sequences. The "balls and pillows" of calcarenite are **load casts** up to 1m wide which have subsided into the softer calcilutites; the latter have risen round the balls in a kind of **flame structure**. Overlying the calcilutites are more calcarenites that become increasingly cherty upwards. The northeast corner of the main quarry face has intersected a small mineral vein and the face is partly one wall of this scrin vein: best seen from within the quarry it shows evidence of historic mining techniques. The top 5m or so have pick marks from pre-explosive days; drill marks can be seen in the next 2m below, showing that gunpowder blasting had been introduced. The lowest part of the vein was not worked.

From the quarry viewpoint look eastwards to the top of the quarry face where the set back shelf below the fence is in nearly a metre of **loessic** soil. On turning back from the viewpoint the low mound ahead is the top of the carbonate mud mound at Locality 5. There are some unusually long articulated crinoid stems and many gigantoproductid shells here.

Locality 5: Return towards the Centre building for about 10m and turn left down the steep path. On the left (east) is the Reef Quarry (formerly Coal Hills Reef Quarry) (Figures 15 and 16) that is largely excavated in a "reef" or carbonate mud mound. The poorly bedded fine-grained reef calcilutite shows little sign of the algae that bound the calcite mud together. There are plenty of stromatactis cavities, which may indicate the former presence of sea-weed with no fossilizable structures; some cavities contain bitumen and there are many hollow shells, mostly reef productids. Parts of the mound limestone have abundant fossils, such as "reef" brachiopods and bivalves including an elongate pinniform type. Occasional cephalopods and trilobites are present as well as numerous fenestellid bryozoans. The crag to the left of the mound shows the contrast with the immediately flanking beds, mostly coarse crinoidal limestones, but with bedding planes crowded with *Gigantoproductus* shells, best seen on the under-sides of overhanging blocks. This section demonstrates that the carbonate mud mound was lithified rapidly so that coarse detritus could be banked up against it. The highest part of the mound limestone shows palaeosol textures under the microscope. A fissure lined with brownish calcite on the far side of the quarry may be a Dinantian cave with stalagmite lining. Stratigraphically the carbonate mud mound lies just beneath the calcarenites seen at Locality 4 in the Northeast Quarry, both within the Eyam Limestone Formation. The lower part of this carbonate mud mound is in the Southeast Quarry (formerly Lower Coal Hills Quarry) which is now largely back-filled and overgrown.

Locality 6: Return to the National Stone Centre building (SK 287522) which lies in an inter-mound area. Small outcrops show crinoidal calcarenites with a scatter of remarkably large *Gigantoproductus* shells, up to 20cm wide! Looking west from the Centre's terrace another carbonate mud mound can be seen in the upper level of West Quarry (formerly Shaw's Quarry). Beware the vertical drop into the lower level. An irregular parting high in the quarry face may represent an erosion surface. Study of the bedding planes in the quarry face beyond the carbonate mud mound shows that the flanking crinoidal calcarenites have built up as a stack of lenticular accumulations of detritus. The lower level of West Quarry is in a stack of carbonate mud mounds separated by undulating bedding planes.

Return uphill through the archway to the lowest level of the Centre's car park and turn left to regain the High Peak Trail. The rough ground to the north of the car parks was once a maze of old lead mine waste heaps. They were removed in the 1980's for re-processing for baryte. Returning the area to grazing will be inadvisable as finely dispersed galena particles are liable to be ingested by animals, with potentially disastrous effects on young stock. On rejoining the High Peak Trail large square blocks of gritstone on the walls were once the sleepers for the early 19th century railway. The next cutting has the crest of the West quarry reef exposed low down on the left, whilst the Coal Hills Quarry on the right (north) is in inter-mound crinoidal calcarenites with many chert nodules.

Locality 7: Some 200m along the Trail, 20m after a walled section, go left for 10m through a gap in the trees to a small terrace (SK 284552), where one can get a view down the shale-floored embayment of the Gulph towards Wirksworth. This depressed area between two limestone fault scarps is a graben or rift valley. The crag on the left is Ranter (corruption of Ravenstor) and is on the upthrown side of the Ranter Fault. The basal Edale Shales are downthrown by a maximum of about 50m to the southwest. Some 400m to the west (right)is the Gulf Fault with a maximum displacement up to the southwest of about 150m. The small graben between the two faults is unusual in that such structures can rarely be seen in a single view. The outcrop of the Edale Shales gives rise to low ground between the two fault scarps. The Gulf is marked by the waste heaps of many old lead mines sunk through the shale to reach veins in the limestone. These veins are mostly parallel to the Ranter and Gulf Faults and were well mineralized. The Ranter Fault dies out to the northwest, leaving a half-graben, whilst to the southeast neither fault can be traced in the Millstone Grit outcrop. Return through the trees to the High Peak Trail proceeding westwards.

Locality 8: Just before the Trail starts going up the Middleton incline a pit on the left houses a large iron wheel, which was the bottom pulley for the railway's wire-rope haulage. A few metres up the track a mine hillock on the right contains a shaft into the complex workings of Ratchwood Mine (SK 282552) which extends under the Trail and under the upper end of the Gulph.

Locality 9: Proceed up the incline until the bridge over the B5023 road is reached (SK 281552). It is worth pausing on the bridge to note that the Gulf Fault runs approximately along the road and if the fault ever moved again it might be a case of "tear along the white line". The limestones on the upthrown side of the fault are part of the Monsal Dale Limestone Formation, which has been concealed beneath the Eyam Limestones seen hitherto. Drivers may wish to walk back from here and bring the cars up from the National Stone Centre car park to the Middleton Top car park (SK 275551).

Locality 10: From the bridge over the B5023 continue up the Middleton Incline through a cutting on the High Peak Trail. The Monsal Dale Limestone Formation is exposed on both sides. About 80m from the bridge opposite a large dressed gritstone block the limestone on the right (north) contains two rubbly beds. The lower lies on a thin clay parting or wayboard. From 1 to 5cm thick, the greenish-buff clay is an altered volcanic ash that contains a few scattered productid valves; living on the sea-floor they were overwhelmed by the ashfall. Continue up to the top of the incline.

Locality 11: The Middleton Top engine house (SK 276552) was last used when the railway closed in 1967 but the beam engine has been preserved and is open to the public at weekends and holidays. A small visitor centre is by the adjacent car park. Proceed westwards along the High Peak Trail for about 400m. The disused Intake Quarry (SK 270550) lies on the right behind a landscaped waste heap. There is no public access to the quarry.

Locality 12: Continuing a further 400m westwards the Trail passes through the 100m long Hopton Tunnel under Gallows Knoll (SK 267548). The eastern cutting goes through the irregular contact between unaltered and highly dolomitized Monsal Dale Limestones. The lower part of the cutting is in light grey limestones whilst the dolomite above weathers grey-brown. Freshly broken surfaces of the dolomite are cream-coloured.

Both limestones and dolomite contain chert nodules, indicating that chert formation preceded dolomitization. The western cutting has a rubbly limestone band in the right-hand (north) cliff with a thin clay wayboard at the base. Brownish dolomitized limestones occur in the higher cliffs. From the cutting there is a view ahead of Griff Grange Quarry (SK 256548). Opened in the 1960's, it was intended to extract magnesium metal from dolomite but this soon proved uneconomic. The buildings were later adapted as a fluorite processing plant but this too proved uneconomic. Some dolomite is now quarried for aggregate and reconstituted decorative stone. The gorse bushes in a field to the south of Gallows Knoll mark the restored site of one of the Mio-Pliocene silica-sand pockets of which working examples may be found around Brassington some 3km to the west.

Return to the Middleton Top car park and thence to the B5035; turn left and then right onto the B5023 towards Wirksworth. Go past Middlepeak Quarries and bear right at the road junction. Park on Harrison Drive opposite the petrol station in the former Baileycroft Quarry (SK 287542).

Locality 13: Here, on both sides of the mouth of the cutting, thin dark limestones of the Eyam Limestone Formation rest with marked unconformity on a deeply channelled erosion surface cut into the more massive calcarenites of the Bee Low Limestone Formation. Compaction on to the channelled surface has induced small folds in the Eyam Limestones. The sequence is best seen on the left (east) side but is liable to be partly hidden by the Highways Dept. salt heap. The grassy slopes behind the petrol station conceal a former outcrop of the Edale Shales that rest non-sequentially on the Eyam Limestones. Thus two unconformities occur within a few metres of each other here.

EXCURSION 5. CARBONIFEROUS ROCKS AND MINERALISATION OF THE ASHOVER ANTICLINE

I D Sutton, University of Nottingham

Objectives

This field trip will enable participants to gain an understanding of the Dinantian limestone and **volcaniclastic** sedimentary sequence in the core of the Ashover Anticline. It will also give the opportunity of studying the Namurian, wholly argillaceous Edale Shales and succeeding sandstone sequence overlying the Dinantian strata.

Additionally the relationship between the topography and underlying geology should become apparent in an area that is an excellent venue to attempt geological mapping exercises. Mineralization and historical mining aspects can also be recognised.

Logistics

Most of the exposures and viewing points are within easy walking distance of Ashover village that can easily be reached by car from Alfreton via the A61, B6014 and B6036, from Chesterfield via A632 to Kelstedge and the B6036, and from Matlock also via the A632 to Kelstedge (Figure 17). A large car park is available in Ashover by the parish hall (SK 352633), an excellent meeting point. There is also a rather irregular bus service from Chesterfield and Matlock (no Sunday service). If two vehicles are available a considerable reduction in walking can be accomplished. Nearly all the walking is on roads or footpaths and two quarries are in the itinerary wherein protective clothing should be worn. The area is shown on the O.S. Landranger 1: 50,000 Sheet 119, the O.S. 1: 25,000 Sheet SK36 Clay Cross, and on the British Geological Survey one-inch series Sheet 112 Chesterfield, and 1: 25,000 Geological Special Sheet Matlock.

The itinerary should provide ample interest for a full day field activity. The area is well served by public houses in Ashover and nearby at Woolley Moor where the White Horse (SK 367615) is highly recommended for food and ale. The area is much visited and although none of the sites have any hammering restrictions, you are requested to observe great care in order to maintain the quality of the exposures, and to hammer rock exposures only in exceptional circumstances.

It is suggested that the first part of this field visit should be a traverse from the SW part of the area to Ashover village. If only one vehicle is available this should be left in Ashover and a walk of about 1.5km will be required to reach Locality 1. To do this, take the footpath (Salters Lane) adjacent to the Red Lion Inn down to the River Amber, cross the footbridge and ascend to the top of the valley slope using the slab-paved footpath.

Continue on the bridleway and cross the road leading to Overton Hall on your left. Follow the footpath through the wood and then above the old mine spoil heaps before ascending the escarpment on an ill-defined path, alongside the field boundary, to the right of the footpath and to the left (south) of the very prominent sandstone outcrop.

If two vehicles are available, leave one in Ashover and travel in the other from the village past the church along Church Street and turn right by the Red Lion. Follow this road to where it joins the Chesterfield-Matlock road (A632) at Kelstedge. Turn left towards Matlock and ascend Slack Hill, a steep 1 in 7 gradient, rising up over the Ashover Grit escarpment.

At the top of Slack Hill turn left signposted 'Matlock (avoiding steep hill) Woolley, Bradenfield and Wessington'. After about 1.5km the entrance to Holestone Moor Farm (SK 339615) is on the right. Park on the left-hand side as far off the road as possible. Directly opposite the entrance to Holestone Moor Farm is a footpath that leads to Locality 2.

Geological Background

The Ashover area has long been famous from a geological viewpoint because of its structure, which is an eroded anticline or dome (Figure 17).

Although Pleistocene ice processes may have played a small part in its erosional history there is little doubt that the River Amber and some of its small tributaries have been largely responsible in the carving of the valley through the structure.

In a small area around Ashover, Dinantian and Namurian rocks are well exposed and **hydrothermal** mineralization has resulted in considerable lead mining and fluorite working from the large number of mineral veins in the limestone. The oldest rocks exposed are basaltic volcanic tuffs that occur on either side of the River Amber. These tuffs represent part of a substantial amount of volcanic activity during the Dinantian in the Derbyshire area.

The NW – SE elongate outcrop of the tuffs in the core of this anticline are succeeded by a wider but similar shaped outcrop of the Dinantian limestones that have been quarried for building stone, road metal, etc. The hydrothermal mineral veins which typically contain galena, sphalerite, purple and pyritic fluorite (clear to yellowish fluorite with pyrite inclusions), some calcite, quartz and pyrite, have a long history of mining, particularly from the 17th to 19th centuries for lead and during the 20th century for fluorite. The formation of the Ashover anticline has produced faults and major joint planes, which have been admirable avenues for the uprising hydrothermal fluids to move and precipitate out the typical minerals present. The tectonic activity producing the structures was imposed on the area by **Variscan** earth movements in late Carboniferous times. The hydrothermal mineralization is considered to be largely of Permian age but it may well have continued into the Triassic.

Overlying the limestones, but forming an area of comparatively low relief with frequent waterlogged conditions are the Namurian Edale Shales, which at some horizons contain abundant fossils of marine **goniatites** and **bivalves**.

The shale is, in turn, overlain by the Ashover Grit of the Namurian age, which

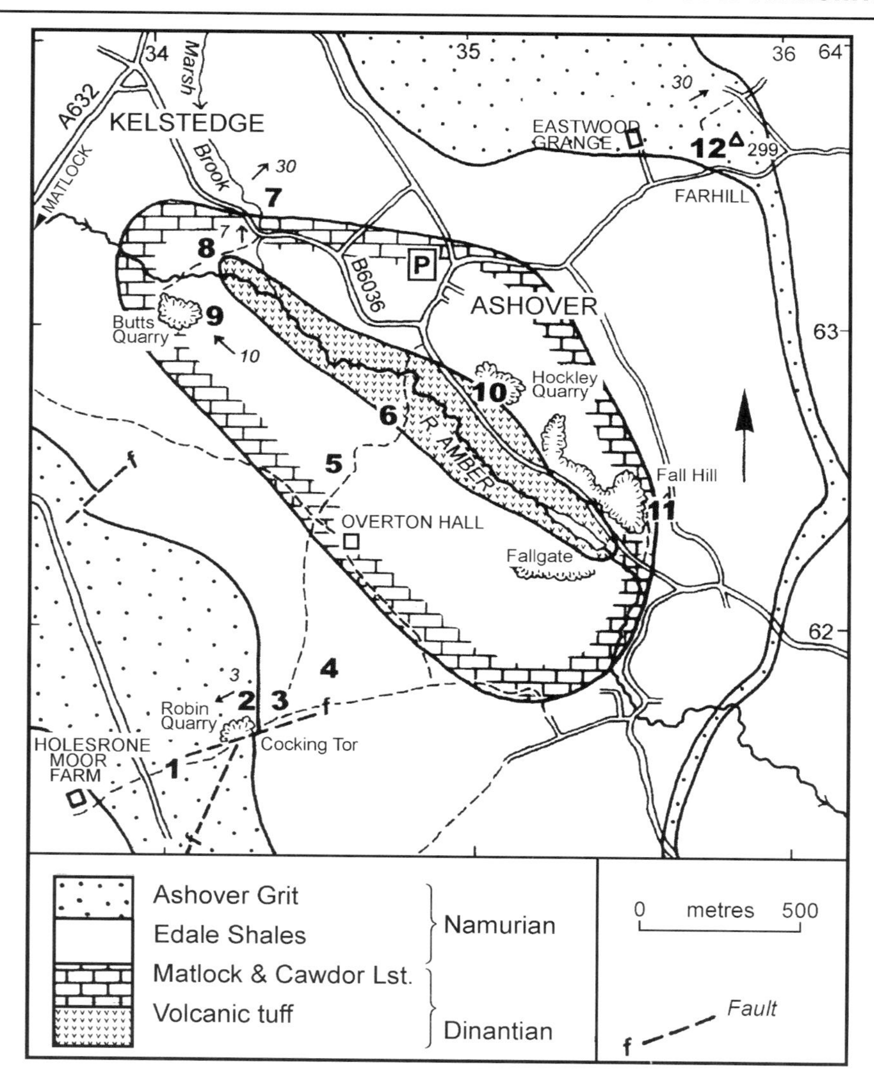

Figure 17. Simplified solid geology map of the Ashover Anticline showing localities.

forms escarpments to the NE and SW. Because of the much shallower dip (3° to the SW) the SW escarpment is much more prominent than that to the NE where dips reach as much as 50°.

The Ashover area is an excellent area to attempt geological mapping exercises and one where the topographical features can be readily linked to the rock types and structure.

Locality Details

Locality 1: (SK 339615). Viewpoint on roadside by entrance to Holestone Moor Farm. In reasonable weather conditions excellent views can be obtained in a westerly direction towards the main Dinantian limestone outcrop of the Peak District in the neighbourhood of Matlock. From the viewpoint the ground slopes westward down the dip slope of the Ashover Grit to the small escarpment produced by the overlying Chatsworth Grit on Tansley Moor. Riber Castle can be seen in the distance. The ground in front of the castle slopes towards the northeast and marks the dip slope of the Ashover Grit once more, this time on the other (southwestern) side of the small and gentle **synclinal** downwarp between Locality 1 and Riber Castle. Beyond Riber is the Derwent Valley, cut into the Dinantian limestones, which also form the upland area further away.

Locality 2: Robin Quarry (SK 342616). Walk eastwards along the footpath for about 200m from the road. At the entrance to the quarry is some evidence, in the form of millstones, of the use to which the Ashover Gritstone was put. It was also quarried for walling and kerbstone.

Robin Quarry was actively worked until the middle of the 20th century. The 12m of sandstones dipping in a southwest direction at about 3° can be divided into two units.

The lower unit, at least 9m thick, consists of two parts. The lower part is massive, and at the floor of the quarry, includes a pebbly sandstone with clasts up to 10mm in diameter. The latter passes up into an apparently unbedded sandstone containing quartz with subordinate feldspar and a little mica. The proportion of feldspar is sufficient to describe the sandstone as a **sub-arkose**. The feldspars have been weathered to clay minerals, giving a buff appearance to the freshly exposed rock that develops a dark grey coating in time.

There is a distinct boundary within the upper part of the lower unit indicated by a basal ripple-laminated sandstone up to 0.2m thick, overlain by a poorly bedded (possibly with ripple structures) dark grey, poorly sorted, highly micaceous and carbonaceous, medium-grained sandstone with large plant fragments. This sandstone is best seen from the bench furthest from the gate.

The entire lower unit comprises an upward-fining sequence, which is terminated by a major change in sedimentation.

The uppermost 3m of the upper unit consist of a thick bed with thin gently inclined parallel bedding, which weathers to sandstone flags. The basal bed, 0.3 to 0.8m thick, is intensely burrowed and has an irregular base which is probably a consequence of shallow erosional scouring.

Leave the quarry at the far end and walk round above the eastern edge of the quarry face for a distance of 100m, in a NE direction, through heather, bilberry, gorse and bracken, typical of flora on upland acid soils.

Locality 3: Cocking Tor Edge (SK 344617). The escarpment edge will soon be reached where, from a graffiti covered bedding plane in the Ashover Grit, a magnificent panorama of the Ashover Anticline can be obtained. From here one gains a clear impression of the trend and morphology of the outcrops of the different rock types comprising the structure.

The first thing to note is the nearly vertical and impressive escarpment face, which gives way to progressively gentler vegetated slopes consisting of scree and head debris. The Ashover Grit is approximately 60m thick here and with the shallow dip of about 3 degrees.

Below the escarpment face is an area of low-lying ground occupied by Edale Shales that underlie the sandstone. Typically their outcrop is a poorly drained area but nevertheless provides reasonable quality grassland. Immediately below the escarpment are the quite extensive spoil heaps of the Gregory Mine (Locality 4). Across the low ground of the Edale Shales, Overton Hall (SK 346622) is located where the ground begins to rise once more and this is the dip slope of the Carboniferous Limestone on the western side of the Amber valley. Around Overton Hall the limestone outcrop is pock marked with grassed over spoil heaps of numerous small mineral workings. The central part of the Amber Valley is obscured from view by the extensive quarrying of the limestones near Fallgate (SK 353622).

To the NE of the River Amber Ashover village and particularly the spire of All Saints Church, which is built on the outcrop of the limestone, is clearly visible. Beyond and above the village an area of gentle sloping grassland represents the outcrop of the Edale Shales and rises to the Ashover Grit escarpment beyond with a small knob, Fabrick Rock (SK 358636), as a distinctive feature. These beds are on the NE side of the Ashover Anticline.

In the distance is the well populated, rolling country of the Coal Measures and on clear days the many power stations of the Trent Valley further east can be seen.

From this viewpoint walk along the escarpment edge to the SE for a few metres until it is possible to descend the escarpment (with care) on one of the ill-defined paths. At the bottom of the escarpment rabbit scrapes occasionally bring shale to the surface.

Continue descending along the bridleway at the foot of the escarpment in a northerly direction to Locality 4.

Locality 4: Gregory Mine Spoil Heaps (SK 345618). These extensive spoil heaps give evidence of a historically important mineral mining activity in the Ashover area.

The mineralization is confined to the Dinantian limestones that occur above the considerable thickness of volcanic tuffs. The mineral deposits are of hydrothermal origin with the main primary sulphide minerals being galena and sphalerite with subordinate pyrite and the gangue (non-metallic in this usage) minerals being fluorite, calcite, baryte and some quartz. There is an apparent zoning of the gangue minerals in the ore field of Derbyshire as a whole in that higher temperature minerals, such as fluorite, have crystallised freely in the eastern part (that includes Ashover) compared with the west. This is evidence that the mineralizing fluids were sourced from the east. It is now considered that the source was brine-rich fluids circulating at considerable depth in the mud-rocks of adjacent basins that subsequently migrated westward into the Dinantian limestones where a reducing environment caused precipitation of the dissolved minerals. It appears that the mineralization processes took place over a considerable period from late **Palaeozoic** into **Mesozoic** times.

Although the tips have been scoured by countless field parties it is still possible to collect some of the minerals. Sphalerite is quite common in little veinlets and is often associated with galena and fluorite. The fluorite varies from colourless varieties, often enclosing specks of pyrite to a very dark bluish-black, often enveloping pyrite. Calcite and barytes are less abundant.

Lead mining in the Ashover area has a long history. It reached its acme towards the latter part of the 18th century when records show that it was one of the most important lead mining areas of the Peak District. The Gregory Mine, however, closed at the turn of the 19th century and in 1856 the nearby Milltown Mine also closed. Since then, in spite of the resurrection of mining at Milltown in the 1910s and 1920s, most of the subsequent activity has been hillocking for lead and later for fluorite. In the 1950's considerable demand for fluorite led to opencast working at Fall Hill (Locality 11) for a short period.

Having satisfied appetites for mineral collecting, walk back to the bridleway that continues through the wood at the NW corner of the tip heaps. At the far end of the wood the ground is boggy where a spring issues out at the gritstone/shale boundary. Continue on the trail and cross the un-paved road that leads from Slack Hill to Overton Hall and then ascend the gentle dip slope of the limestone.

Locality 5: Outcrop of crinoidal limestones (SK 346625). At the top of the dip slope on both sides of the track there are small exposures of richly crinoidal limestone with occasional brachiopods. The rock is best seen in the floor where superb and unusually long still-articulated crinoid ossicles are visible.

Continue along the track and take the left hand footpath adjacent to the stone gate pillars that join Salters Lane and leads to the River Amber.

Note the seepage hollow to the right that is produced by a spring issuing from the base of the limestones.

Locality 6: Outcrops of volcanic tuff in the footpath and verges (SK 348626). These are small exposures and the tuff is better seen at Localities 8 and 10.

Continue along Salters Lane noting the sandy **alluvium** exposed in the banks of the River Amber downstream from the footbridge. Like many other anticlinal structures weathering and erosional processes have picked out the weakest strata exposed within the anticline core, the River Amber having excavated its valley along the long axis of this structure.

On the east side of the river Salters Lane ascends rapidly onto the limestones and into Ashover Village.

Leave the village on the B6036 in a NW direction and park vehicles after 1.1km on the wide part of the road immediately after the hairpin bend at Marsh

Brook Cottage. Above Marsh Brook Cottage a footpath leads from the main road down to Marsh Brook.

Locality 7: (SK 343634). In the bed of Marsh Brook stream and particularly in small river cliffs on the right bank highly fossiliferous dark grey marine Edale Shales are exposed. They are dipping at about 30° in a NE direction. The friable shales have yielded the **bivalves** *Canayella* sp. and *Dunbarella* sp. and the goniatite *Reticuloceras umbilicatum*, which indicate an R1 age for these shales. These are the lowest Namurian beds exposed although shales of the E and H zones have been proved in nearby boreholes.

Return to the road, descend to the hairpin bend and take the footpath to the southwest (right).

Locality 8: (SK 342633). About 130m along the track, two metres of well-bedded volcanic tuff are exposed dipping gently in a NNE direction. The tuffs are purplish-green in colour and vary in grain size considerably with the largest material formed of lapilli up to 5mm in diameter. The beds of tuff exhibit a fining-upwards grading.

Continue along the track cross the River Amber and enter Butts Quarry.

Locality 9: Butts Quarry (SK 341631). Dinantian limestones of the Monsal Dale and Eyam Limestone Formations are exposed in this quarry. The total thickness of the limestones, which dip at about 15° to the NW, is about 38m. The Eyam Limestones tend to be less massively bedded, darker in colour than the underlying massive grey limestones of the Monsal Dale Limestone. The former have yielded a wide range of fossils including crinoidal fragments, many brachiopods including gigantoproductids and rugose corals including *Lithostrotion* sp., *Diphyphyllum* sp. and *Lonsdaleia* sp.

Other features to note in the lower level of the quarry are abundant **stylolites**, much **chert** which forms numerous, almost continuous, bands and considerable fluorite mineralization along the many near-vertical joint planes.

At the upper level of the quarry in the southeast corner a fault with excellent **slickensides** and a very well-developed mineralized **fault breccia** can be seen adjacent to a small scree of fine debris. Mineralization along the fault plane is largely fluorite but strings of galena and occasional barytes can also be found.

The quarry also exhibits a number of exposed post-Carboniferous karstic solution features. At floor level in the southeast corner of the quarry the limestone is underlain by volcanic tuff. The boundary is gradational with volcanic fragments enclosed in the basal limestones that have been altered to a pale green colour and are clayey, though still preserving a gritty texture. The outcrop of the tuff is defined by the seepage of water at its junction with the limestone.

Leave the quarry and return to Ashover.

Locality 10: Hockley Quarry (SK 351627). From the Red Lion Inn at Ashover travel SE along Hockley Lane for a distance of 100m and park just beyond Leonard Wheatcroft cottage (last on left) which dates back to 1676. Obtain permission from the cottage before taking the adjacent track that leads to the disused

Hockley Quarry. The entrances are now overgrown so descend (with care) from the quarry floor, past the limekiln, to the cutting, which was formerly used to transport burnt lime to the road. The cutting shows Carboniferous Limestone resting upon 3m of purplish green volcanic tuff with fragments, up to 4cm in diameter, of limestone and igneous rocks, including vesicular basalt. There are many calcite veins, most of which appear to parallel the bedding. The uppermost beds have been altered to soft greenish smectitic clay, possibly by percolating ground waters. Although the underlying granular unweathered tuff appears porous, this weathered zone is impermeable and creates the spring-line at the base of the limestone outcrop.

Continue along Hockley Lane and park in the disused entrance to Hockley Quarry.

Locality 11: (SK 356624). Views over Fall Hill Quarry. Initially look across the River Amber and note the limestone outcrops, the change of slope and the seepage at the base of the limestone. It is impossible to gain access to the quarry that was reopened for the extraction of fluorite.

Then view the quarry before proceeding down the road to Ash Meadow Cottage. Take the footpath opposite which leads to the southern (or eastern) edge of the quarry. The mineralization in the quarry is partly associated with a fault that runs parallel to the road. The Carboniferous Limestone is downthrown to the south-west, and weathered volcanic tuff is exposed on the quarry floor on the upthrown side of the fault. The mineralization along this rake includes much excellent fluorite, galena, quartz, barytes and sphalerite.

Return to vehicles and continue in along the main road past the Nettle Inn (formerly the Greyhound Inn) (SK 358622). Turn left to the road signposted Littlemoor, which is located on steeply inclined Ashover Grit, and left again in the village towards Farhill. On the approach to Farhill, take the first right fork at the reservoir and park near the next road junction.

Locality 12: Fabrick Rock (SK 358637). This is an excellent vantage point to finish the excursion. The rock is formed of Ashover Grit which here dips at 30° to the NE and hence gives rise to a less steep escarpment face than is common locally. The outcrop provides a superb opportunity to study the three-dimensional character of cross-stratification. Weathering has enhanced the bedding planes that separate individual sets (depositional units) creating a flaggy, stepped appearance. Note the large and small scale **cross-stratification** with grain-size banding, the horizons rich in mica, and the abundance of coarse feldspar and quartz grains.

EXCURSION 6. THE EDALE SHALES AND ASHOVER GRIT OF THE ECCLESBOURNE VALLEY AND ALPORT HILL

Neil Aitkenhead & Ian Chisholm, British Geological Survey, Keyworth, Nottingham

Objectives

The purpose of the excursion is firstly to examine selected rocks in the Edale Shales, some characteristic and some unusual; and secondly, to study the contrasting fluvial and delta slope sandstones of the Ashover Grit.

Logistics

The excursion divides into two, an Edale Shales part (Localities 1 to 7) and an Ashover Grit part (Localities 8 to 10), each taking about half a day. All localities can be approached from the B5023 Duffield-Wirksworth road that follows the bottom of the Ecclesbourne valley (Figure 18). Access by car involves limited parking on roadside verges, and therefore car sharing or use of a minibus or coach would be advantageous. All the localities are on private land except for the summit of Alport Hill (or Height), which belongs to the National Trust.

The Edale Shales part involves about 3km of walking on footpaths and stream sections; dense undergrowth can be a problem in the summer months. Wellingtons are essential for full appreciation of the section at Locality 1 which involves wading across the normally shallow River Ecclesbourne. The Ashover Grit part involves about 2.7km of up- and down-hill walking around Alport Hill, mainly on footpaths and minor roads.

The appropriate maps for the area are: O.S. 1:50,000 Sheet 119, Buxton, Matlock and Dovedale; 1:25,000 Outdoor Leisure Sheet 24 (White Peak), and sheets 794 (Crich and Bullridge) and 811 (Belper); B.G.S. 1:50,000 Sheet 125 (Derby).

Geological background

Between Derby and Wirksworth, the broad valley of the River Ecclesbourne has been eroded into sedimentary rocks of Upper Carboniferous age, the Edale Shale Group and the overlying Millstone Grit Group. The rock succession has a total thickness of about 400m and was formed from sediments deposited in mid-Namurian times (late Arnsbergian (E2c) to early Marsdenian (R2c), approximately 318-328 million years ago). The area lay in the Widmerpool Gulf, a subsiding basin that had a general NW to SE alignment. The Edale Shales were deposited as muddy sediment from suspension, with subordinate beds of quartz sand carried by **turbidity currents** from distant basin-marginal areas. From time to time, world sea-levels rose, allowing free-swimming organisms, particularly **ammonoids** (or **goniatites**), to come into the area. Their remains were usually preserved in black mudstone to form beds known as **marine bands**. During deep burial, their fossilised

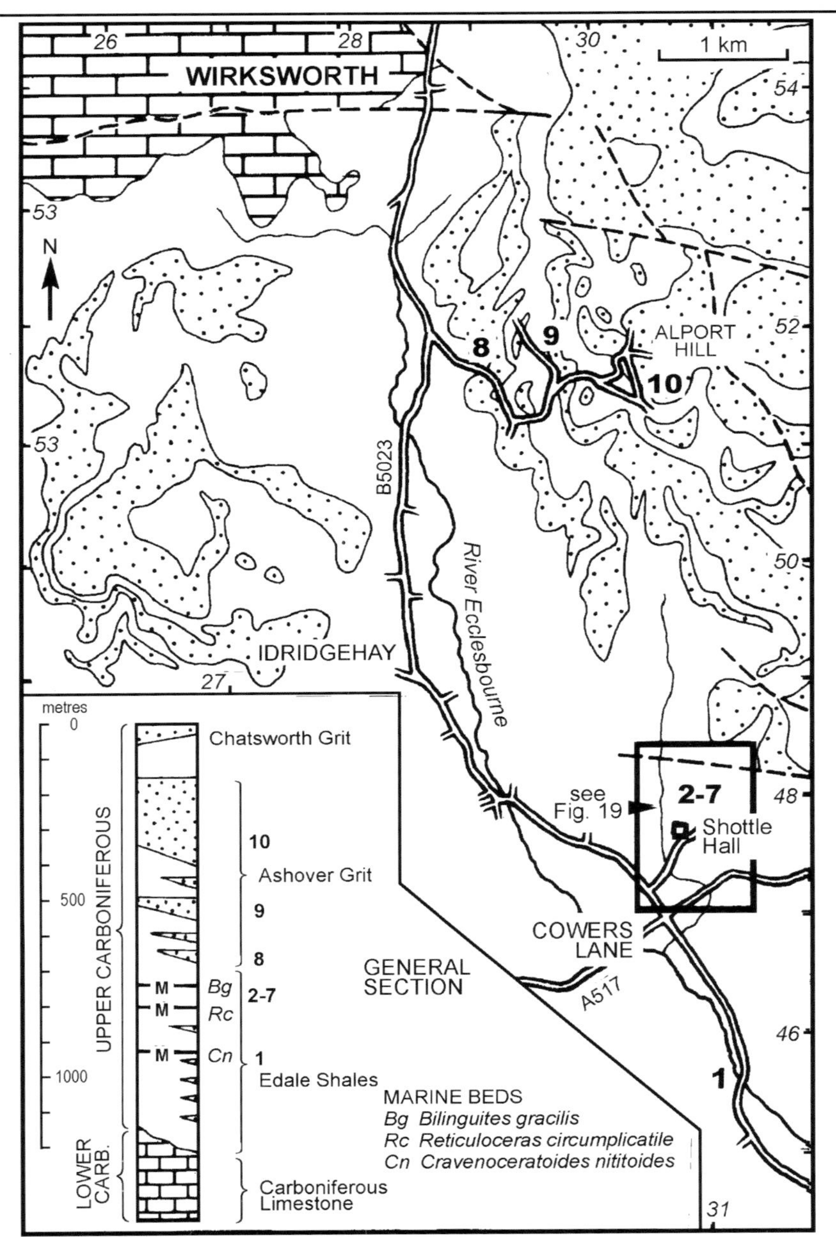

Figure 18. Outline geology of the Ecclesbourne valley and access road to the localities.

shells became flattened by the weight of thousands of metres of overlying rock, and they are usually found in this flattened state. In some marine bands, however, the shells are preserved in their original form in limestone concretions known as **bullions**. The Edale Shales include ammonoid-bearing marine bands at many levels, and several exposures of these can be seen at Localities 1 to 6.

During the course of Namurian time, a great **delta** intermittently extended south-westwards across what is now the Pennine region, eventually bringing thick spreads of coarse sand into this area. The first of these was to form the Ashover Grit. The lower beds of the Ashover Grit tend to be medium-grained and massive (unlaminated), and were probably deposited by turbidity currents on the sloping, unstable sea floor in front of the delta. In contrast, the higher beds are coarse-grained and **cross-bedded**, and were deposited by a large river flowing over the top of the delta. **Syn-sedimentary faulting** affected the Ashover Grit in areas nearby and may account for anomalous dips and truncation of sandstone features in the excursion area also.

The last major ice advance (**Devensian Stage**) of the **Quaternary** glaciations did not reach the Derby district, and the thin patches of till which partially mantle

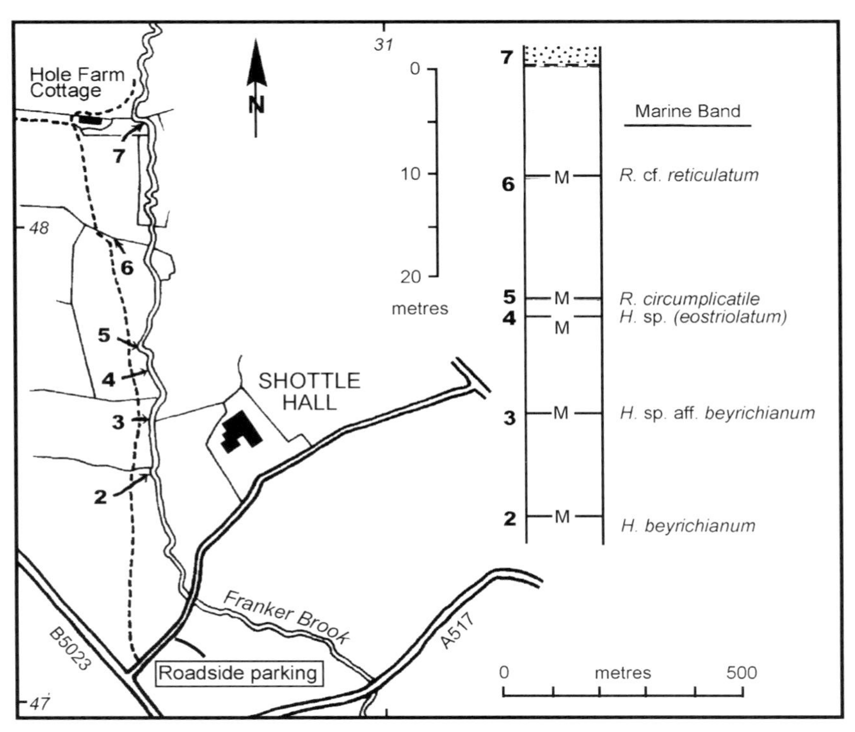

Figure 19. Map of the Franker Brook area showing access to Localities 2 to 7.

the slopes and **interfluves** around the Ecclesbourne valley represent the degraded remnants of an earlier ice advance. However, the ground was deeply frozen during the Devensian cold interval and subjected to various **frost heave** processes, which, in places, have produced **valley bulge** structures made evident by anomalous folding and steep dips.

Locality Details

Locality 1: (SK 31374555) is a meander scar on the north bank of the River Ecclesbourne, 130m downstream from the bridge where the B5023 crosses this small river. Approaching from Duffield (Figure 18), cross the railway bridge and take the 'hidden' farm road to the right about 50m north of the river bridge. There is limited parking at the side of the farm road near the junction. This is used by the Lubrizol Angling Club who have kindly indicated that they have no objection to the occasional geological party using it. The meander scar has to be approached from the south bank, which may be difficult after prolonged heavy rain. Coaches cannot be parked safely and should drop off their passengers on the straight stretch of road on the Duffield side of the railway bridge.

The scar is about 7m high but only the lowest 2m is safely accessible. It contains the *Cravenoceratoides nititoides* and *Nuculoceras stellarum* Marine Bands about 1.2m and 2.7m above the base, respectively. The lower marine band has a rock type unique in the Edale Shales: a pale grey, **decalcified**, cherty siltstone with black streaks running through it. A mass of this rock also forms a small island in the stream immediately in front of the scar. This is either the remains of a rock fall or an *in situ* exposure of the steeply dipping south limb of a minor asymmetrical anticline with an axis orientated approximately NW-SE. Being relatively tough compared with the adjacent ductile shales, this marine band is commonly folded and sheared, and in some places thrust-faulted as proved in the BGS Duffield Borehole, sited about 4km to the south. Fossil collecting is difficult at exposures like this but elsewhere the cherty band has yielded an extraordinarily rich fauna including **brachiopods, bivalves, gastropods, trilobites** and **crinoids**. These are all bottom-dwelling forms and they lived on the sea floor at a time when, for some reason not yet understood, mud and clay deposition was greatly reduced, and the sea must have been temporarily well-oxygenated. In addition, the fossil assemblage contains ammonoids that were free-swimming. Some 15cm above this marine band is a single lamina of soft, pale grey-brown to off-white clay 2-10mm thick. This is a **K-bentonite** (potassium bentonite) representing a fall of wind-blown volcanic ash or **tephra**. A strongly jointed or fractured decalcified carbonate bed, 5cm thick and some 0.85m above the K-bentonite clay, represents the *Nuculoceras stellarum* Marine Band. This has a more normal fauna of compressed ammonoids.

Continue north across the A517 and soon turn right on a minor road towards Shottle Hall. Localities 2 to 7 are all in or near the Franker Brook and are approached from a place (SK 30604726) about 450m SW of Shottle Hall (Figure 19). Cars can be parked at the side of the road here. A gate on the west side of the road leads into a field and Locality 2 is about 400m to the north, on the bed and west bank of the brook. Temporary electric fences may be encountered in places and should be crossed with care. The strata exposed in the Franker Brook have a general low dip to the ENE, with only minor reversals, so that successive exposures upstream are progressively younger. Access may be difficult in the summer because of dense undergrowth.

Locality 2: (SK 30594761). Some 2.5m of dark grey to black shaly mudstone are exposed here with well-displayed bullions. Flattened ammonoids are common in the shale and uncrushed specimens can be seen in loose limestone bullions. A good indication of the degree of burial compression that has taken place may be obtained by following sets of laminae from the shale into the bullions. This also shows how the carbonate-rich sediment must have become indurated or hardened into rock before burial compression took place, a process known as early **diagenesis**. The ammonoids *Homoceras beyrichianum* and *Isohomoceras* cf. *subglobosum* are indicative of the H1a Zone.

Locality 3*:* (SK 30574774). Hereabouts are small discontinuous exposures of contorted black shaly mudstone containing scattered bivalves and ammonoids of the H1b Zone. The contortions may have been caused by valley bulging.

Locality 4: (SK 30594782). This is another small exposure of dark grey mudstone that has yielded poorly preserved ammonoids, here indicative of the H2b Zone.

Locality 5: (SK 30564788). Here about 1.9m of dark grey mudstone with a bullion band are exposed. The fossil assemblage collected from these beds indicates that they belong to the R1a Zone.

Upstream from Locality 5, dense vegetation makes further progress difficult, and it is best to leave the brook and join the public footpath which runs parallel to it and about 20 to 30m to the west here (Figure 19). Proceed north along the path for about 230m to where it meets a footbridge that crosses a tributary stream, half hidden in the undergrowth. Don't cross the footbridge but turn right following the edge of the undergrowth for about 40m before approaching the stream and Locality 6.

Locality 6: (SK30514812). Here the stream has cut down into weathered dark grey shales, which have yielded another age-diagnostic ammonoid, *Reticuloceras reticulatum*, indicative of the R1c Zone. Some 48 km to the north, in Edale itself, several hundred metres of siltstones and sandstones of the Mam Tor Beds - Shale Grit - Kinderscout Grit sequence overlie the probable correlative of this marine band, but these beds are totally absent in this area. Some 1.5 million years later, however, the Millstone Grit river delta system did eventually bring huge quantities of sandy sediment to this area and the first traces of it are to be seen at Locality 7.

Return to the aforementioned footbridge, cross over the stream and follow the footpath north to Hole Farm Cottage ('The Hole' on OS maps). Here the path skirts round the west and north sides of the cottage and then leads, via a stile, to a footbridge over the Franker Brook. Continue straight on eastwards into a field, bearing

Figure 20. Alport Stone (Locality 10) displaying massive sandstone overlying cross-bedded sandstone. (BGS Photo No. L880, copyright NERC 1965.)

right to a gate that leads back to the brook and the last locality in this part of the excursion.

Locality 7: (SK 30574839). This is located at the bottom of the garden of 'Hole Farm Cottage', and visitors should therefore contact the owner (currently Mr. K C Wigley, telephone number 01773-550557) before their visit. The stream here exposes beds of rather muddy grey-brown sandstone with conspicuous large white mica flakes. Steep dips here are probably caused by mass movement (slumping) of the bedded sediment down the delta slope shortly after deposition.

After examining the beds at this locality the route should be retraced, using the public footpaths, back to vehicles. If refreshment is required after this first half of the excursion, then the small town of Wirksworth at the head of the Ecclesbourne valley provides an ample choice.

Locality 8: Vehicles should turn southeastwards at a junction about 2km south of Wirksworth (SK 286519) onto a fairly narrow lane signposted to Ashleyhay and Alport. About 800m up this lane, there is a wide-enough verge on the right for vehicles to park (SK 29255148). A disused hillside quarry (SK 29215175) is reached by walking down the lane and taking a public footpath leading off to the northwest just before a stone cottage and opposite a farm access road to Beighton Hill. The path immediately descends to a small marshy valley. From here, bear half left ascending gradually along the uphill side of an overgrown hedge on the left and below a steep gorse-covered slope (a sandstone scarp feature) on the right. After about 100m, the overgrown spoil heaps of a disused quarry will be seen on the right. The quarry exposes some 6m of fine-grained sandstone in thick, sharp-based beds 1.5 to 3m thick with parallel lamination in their finer-grained upper parts. These beds are interpreted as proximal **turbidites**, probably part of a lobe of such beds deposited on a delta slope. They dip at 10° to 20° into the hill, perhaps tilted back (relative to the near-horizontal regional dip) in the **rollover** of a syn-sedimentary **listric fault**.

After visiting Locality 8 there are three recommended options: (i) walk to Locality 9, return to the vehicles and then drive to the top of Alport Hill (Locality 10); (ii) walk to Locality 9, continue on foot to the top of Alport Hill (Locality 10) and then walk back down to the vehicles via minor roads (Figure 20); (iii) return directly to the vehicles and drive to the top of Alport Hill, missing out Locality 9. Allow about one hour for the first option and two and a half hours for the second.

To follow the first or second option, retrace the route from Locality 8 for about 100m as far as the small marshy valley and then turn sharp left up this valley where a well-defined track is soon joined to the left of a small stream. Follow this track for about 250m, to where it divides immediately beyond a stile and a gate. Take the right fork until it intersects a road called Taylor's Lane opposite a farm called New Buildings. The owner of the farm also owns the disused quarry at Locality 9.

Locality 9: (SK 29745181). Mr. Wiltshire (telephone number 01629 823191) wishes to be advised in advance of visits to his quarry that is situated at the top of the field above New Buildings farmhouse. Access is via a stile about 20m to the north of the farmhouse, and a gate through the lower side of the fence encircling the quarry. The quarry face is fortunately being preserved but some trees have recently been planted and, in order to avoid damaging these, close inspection of the face is not advised. From the bank opposite, about 6m of massive fine-grained sandstone are clearly visible in the quarry face. The top of the sandstone is partly obscured but appears to be sharp and irregular; the base is not exposed. At the north end the sandstone is overlain by 2m of shaly micaceous siltstone dipping about 16° to the north, but at the south end 1.5m of brown to grey mudstone rest on 2m of thinly bedded fine-grained sandstone on up to 0.8m of silty micaceous mudstone. A gap of about a metre with some disturbed (?faulted) siltstone separates these beds from the massive sandstone whose irregular sharp top dips at about 16° to the NW in contrast to the dip in the overlying beds (17° to the east). The detailed relationships in this quarry are difficult to explain, but deposition was probably on a delta slope. The massive sandstone is probably lenticular in cross section and may have been deposited in an incised channel that fed sand to turbidite lobes such as those represented by the beds seen at Locality 8. The overlying beds may represent general delta slope deposits between channels, and their eastward dip is probably related to **syn-sedimentary faulting** like that suggested for Locality 8.

From Locality 9, if taking the first option, return to the vehicles, either by the route just taken, or by an easier (but longer) route via Taylor's Lane and Mallinscommon Lane, and then drive to the car park at the top of Alport Hill, immediately above Locality 10. While travelling, note the peculiar lumpy discontinuous character of the topographical features produced by these delta-slope sandstones. This is likely to express both their lenticular nature and the effect of syn-sedimentary faulting.

If taking the second option, join a footpath off Taylor's Lane about 180m south of New Buildings, and ascend steeply to join a road (Mallinscommon Lane) leading eventually to Locality 10.

Locality 10: (SK 30425160) is the disused Alport Quarry in which there is a prominent pillar of undisturbed rock known as Alport Stone (Figure 20). This was presumably left by the quarrymen as a landmark, and perhaps a virility symbol, for posterity. The pillar also provides the best section hereabouts of the top leaf of the Ashover Grit (the 'Main Bed'). It comprises about 5m of massive coarse- to granule-grained sandstone with a few scattered pebbles up to 2cm in diameter, resting on similar sandstone forming a single cross-bedded set 2.4m thick. The massive sandstone probably occupies a former channel whose base appears to have been eroded into the underlying cross-bedded set, although the contact is mostly annealed and indistinct. Both sandstones were probably deposited in the channel of a large braided river, but under different flow conditions. The cross-bedded sand would have formed subaqueous dunes when the flow was steady, whereas the massive sand must have accumulated much more quickly, perhaps in the immediate aftermath of a large flood. The cross-bedding dip (to 332°) is consistent with the regional NW palaeocurrent direction.

The Alport Stone appears to be more severely weathered in its upper part than its lower part, suggesting that the upper part formed a tor on the hillside before the quarry existed. The main quarry face opposite the Alport Stone, consisting mainly of massive coarse-grained sandstone, is of interest for the large barytes crystals, up to 8cm long, coating the joint planes. Lead ore (galena) has been worked in the vicinity and the remains of a probable shaft and overgrown spoil heaps can still be seen adjacent to Mallinscommon Lane (SK 30285173), 190m NNW of Alport Stone. Proceed from here to the summit of Alport Hill (314m) owned by the National Trust to view the broader aspects of the surrounding geology.

To the west across the Ecclesbourne valley there is an irregular plateau with uneven scarp features formed by sandstones in the lower part of the Ashover Grit succession. Beyond this, one can just glimpse Carsington Water Reservoir in another valley eroded in Edale Shales flanked on its far side by rolling hills formed by interbedded limestones and shales of the underlying Widmerpool Formation of Dinantian age. This is the basin **facies** (deep water) equivalent of the shelf (shallow water) limestones of the Derbyshire Massif **carbonate platform** which forms the plateau visible to the north and NW. Part of the original (submarine) steep and embayed south-facing margin of the carbonate platform can be seen, with the hamlet of Hopton and the village of Carsington at its foot. Crags on the NW skyline are the dolomite tors of Harborough Rocks (379m). Beyond the town of Wirksworth to the NNW are several large limestone quarries. The most prominent face (in Middlepeak Quarry) shows the thick flat-lying beds of pale limestone which are so characteristic of the carbonate platform and so important to the scenery and economy of the Peak District. To the north, the escarpment of the Ashover Grit continues towards the Derwent valley at Cromford while below and to the left, the lower leaves form irregular subordinate features. The folly of Riber Castle picks out the escarpment on the east side of the Derwent valley. Beyond is a plateau formed mainly by the overlying Chatsworth Grit. The middle ground to the NE and east is formed by the generally eastward-inclined dip slope of the Ashover Grit. The dip slope forms the near side of a broad N-S **syncline**. The flattish axial hinge area of this is occupied by the River Derwent that flows north to south in a deeply incised valley below the line of sight. Beyond, the dip slope on the far side of the syncline rises towards the next major fold and inlier, the Crich Anticline, a much tighter (steeper-limbed) structure. The Carboniferous Limestone pushed up into its core is conspicuously visible to the NE in a quarry at the crest of this anticline. Views to the SE quadrant take in more distant areas including the southern part of the Derbyshire-Nottinghamshire Coalfield, and the Trent valley marked by the vapour plumes from Ratcliffe-on-Soar Power Station. Better defined, on the horizon slightly to the right, are the hills of Charnwood Forest, where the Precambrian **basement** of the region comes to the surface. Other more distant landmarks are indicated on a 'topograph' situated 50m south of the car park.

EXCURSION 7. THE UPPER CARBONIFEROUS SEQUENCE NEAR HOLYMOORSIDE, SOUTHWEST OF CHESTERFIELD

John Marriott, Brockwell, Chesterfield.

Objectives

This excursion examines geology of the Carboniferous Lower Coal Measures. In particular it will focus on how different lithologies of **deltaic cyclothems** have shaped the landscape and given rise to the traditional industries of the area.

Logistics

The excursion is a circular walk of 8 to 9km starting and finishing in Holymoorside, a village about 6km southwest of the centre of Chesterfield (Figure 21). It may be approached from several directions but the best route is via the A619 Chesterfield - Baslow road. Cars may be parked in the village hall car park (SK 338694) or on nearby roads. A public bus service operates from Chesterfield. Shops and public houses are available in the village, and the Red Lion Inn at Stone Edge is located at the halfway stage. The walk involves some gradients and fairly rough paths so strong footwear should be worn. In addition, warm clothing may be needed as parts of the walk are in exposed locations. A long half-day or a day should be allowed for the walk.

The Stone Edge Cupola can be viewed from a nearby footpath; permission for access should be obtained from Mr Paul R Marriott, a drilling-rig operator who lives at Spitewinter House on the A632 road.

The area is shown on O.S. Landranger 1:50,000 Sheet 119, and 1:25,000 outdoor Leisure Sheet 24 (White Peak Area) and on BGS 1:50,000 Sheet 112 (Chesterfield) and 6 inch to 1 mile map SK36NW.

Geological background

The Lower Coal Measures to the southwest of Chesterfield overlie the Millstone Grit and continue a similar sequence of interbedded sandstone, siltstone and shale including some thin coal seams and **seatearths**.

As the rocks dip in a northerly direction (Figures 21 & 23), their lithological features are reflected in the local topography with sandstone escarpments alternating with vales and benches marking the outcrop of softer **argillaceous** rocks. Landscape features are similar to those on the Millstone Grit but more subdued.

The Pot Clay Marine Band marks the base of the Coal Measures and is a black shale that represents a **marine transgression**. It contains marine fossils including the **goniatite** *Gastrioceras subcrenatum* and the **brachiopod** *Lingula*. The grain size of the sediments above the marine band coarsen-upward (reflecting a regression) passing from mudstone to siltstone then up to the Crawshaw Sandstone upon which lies the Belperlawn Coal developed on a seatearth. This succession consti-

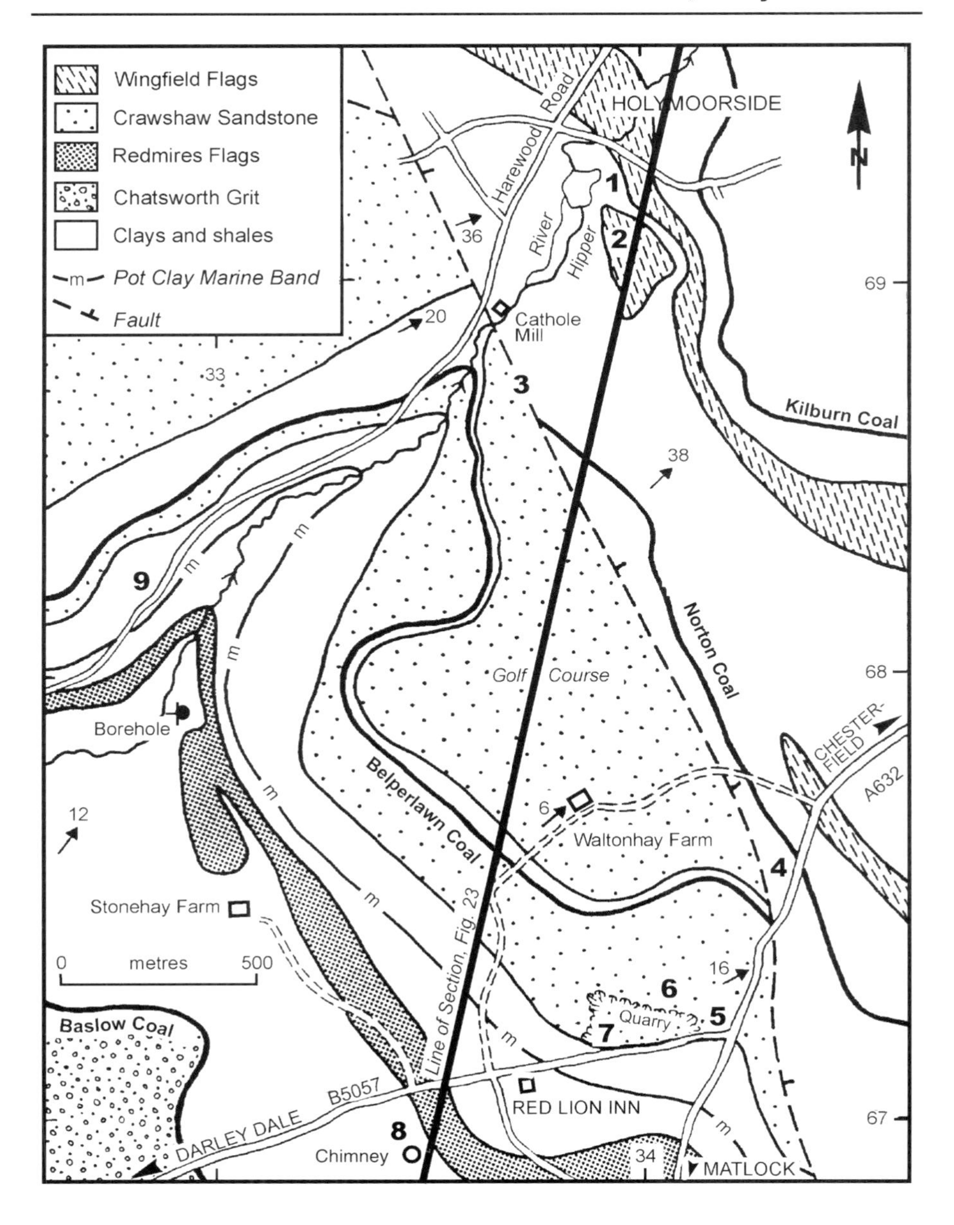

Figure 21. Geological map of the Holymoorside area showing the route and localities

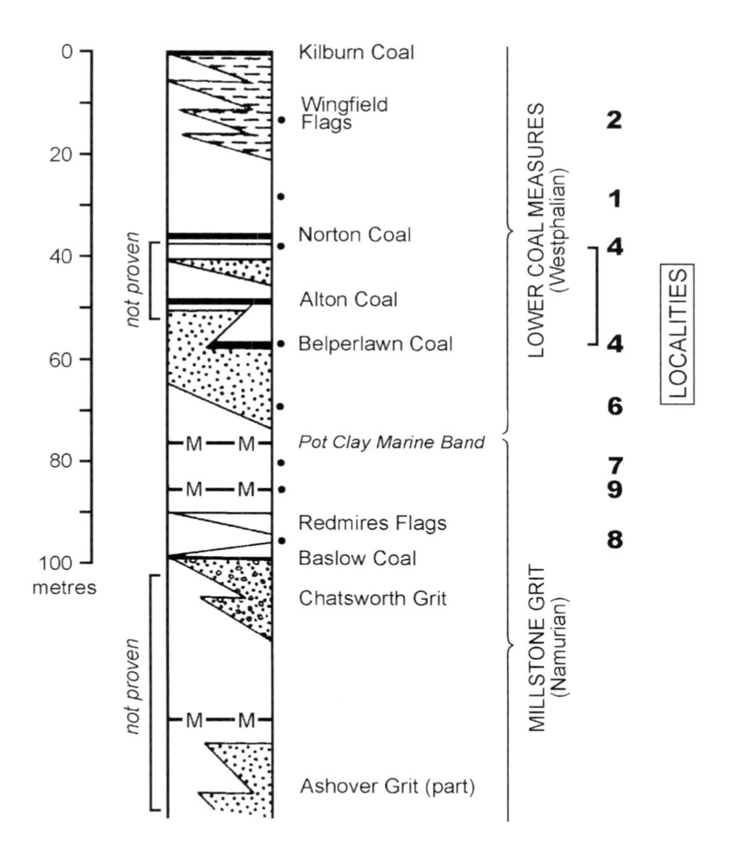

Figure 22. Upper Carboniferous succession in the excursion area.

tutes a cyclothem. Further evidence of repeated cyclothemic or **cyclic sedimentation** is present in the succeeding beds. The seatearths beneath the thin coals are either **ganister** or **fireclay** both of which have been of economic value in the past. Slump structures, lamination and **cross-bedding** occur within many of these beds.

Distinctive Coal Measures fossils including plant debris, non-marine bivalves (mussels), fish remains and brachiopods occur within the sequence. Figure 22 shows the stratigraphy of the area and the stratigraphical position of the succession examined at each locality.

Locality Details

Turn left from the village hall, proceed to the Bulls Head Inn and take the road signposted "Walton". Turn right onto the footpath beyond the United Reform Church and a house. The footpath reaches two stiles; take the left-hand stile. The

Figure 24. The Stone Edge Cupola, a former lead smelting site.

fault that is a continuation of the structure mentioned at Cathole Mill.

These workings occur above and below the outcrop of the Norton Coal. This horizon was extensively worked locally for the refractory seatearth, which underlies the seam. It is interesting to note that two other mines occur just north of the wood, the Sitwell Clay Mine, working ganister and fireclay, and the Stone Edge Clay Pit, working fireclay; these were abandoned in 1926 and 1927 respectively.

Continue downslope a short distance southeastwards towards the A632 road, to a narrow trench (SK 34326756) on the side of which a mudstone rests on a 0.15m coal smut (seam) above a seatearth, which in turn, passes down into a silty mudstone. This was probably the adit to the Slate Pit Mine in which a fireclay of 0.76m thickness and an unnamed coal seam with a thickness of 0.38m were worked. The mine was abandoned in 1895. Further shallow workings can again be seen a little up-slope from the adit. These occur above the Norton Seam and are parallel to its outcrop.

Walk down hill in a northeast direction, towards the corner of the wood, and exit onto the main road (A632).

Locality 5: (SK 342672) From a roadside location there is an excellent view eastwards across the exposed coalfield. Differential erosion has shaped a landscape where sandstones crop out to form the tops of discontinuous ridges. These result from the presence of lens-shaped beds that wedge out and pass laterally into weaker shales and mudstones. Often the older settlements, conspicuous by their churches, are located on the ridges.

The prominent east-west scarp at the edge of the valley, immediately north-east of the viewpoint, marks the outcrop of the Wingfield Flags. The tract of country beyond this has an approximately north-south grain.

Chesterfield is located in a south-southeasterly trending syncline, to the east of which is the Brimington-Heath **Anticline**, which has been drilled for oil in the past. Further east, the Permian Magnesian Limestone escarpment forms the horizon on which can be seen the town of Bolsover and its castle.

Locality 6: Stone Edge Plantation (SK 340673). The Crawshaw Sandstone, towards the base of the Coal Measures and a former source of building stone, is exposed in a 30m high quarry face, which has been excavated into a steep scarp feature. A house has been built into the overhang. Having a coarse to medium-grained texture, the sandstone has 'gritstone' features, being coarser than other Coal Measure Sandstones. Although massively bedded it reveals planar and cross-stratification, with plant material on some bedding planes. The upper face of the quarry shows very large irregular **concretions** resulting from patchy **sideritic cementation**. Oxidation of the iron carbonate and subsequent dissolution has resulted in residual brown-stained cavities. The section also shows **slickensides** associated with minor faults. Closer examination of the rock shows it to be a feldspathic sandstone, mostly quartz grains but with feldspar, clay and iron oxide minerals. Since feldspar readily weathers in hot wet conditions, this suggests that the original source rock may have been rapidly eroded from a relatively unweathered terrain and the debris quickly deposited and buried before further breakdown of the feldspar could take place.

Locality 7: (SK 337672). The low ground to the west and south of the Crawshaw Sandstone ridge marks the outcrop of argillaceous strata of basal Coal Measures and top Millstone Grit age. The base of the Crawshaw Sandstone is marked by a change of slope and a line of water seepage. The Pot Clay Marine Band, which defines the base of the Coal Measures, crops out in the central zone of this poorly drained clay vale, and passes immediately to the northeast of the Red Lion Inn. The sandstones of the Redmires Flags form the higher ground to the south and southeast. The poor agricultural potential of the land reflects the nature of the underlying strata particularly where there are superficial deposits of **head** containing boulders of sandstone set in a stiff clay matrix. Very large detached blocks of sandstone occur in the plateau area. A good example is the Toadstone rock, a toad-shaped sandstone block located opposite the Red Lion Inn, on the B5057 road. These blocks may result from glacial plucking from the escarpment and **solifluxion** processes.

Locality 8: The Stone Edge Cupola (SK 334669). A footpath runs through the site but permission to explore further should be obtained. This former lead smelting site, dating from at least 1770, is now designated an Ancient Monument. It has the oldest industrial chimney in Britain (Figure 24). Operations appear to have been terminated in 1860. It is located on the gritstone moorland about halfway between the lead-mining limestone areas to the west and the user markets, via Chesterfield. Its exposed position may have favoured the creation of up-drafts in the furnaces during smelting, and the dispersal of the poisonous fumes produced. Furthermore, wood and subsequently coal supplies were available locally. The nearby pond collected the drainage from the peat-covered moor to the south, and provided a constant source of waterpower for the bellows. Local names such as 'Pig of Lead', Belland (lead-poisoned ground) and Lead Lane testify to the former activity. Slag tips are present. Features of the complex site may be interpreted by referring to the recommended literature. Further information on the cupola may be obtained from the Peak District Mining Museum, Matlock Bath.

An outcrop of **boulder clay** occurs to the southwest of the site. The site has been built partly on the outcrop of the Millstone Grit. Traces of the younger Redmires Flags can be seen in the quarry face alongside the road. The view northwards from this locality follows the northeasterly dip slope of the Crawshaw Sandstone and the underlying Redmires Flags. To the northeast one can follow the steep apparent dip of the basal beds of the Lower Coal Measures down to the main valley in the Cathole area.

The Lower Coal Measures crop out on the steep northern slopes of the valley, the higher ground. Holymoor is founded on two leaves of the Crawshaw Sandstone.

Leaving the cupola site walk downhill, turn left past the Pig of Lead Cottage then right down the track to Stonehay Farm (SK 332674). The Pot Clay Marine Band and overlying Lower Coal Measures crop out to the right, as the track follows the dip slope of the Crawshaw Sandstone.

Follow the path through the woods noting the mini-landslip into the small tributary valley. The steep scarp slope on the other side of this valley marks the outcrop of the Redmires Flags. These dip more steeply than the gradient of the stream, and the basal sandstone can be seen a short distance downstream of the point where the path crosses the stream. Continue to the River Hipper valley where there is an abandoned waterworks (SK 32976698). Caution is necessary because several manhole covers to the deep storage tanks are missing. The works are located close to the point where the northerly dipping Chatsworth Grit passes beneath the alluvium giving rise to strong springs. The Millstone Grit Sandstones are major aquifers and a borehole at SK 329678 down to 142m once drew artesian water from the Chatsworth and underlying Ashover Grits, for public supply.

The Cathole section of the River Hipper valley has asymmetrical slopes due to the northerly inclination of the strata and orientation of the river, which flows eastwards along the **strike.** Having risen on the gritstone moor to the west, it is fast flowing and has deeply incised the soft rocks immediately above the Pot Clay Marine Bed, at the base of the Coal Measures (Figure 24).

After crossing the Hipper, walk up the former waterworks access road to the Harewood Road, turn left and proceed up the road for about 100m.

Locality 9: (SK 328683). There is ample evidence of slope instability in the form of landslipping and solifluxion in this steeply sided valley, where weak, incompetent shales are overlain by the highly porous and thick Crawshaw Sandstone.

The back scar of the main landslip can be clearly seen as the change in slope in the road at this point. Continuous movement is reflected in the repeatedly repaired road surface. On the way back, pause to look north to see the much-disturbed ground (hill and dale topography) resulting from the multiple break-up of the original landslip mass into subsidiary back-tilted blocks, which have been further degraded by mudflows.

Continue past the water works lane to the point where a small tributary stream is carried southwards in a culvert beneath the road. The area to the south of the road has been mined for clay to supply local potteries.

The source material extends from the Pot Clay Marine Band, which here has yielded specimens of *Gastrioceras subcrenatum* and is about 8m below the road surface, upwards to include the seatearth below the Belperlawn Coal. About 100m further down the road on the left there is an exposure of siltstones and shales, part of a gradual upward passage into the Crawshaw Sandstone, which forms the strong scarp above.

Continue along Harewood Road back to Holymoorside, noting the various quarries on the left where the Crawshaw Sandstone was worked in the past.

PART 3: THE PERMIAN TO MIDDLE JURASSIC GEOLOGICAL HISTORY OF THE EAST MIDLANDS

Andy Howard, British Geological Survey, Keyworth, Nottingham

The bedrock underlying most of Nottinghamshire, Leicestershire and adjacent parts of Lincolnshire is formed by strata of Permian to Middle Jurassic age, spanning a period of the Earth's history from 290 to 160 million years ago. The succession consists of sedimentary rocks deposited in a wide variety of environments and palaeogeographic settings with, generally speaking, the Permian and Triassic rocks originating in terrestrial environments and the Jurassic rocks being largely marine. These strata have provided not only the physical but also the economic foundations for the industrial growth of the East Midlands. In the past, virtually every formation has been exploited for some form of raw material to supply manufacturing and construction industries both locally and nationally. Today, however, only the quarrying of gypsum from the Mercia Mudstone Group remains of national importance. These quarrying activities have, however, left a legacy of good surface sections within these otherwise very poorly exposed formations. Former quarries, together with disused railway cuttings, provide most of the localities described in the following itineraries in this guide.

North of Nottingham, the Permian to Jurassic sequence is structurally very simple, dipping gently towards the east with only minor disturbance by faulting. The landscape of Nottinghamshire and adjacent parts of Lincolnshire is characterised by a series of dissected escarpments formed by gently-dipping, more resistant units, notably the Lower Magnesian Limestone, the Nottingham Castle Sandstone Formation, the Barnstone Limestone Member, the Marlstone Rock Bed and the Lincolnshire Limestone Formation. The intervening clay vales are formed by the less resistant mudstone units within the succession, such as the upper part of the Mercia Mudstone and the lower parts of the Lias. In Leicestershire, the dip is generally towards the southeast and the outcrop is more disturbed by faulting than to the north of Nottingham. The stratigraphical relationships at the base of the succession are also more complex, with Permian and Triassic sediments accumulating on a buried topography of Charnian and Carboniferous rocks.

In the late Carboniferous period (about 310 million years ago), continental drift and collision resulted in the assembly of all the world's continents into Pangaea, a single, huge supercontinent. During this period, the Variscan Orogeny, enormous forces of compression were generated as the continental plates collided, crumpling and fracturing the Earth's crust and throwing up vast ranges of mountains. One such range, the Variscan Mountains, extended from what is now southwest England through central France and southern Germany into Eastern Europe. North of the Variscan Mountains, the Carboniferous rocks were uplifted, weathered and denuded over a period lasting many millions of years, continuing well into the

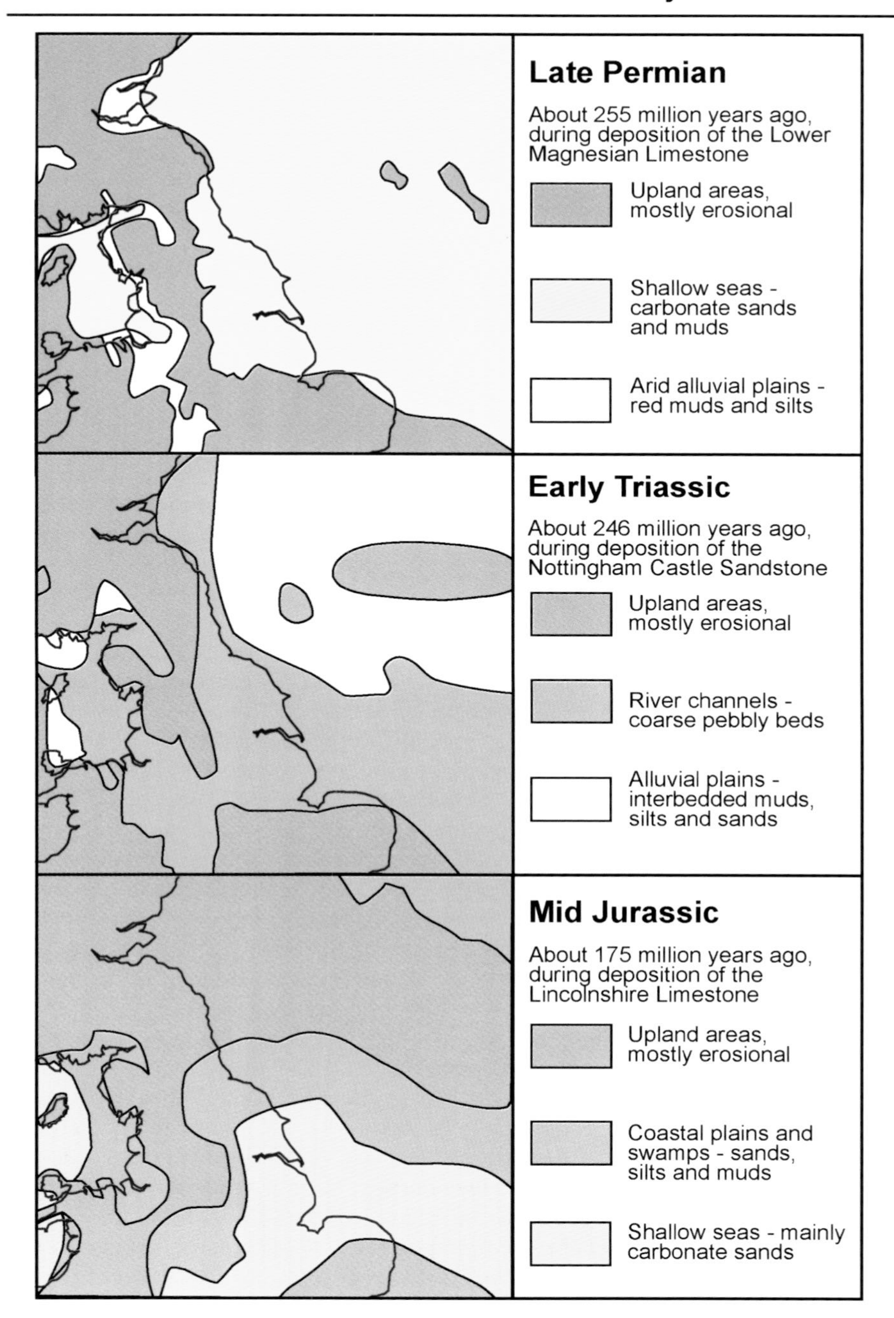
Late Permian
About 255 million years ago, during deposition of the Lower Magnesian Limestone
Upland areas, mostly erosional
Shallow seas - carbonate sands and muds
Arid alluvial plains - red muds and silts
Early Triassic
About 246 million years ago, during deposition of the Nottingham Castle Sandstone
Upland areas, mostly erosional
River channels - coarse pebbly beds
Alluvial plains - interbedded muds, silts and sands
Mid Jurassic
About 175 million years ago, during deposition of the Lincolnshire Limestone
Upland areas, mostly erosional
Coastal plains and swamps - sands, silts and muds
Shallow seas - mainly carbonate sands

early Permian period. By this time, about 290 million years ago, Pangaea was already showing signs of breaking up. The crust beneath much of northwest Europe started to thin and subside, and many fault-bounded basins or 'grabens' began to form, notably in the English Midlands. At the same time, a much larger subsiding basin, the 'Zechstein Basin', formed over much of northwest Europe. By about 270 million years ago, towards the end of the early Permian, most of this basin had subsided to well below sea level, but remained landlocked in the continental interior of Pangaea. The East Midlands lay on the southwestern edge of the Zechstein Basin and more or less on the equator, within a hot, stony desert underlain mainly by deep red-weathered, Carboniferous rocks.

At the beginning of the late Permian, about 265 million years ago, the Earth's climate began to warm up and the polar ice caps started to melt. Global sea-level rose and marine waters spilled into the interior of Pangaea from the north. The Zechstein Basin was flooded in just a few years, the blink of an eye in geological terms. The 'Zechstein Sea' extended as far south as Nottingham, and lagoonal silts (Permian Lower Marl) and then carbonate sand banks (Lower Magnesian Limestone) were deposited in its warm, well-agitated waters (Figure 25). The area to the south of Nottingham remained above sea-level and no marine Permian deposits are known. The Lower Magnesian Limestone of Nottinghamshire and Derbyshire was originally deposited as an oolitic lime sand, but was later replaced by dolomite due to reaction with alkaline, magnesium-rich groundwaters following retreat of the Zechstein Sea in later Permian times (Excursions 8 and 9). The Lower Magnesian Limestone now forms a prominent escarpment extending northwards from Nottingham, along the Derbyshire-Nottinghamshire border and into South Yorkshire. Neolithic Man occupied natural caves in the limestone at Creswell Crags. The dolomite rock (or dolostone) has long been prized as a building and ornamental stone of national importance and most remaining exposures, including those described in this Guide, are located in disused quarries.

Global sea-level continued to fluctuate during the late Permian, and the Zechstein Basin experienced at least five more major marine flooding events. Each flood was less extensive than its predecessor, so that the Basin gradually dried out as time progressed. Damp coastal and alluvial plain mudflats (Edlington Formation, Excursions 8 and 9) were succeeded by a sandy desert with aeolian dunes. These sands, now preserved as the Middle Permian Sands of north Nottinghamshire and the Lenton Sandstone Formation (Excursions 8 and 9) of the Nottingham area, were much prized as self-binding moulding sands for brass and iron foundries and, in the Worksop area, as a source of silica sand to support the local glass bottle industry.

By the early Triassic, 250 million years ago, northwards continental drift of Pangaea had resulted in a change to semi-arid climates over much of northwest

Figure 25 (page 68). Palaeogeography of central England and adjacent areas during Permian to Jurassic times (Adapted from Cope et al. 1992, and other sources).

Europe. Monsoonal rains fell on the Variscan Mountains, accelerating their erosion and feeding a major 'Triassic river' system that flowed northwards across southern and central England (Figure 25). This deposited thick sheets of fluvial sands and gravels over much of the English Midlands. During much of the early Triassic, the rivers drained northwards towards Cheshire and the Irish Sea but, from time to time, diverted northeastwards towards the East Midlands. Pebbly sands (Nottingham Castle Sandstone Formation, Excursion 9) spilled into the East Midlands. Finer grained sands and silts were carried farther northeastwards and deposited in Lincolnshire and Yorkshire, as the rivers flowed into a continental drainage basin occupying what is now the North Sea. The pebbly sands of the Nottingham Castle Sandstone Formation now underlie much of the western half of Nottinghamshire, the area once covered by Sherwood Forest. The outcrop forms gently rolling countryside with numerous dry valleys, with the thin, poorly drained soils exploited for arable farming and forestry. The sandstone itself has been extensively worked for aggregate and is a major aquifer, supplying between one third and one half of Nottinghamshire's water supply.

A phase of regional tectonic uplift towards the end of the Lower Triassic, 240 million years ago, disrupted the earlier river drainage patterns and ended deposition of pebbly fluvial sands in the Nottingham region. As the climate once again became more and more arid, alluvial plain and lacustrine sands, silts and muds (Sneinton and Radcliffe Formations, Excursion 9) gave way to saline mud and sandflats (Gunthorpe Formation, Excursion 9), with deposition mainly by accumulation of windblown dust punctuated by more rapid deposition by **flash floods**. The ancient rocks of Charnwood Forest, which formed **inselbergs** standing proud of the surrounding deserts and fluvial plains in early Triassic times, were finally buried by muds and silts in mid to late Triassic times. Aridity continued to increase during deposition of the upper formations in the Mercia Mudstone Group, leading to precipitation of **evaporitic** sulphate deposits. These sulphates, now preserved as gypsum, are of considerable economic value in the East Midlands and have been mined both at surface and underground in Leicestershire and Nottinghamshire. Most formations in the Mercia Mudstone Group have also been exploited for brick clay, with quarries still working at Ibstock in Leicestershire and Arnold near Nottingham.

In the late Triassic, about 210 million years ago, a global rise in sea-level resulted initially in the deposition of silts and muds in brackish water lakes (Blue Anchor Formation) followed by flooding of the region by the sea to deposit the marine and lagoonal mudstones of the Penarth Group. In the ensuing Lower Jurassic period, the region remained submerged under the sea for around 30 million years, while the fossiliferous mudstones, limestones and ironstones of the Lias Group (Excursion 10) were laid down. Limestones at the base of the Lias, once known as the Hydraulic Limestones (now Barnstone Member) have been exploited both as a source of lime and for hydraulic cement manufacture, but all quarrying in the region has now ceased.

The ironstones of the Marlstone Rock Formation have been both mined and quarried in Leicestershire and Lincolnshire as a source of iron ore, and have also been used as a distinctive, rust-coloured stone in older buildings in Leicestershire and Rutland.

The Middle Jurassic strata in Eastern England form a complex, inter-fingering succession of shallow marine, deltaic and estuarine sediments punctuated by a series of erosion surfaces, (Figure 25, Excursion 11). This complexity arose from major sea level fluctuations during the period, leading to a series of marine **regressions** and **transgressions**. These fluctuations were partly caused by global **eustasy**, supplemented by episodes of uplift associated with rifting and volcanism in the central North Sea. The first major sea-level fall took place at the beginning of mid-Jurassic times, resulting in the erosion of a substantial thickness of Lower Jurassic strata and deposition of a thin, condensed series of marginal marine, ferruginous sands (Northampton Sand Formation). As sea-level began to rise once more, marginal marine muds, silts and sands (Grantham Formation) deposited in deltaic and estuarine environments, gave way to shallow marine oolitic sandbanks and patch reefs (Lincolnshire Limestone). A second major regression later in the mid-Jurassic, at the boundary between the Bajocian and Bathonian stages, led to a repetition of this cycle of erosion and deposition. The erosion phase locally cut deep channels into the top of the Lincolnshire Limestone, and was again followed firstly by deposition of deltaic and estuarine muds, silts and sands (Rutland Formation) and then by shallow marine carbonate sands (Blisworth Limestone). Another regression led to deposition of the lagoonal, green and grey clays of the Blisworth Clay Formation. These contain an appreciable proportion of the clay mineral **smectite**, an alteration product of air-fall volcanic ash, possibly derived from contemporary volcanism in the central North Sea area. A major marine transgression then ushered in the deposition of the highly fossiliferous, nearshore marine deposits of the Cornbrash and Kellaways Formations.

The Lincolnshire Limestone has long been quarried in Lincolnshire for a variety of uses including building stone (the famous Ancaster Freestone), cement manufacture, crushed rock aggregate and agricultural lime. Other Middle Jurassic strata have been exploited on a smaller scale in the East Midlands, although the Northampton Sand Formation was formerly quarried extensively for iron ore in Northamptonshire. Silica sands within the Grantham Formation were once exploited on a small scale for manufacture of high-grade refractory products.

The Kellaways Formation represents the youngest Mesozoic strata described in this guide. Permian to Middle Jurassic strata were buried beneath substantial thicknesses of Upper Jurassic and Cretaceous sediments, including the Oxford Clay, Kimmeridge Clay and Chalk, most of which were deposited in open marine settings. The region was uplifted and eroded in the Cenozoic era, a process that is continuing at present. In the Palaeogene (65 to 25 million years before present), a drainage system of parallel, eastward flowing master rivers was converted, by the Neogene period (25 million years ago), into a trellised pattern of major northward flowing rivers and minor eastward and westward flowing streams. This drainage system, modified in response to glacial advances and sea-level fluctuations in the **Quaternary,** has produced the familiar, scarp and vale topography we see today.

EXCURSION 8. THE PERMO-TRIAS OF NORTH NOTTINGHAMSHIRE

R. Toynton. School of Education, The Institute for Lifelong Learning, University of Sheffield.

Objectives

The objective of this itinerary is to examine the Permo-Triassic rocks in north Nottinghamshire to demonstrate the nature of the stratigraphic succession. Variations within this succession between the north and south of the area can be shown, as can the way in which evidence given by the rocks, in the absence of fossils, can be used to interpret the palaeoenvironmental conditions.

Logistics

The itinerary is designed for use with a car, though at Localities 7 and 8 a circular walk of around 3km is more appropriate, and at Locality 9 a similar length walk can be included if desired. From the starting point at the Visitors Centre, Creswell Crags (SK 538744), the itinerary (Figure 26) progresses eastwards up through the succession viewing exposures in the north of the area, and then returns down through the succession, looking at other stratigraphic levels, and at differences in lithologies and palaeoenvironments further south. The whole itinerary is possible within one long field day. All of the sites have free access.

The itinerary falls within the O. S. 1:50,000 Sheet 120 (Mansfield, Worksop and surrounding area), but is divided between four One Inch British Geological Survey maps: Sheets 100 (Sheffield), 101 (East Retford), 112 (Chesterfield) and 113 (Ollerton).

Geological background

The Permian and Triassic within north Nottinghamshire was a time of both erosion and deposition, of deserts and coastal plains, and of a sea (the Zechstein Sea of the Permian) expanding and shrinking in response to climatic conditions and global sea-levels. At times this sea extended across the area, with carbonate deposition in the shallower water, at other times it shrank away to the east leaving evaporite deposits in its wake. The sedimentary succession within this area is not uniform in lithology when traced laterally. Contemporaneous deposits vary in character (facies) from place to place. The evolving geography influenced the occurrence and nature of the material being deposited.

This itinerary progresses up through the succession in the northern part of the area, and then back down through the succession slightly further south (Figure 27). This illustrates the changes in the lithologies, and thereby through interpretation, of the environments, both through time and across the area at the same time.

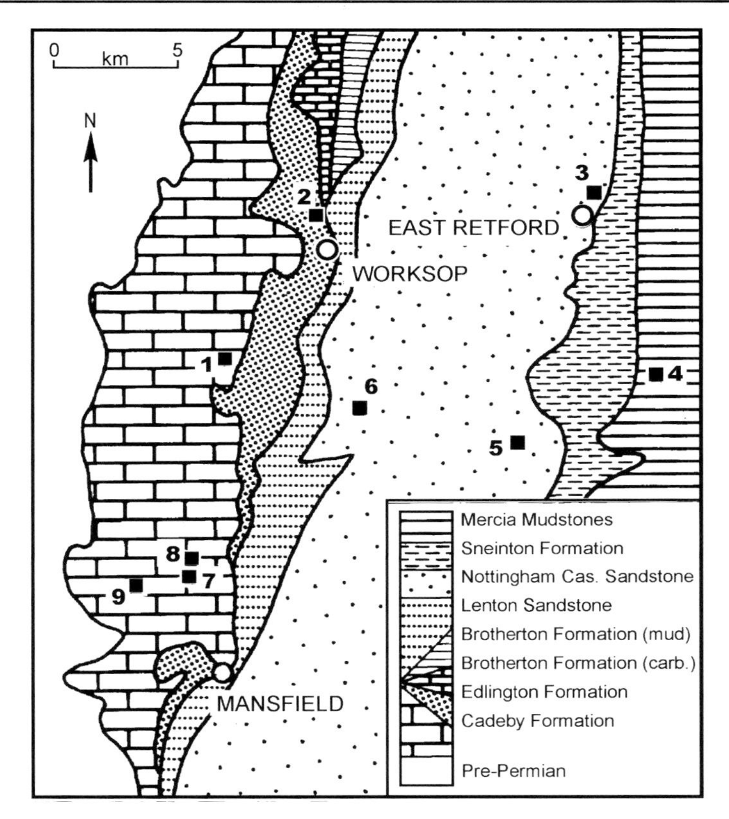

Figure 26. Location of Permo-Trias sites of north Nottinghamshire.

Locality Details

Locality 1: Creswell Crags (SK 538744). This is a site of great archaeological importance. The crags also provide spectacular exposures of the higher levels of the dolomitic limestone, which forms the carbonate facies of the Cadeby Formation.

The original calcareous sediment was deposited in the shallow marginal waters of the Zechstein Basin during periods when it was flooded with seawater. At other times, cut off from the world's oceans, the sea shrank back towards the centre of the basin and, as the desiccation of the basin progressed, evaporite minerals were deposited. During these periods of drying out, the remaining seawater would become hypersaline. With fluctuating levels of the sea, highly saline sea- and ground waters percolating through relatively recently deposited calcareous sediment resulted in the dolomitization of the calcite.

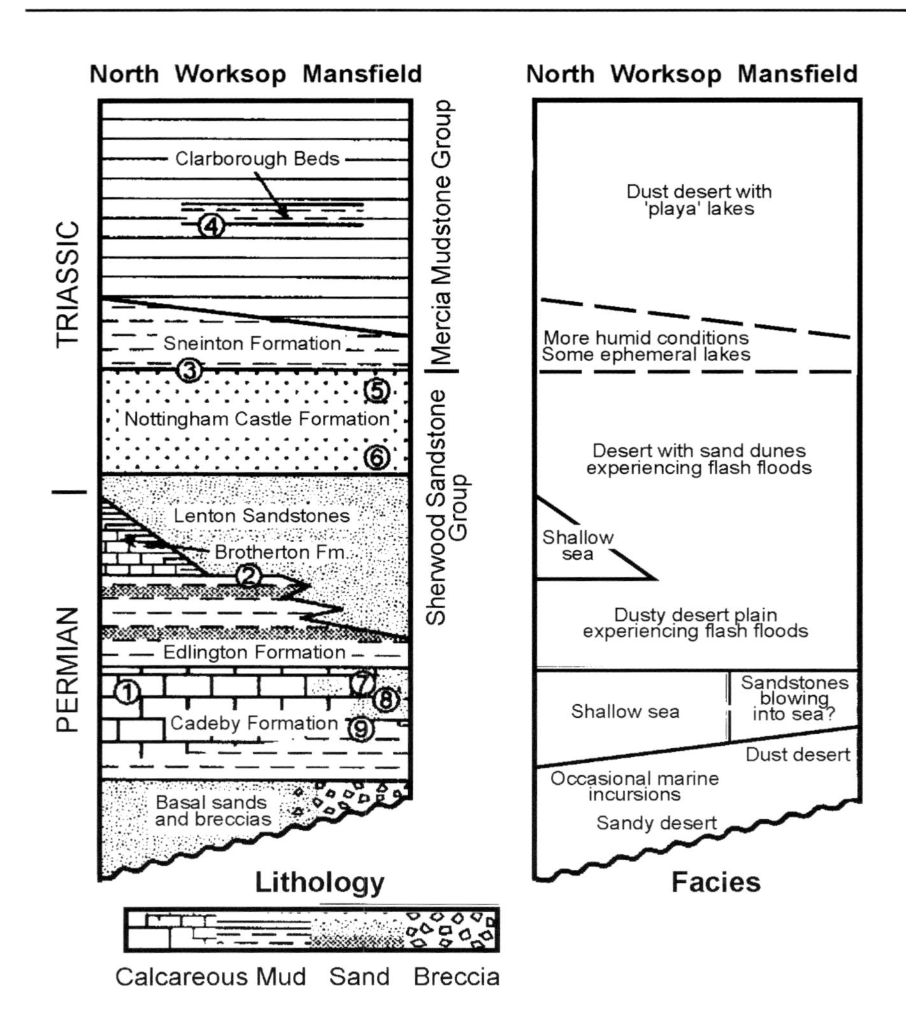

Figure 27. Stratigraphic succession, lithology and facies in the Permo-Triassic of north Nottinghamshire.

From the car park follow the path 'to the crags'; the view on reaching the lake shows massively bedded dolomites dipping gently eastwards. All of the features within the dolomites can be illustrated in the crags to the left of the lake.

By Boat House Cave, the massive hard crystalline dolomite typical of the upper part of the carbonate facies of the Cadeby Formation can be examined. The rock has a saccharoidal (sugar-like) texture owing to the presence of rhombic dolomite crystals. In the bluff just beyond this cave, two other features typical of this level are seen. Large-scale **cross-stratification** suggests deposition in high energy conditions in shallow water close to the margins of the sea.

Small **vugs** (bubble-like voids) occur within the rock. These might have formed by the dissolving of evaporite minerals which replaced some of the original carbonate at an early stage of **diagenesis**. The vugs may also be linked to dolomitization, during which the volume of individual calcite minerals in the original sediment is reduced by 12 per cent allowing voids and/or replacement by evaporites to occur. Further along they become very common at particular levels. Some have a 'keyhole' shape due to the flow of water through connecting vugs.

Stylolites also occur here. These are subhorizontal surfaces within the rock, giving a further false impression of bedding in many places. They are distinguishable from planes of sedimentation by the jagged nature of the surfaces. The name refers to protruding 'styli' or vertically striated pillars, though here they are not very sharp. The smaller scale and much more jagged microstylolites present are often marked by a clay traces representing surfaces of solution and impurity concentration, caused by the disssolution of the dolomite under pressure.

There are several other gorges similar to this one at Cresswell Crags on the dip slope of the Cadeby Formation. Some streams, e.g. the River Meden, flow through the escarpment and then occupy steep-sided valleys such as Pleasley Vale (SK 520650). There is no agreement on the origin of these features, but possibilities include: 1) erosion by overflow streams from glacial Lake Humber, though there is no evidence of **glacio-lacustrine** deposits locally and the known lake levels of this feature are much lower; 2) origin as sub-glacial meltwater channels during the **Wolstonian** Glaciation, but there is no evidence locally of this event; 3) fluvial erosion either throughout the **Pleistocene** Epoch (the last 1.8 million years) or during the final stages of that epoch, which is difficult to prove, but there is some evidence of superimposed drainage; and 4) the exhumation of a buried dissected **karstic** drainage system developed on the Cadeby Formation soon after deposition in late Permian times, and exhumed during the Tertiary and **Quaternary** Periods, with enlargement of the gorge and cave system. Although there is evidence of post-Cadeby Formation channelling, there is no evidence of fissure deposits or extensive karst features at that time.

The excursion could include a visit to the caves, of which Robin Hood's Cave is open to the public.

Turn right out of the car park. In Creswell, turn left on the A60 towards Worksop. At the Worksop by-pass take the A57 towards Sheffield. Three roundabouts later take the third exit marked B6041 Kilton. Take the second right, Kingfisher Walk, and park at the end of the road.

Locality 2: Gateford old sand pit (SK 574812). Two exposures remain in this largely restored sand pit. The first is to the left, towards the top of the bank close to some new houses.

The lower exposure reveals grey-green sand and silty sand of the Edlington Formation. Pebbles, many of them quartzose, up to 10cm long occur within layers in the sand, though do not form continuous bands. There are also small discontinuous bands of deep red clay, in some instances very noticeably disturbed, probably by loading by further influxes of sediment.

The overlying Lenton Sandstone Formation is exposed near the top of the bank, near some new houses. It comprises strongly cross-stratified red sandstone. North of Worksop these formations are separated by the Brotherton Formation (Upper Magnesian Limestone), which thickens northwards, where it consists of mudstones with an upper dolomite. Its absence at Gateford indicates that the second **transgression** of the Zechstein Sea halted to the north and east of this locality.

The cross-bedding appears fluvial, with these beds representing the silting-up of the first phase of the Zechstein Sea as the sands were washed into the marginal area by **flash floods**. The thin red clays represent finer material collected in shallow hollows where water remained for a little longer.

Return to the Worksop by-pass, turn left and follow signs to Retford (A57(T), A1 and A620). In Retford keep to the A620 Gainsborough road. After the traffic lights, and just beyond 'The Brick and Tile Inn' turn left into Bolham Lane. The section is about 100m on, with plenty of parking space.

Locality 3: Bolham Lane, Retford (SK 707821). The uppermost part of the Nottingham Castle Sandstone is exposed here. The red sandstone is strongly cross-bedded, though no distinct channel margins can be seen. The sand is highly **micaceous,** and pebbles are rare. An example of a solitary pebble can be seen to the right of the section about 1.7m up. Red clay bands are rare.

There is an upward transition into the Sneinton Formation which here consists of green- and red-banded silty mudstones. This lithology contrasts with the predominantly sandstone character of the formation at Nottingham. Elsewhere in this itinerary the green colour is patchy and commonly associated with the development of reducing conditions around plant debris. Here, the apparent absence of such debris at this particular location suggests reducing conditions resulting from the movement of pore-water through the sediment.

The Nottingham Castle Sandstone was deposited by fluvial sheet-flow in a desert lowland environment. The infrequency of pebbles in the formation reflects the increasing distance from the source area. The recording of plant remains in the Sneinton Formation here, which probably accumulated in ephemeral lakes, is evidence of more humid conditions. The rainfall necessary for plant-growth probably derived from the **Muschelkalk** Sea which at this time covered part of northern and central England.

Return to the A620(A638) and turn right, back to the traffic lights, and turn left on the Newark/Lincoln road. Follow this road to its junction with the A1 at Markham Moor. Take the first exit (A57 Lincoln) and park in the unmade lay-by about 100m beyond on the left. The site is on the same side of the road towards the top of the hill. There is nowhere to park safely further up. There is a pavement.

Locality 4: Markham Moor road cutting (SK 726737). Towards the top of the hill there are exposures in the Mercia Mudstone Group on the left side of the road either side of a walled section. Downhill from the wall the rock is dark red mudstone with only very occasional greenish patches. It is intersected by a series of sub-horizontal anastamosing bands of gypsum in its 'satin spar' habit. On closer inspection, crystalline gypsum **cements** much of the mudstone, making it particularly hard.

Uphill of the wall the rock has the grey-green and red striped appearance more typical of the Edwalton Formation of the Mercia Mudstone. Again, the satin spar gypsum forms layers up to 6cm thick. Some of the green beds consist of well-cemented sand forming laterally persistent beds, or **skerries**. The increase in skerries and the widespread gypsum at this level distinguish these as the 'Clarborough Beds', which may be equivalent to the Hollygate Sandstone Member of the Nottingham district. The greater resistance to weathering thus imparted has formed an escarpment, which can be seen clearly from the crest of the hill to run in a north-south direction. The mudstones represent sediment transported by flash floods and wind, deposited in hot and dry (evaporitic) conditions in ephemeral **playa lakes.** The skerries represent sheets of coarse sand swept into the area by flash-floods.

Return to the Markham Moor roundabout and take the third exit onto the B6387 (left at the Little Chef), to Milton and Walesby. At the main road in Walesby turn left and then right by the 'Carpenters Arms'. About 1.6km beyond, having passed through woodland, the road turns sharp right and then sharp left. On this last corner there is parking to the right of the road.

Locality 5: Robin Hood's Cave, Walesby (car park SK 665702 / locality SK 664708). Follow the path straight ahead from the car park for 400m. Just after passing under the electricity wires there is an unvegetated area off to the left. At this locality the upper part of the Nottingham Castle Sandstone is exposed on a bare surface above and also in the face of a cliff, adjacent to the River Maun. In the face of the cliff the light pink sandstone displays impressive cross-bedding. Pebbles are scattered throughout, but are more common at certain levels. These form lag deposits at the base of channels or on **foresets** within fluvial bars.

In one of the higher parts of the face patches, wedges and spots of green sandstone occur. On the steep steps to the right of the exposure (when facing the river) these patches are connected by beds containing slightly eroded angular sandstone fragments that were cemented before being eroded and incorporated into this deposit. Two pebble-rich bands are also traceable here.

Descending the steep chasm to the left of the exposure, and turning right, it is possible at normal river flow to reach the cave. Here, there is a distinct pebble band about 2m above river-level, with the pebbles supported within the sand matrix. The green **reduction spots** stand out throughout much of the section as hardened spheres. To the right in the front of the cave, mudstone fragments, up to 11cm long, are incorporated into the sandstone. The presence of clay and indurated sandstone fragments indicate erosion and redeposition of older sediment by a torrential current, possibly during a flash flood.

Continue to the A614 and turn right. Ignore the Perlethorpe turn, but take the next left to Thoresby. Continue to the B6034, and turn right towards Worksop. At Carburton turn left for Norton and Cuckney. After 2km the road goes through a low cutting. Just beyond, there is parking on the right.

Locality 6: Corunna Hill Plantation; a road cutting approximately 2km east of Norton along a minor road (SK 591722). The exposed section is lower in the Nottingham Castle Sandstone than Locality 5. To the south of the road there are two pebble beds within the sand. The upper contains pebbles up to 8cm long and the bed thickens markedly eastwards. These are gravels deposited by flash floods near the margins of a desert basin.

Well-rounded pebbles of locally derived Carboniferous limestone, sandstone and Permian dolomites are present. In addition a further-travelled suite of pebbles has been recorded derived from Devonian **quartzites** and lower **Palaeozoic** calcareous sediments, some of the latter containing fossils.

Continue to Cuckney. At the first main road (A616), turn right, and then turn left on the A60 towards Mansfield. At Church Warsop take the right turn (B6031) to Shirebrook. Continue through Shirebrook on the B6407 towards Pleasley. Just before Pleasley turn left for Pleasley Vale Business Park. Follow this lane for 800m and park in the car park to the right of the road.

Locality 7: Pleasley Vale disused railway cutting (Car park SK 510649 / locality SK 520649). Take the footpath eastwards from the car park, parallel to the lane. Follow this down and across the river. Then take the path up the slope rather than following the River Meden. This emerges onto the disused railway. Turn left and continue to the cutting. The first part is overgrown with poor exposures, but towards the bridge there are good exposures to both sides.

The rock resembles the dolomitic limestone seen at Creswell Crags, including relatively massive beds, large scale cross-stratification and stylolites. However, the rock here is a sandy dolomite, with many quartz and some feldspar grains. Stylolites and **flowstones** are present to both sides of the track on approaching the bridge, but vugs are very scarce. Faults with **fault breccias** are common, again on both sides of the track, with some angular blocks being over a metre across.

In this southern area of outcrop of the carbonate facies of the Cadeby Formation, horizons containing significant amounts of quartz and feldspar are found at several localities. Even further south, outside the area of this itinerary, littoral facies with large amounts of sand and quartz pebbles occur, while at Bulwell at one horizon up to 20% by volume of the dolomite comprises quartz and feldspar grains. This is interpreted as material washed or blown seawards from the shoreline by storm action. The sandy dolomites in Pleasley Vale may similarly indicate that the shoreline was not far distant.

Continue along the disused railway to the road. Turn left and then take the left fork, passing to the left of the row of cottages. A few metres beyond, there is an exposure on the left, behind another group of cottages.

Locality 8: Meadow Houses, Pleasley Vale (SK 520650). The Lower cadeby Formation (Upper Permian) exposed here comprises pale yellow dolomite, which rests with a sharp horizontal boundary upon a friable red sandy rock with quartz and feldspar grains. The red colour comes from haematite, which impregnates the carbonate, and coats the other detrital grains. The red sand rock is very localized and passes laterally into pale dolomite within 40m. Its origin is unknown.

Continue into the bottom of Pleasley Vale, turn left and follow the road to the car park. Note the roadside exposures of typical pale yellow and pink dolomite. Return to the main road, turn left and take the second exit at the roundabout, into Pleasley village. After 430m take the right turn to Teversal and Skegby. Once out of the village, take the next right, Batley Lane. Park on the left, about 430m up the lane, just before the railway bridge.

Locality 9: Pleasley to Teversal disused railway cuttings. (SK 494640 to SK 481625). Walk under the first bridge and turn left through the green barrier, and then turn left and left again onto the old railway line. Continue northeast into a wide cutting.

The exposed dolomites are close to the base of the Cadeby Formation. The dolomite is composed of granular dolomite crystals with numerous small rounded quartz grains. Thin red **marl** layers also occur, and there is some red staining of the dolomite. Vugs are scarce, but visible high on the south side of the cutting. In contrast with the stratigraphically higher dolomites of Creswell Crags, the rocks here are thinly bedded. Cross-stratification, though no less common, is on a smaller scale, and contains some channel features. Stylolites are common.

Return along the cutting but continue across the bridge and over the embankment to the next cutting. A series of small outcrops show increasingly silty dolomite, in places very thinly bedded. Red and green marl partings appear between many of the beds, and stain the dolomite. Since the exposed rocks are progressively lower in the sequence, and therefore older, you are passing down through the upward transition from the mud facies (formerly Lower Permian Marl) to the carbonate facies of the Cadeby Formation. This represents the gradual establishment of carbonate deposition in the shallow margins of the transgressive Zechstein Sea.

EXCURSION 9. THE PERMO-TRIASSIC ROCKS OF NOTTINGHAM

Andy Howard, British Geological Survey, Keyworth, Nottingham

Objectives

To demonstrate the various Permian and Triassic sedimentary rocks exposed in the Nottingham area and describe their stratigraphy and environments of deposition.

Logistics

The localities are widely separated and best treated as individual mini-excursions, allowing 1 to 2 hours for each site. All lie adjacent to public rights of way and within short walking distances of current bus routes. A stout pair of shoes will suffice for Localities 1, 2 and 3, but walking boots or wellingtons are more suited for Localities 4, 5 and 6. Hard hats should be worn at Locality 5. Locality 5 is a Site of Special Scientific Interest (SSSI) and the remainder are classified as Regionally Import Geological Sites (RIGS). They should not be hammered.

The geology of Nottingham is covered by the BGS 1:50,000 series Sheets 125 (Derby) and 126 (Nottingham). The BGS memoir for the Nottingham sheet is in press; that for the Derby sheet was published in 1979. Nottingham is included on the OS 1:50,000 Landranger Series Sheet 129. Street plans and guides of Nottingham are useful for locating individual sites.

Geological Background

The city of Nottingham owes much of its prosperity to the valuable mineral and groundwater resources obtained from the underlying Permian and Triassic rocks. Almost every formation within the Permo-Trias has been exploited to provide the raw material for one or other form of local industry, and has thus made its own important contribution to the economic development of the region. Though largely unfossiliferous, these rocks display considerable variety and provide a fascinating record of the environments and climates of the region during Permo-Triassic times, between 300 and 200 million years ago. This itinerary describes some of the best and most well known exposures of these rocks in the Nottingham area and provides an introduction to the local geological history during the Permo-Trias.

A generalised section showing the stratigraphy of the Permo-Triassic rocks of Nottingham is given in Figure 28, and a simplified geological map of Nottingham showing each locality is illustrated by Figure 29.

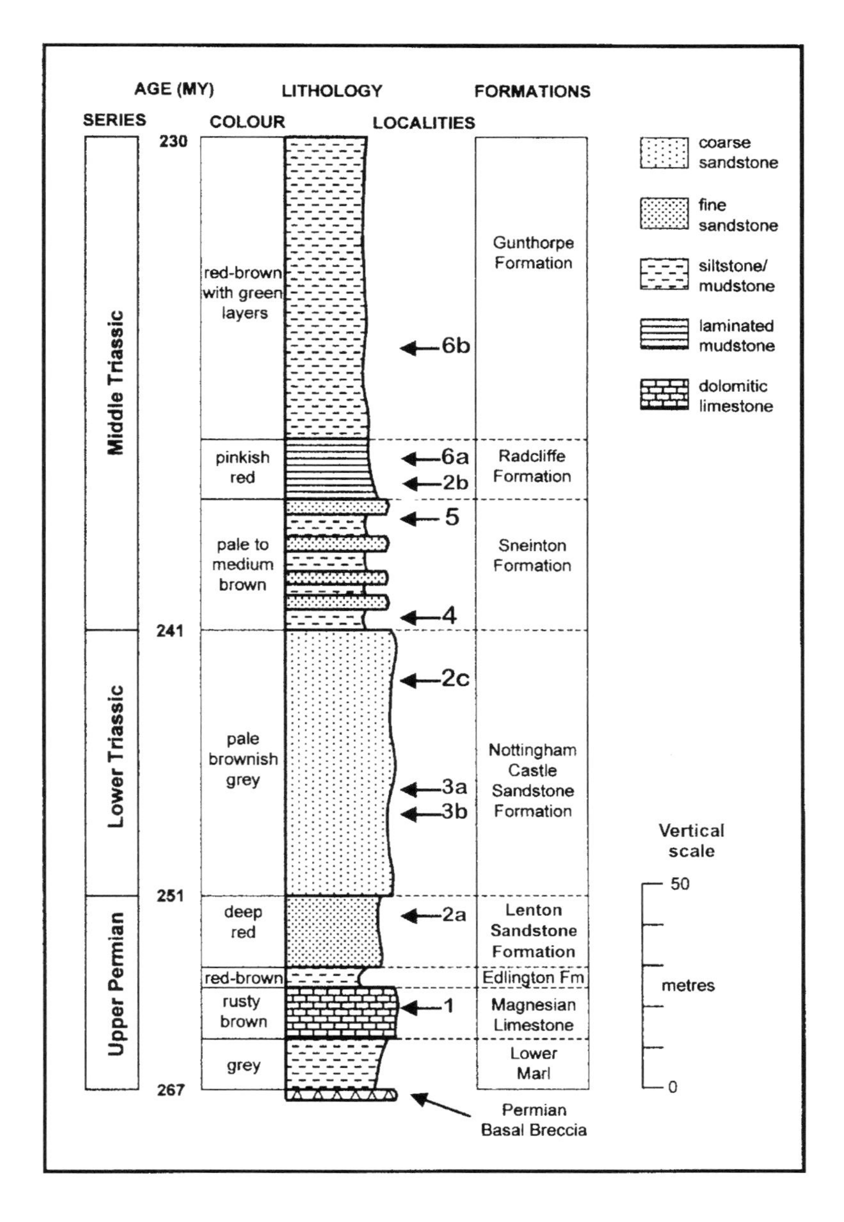

Figure 28. Generalised vertical section of the Permian and Triassic rocks of Nottingham. (1 = Lower Magnesium Limestone)

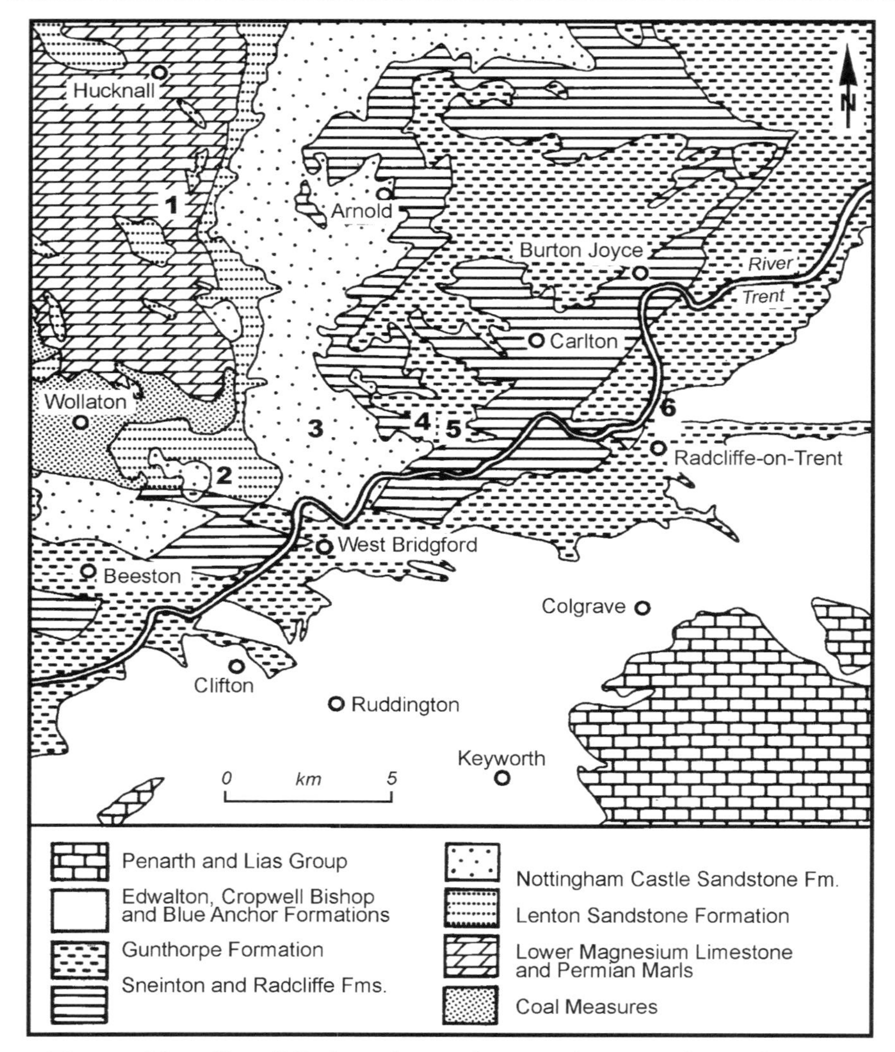

Figure 29. Simplified geological map of Nottingham showing the excursion localities.

Locality Details

Locality 1: Disused Quarry in Lower Magnesian Limestone, Bulwell, north-west Nottingham (SK 53304542) reached via the A610. The section is accessible via Key Close, Bulwell, which lies off Belgrave Road. The Lower Magnesian

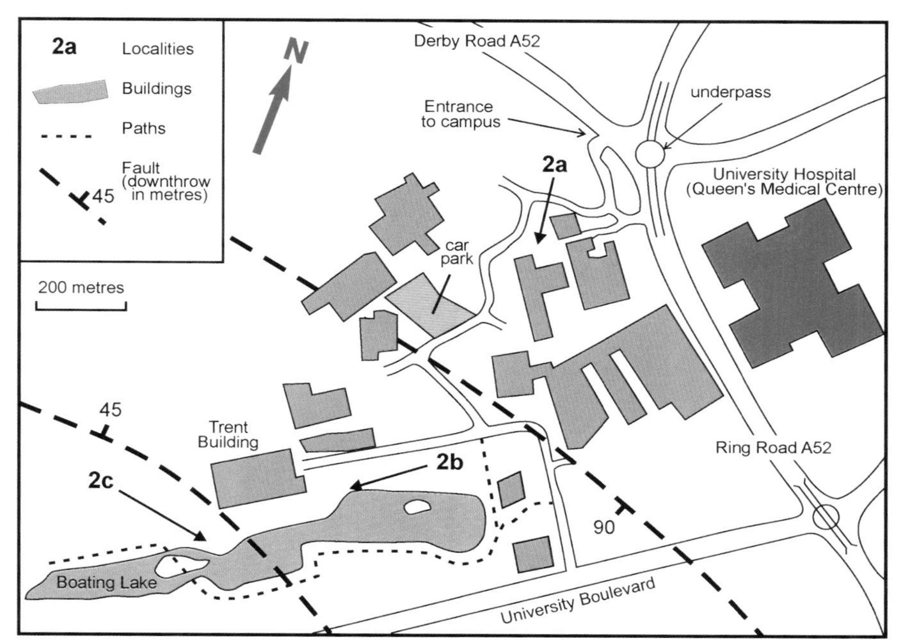

Figure 30. Sketch map showing the geology of the eastern part of the Nottingham University campus (Localities 2a, 2b and 2c).

Limestone has been quarried extensively in the Bulwell area for building stone, from which many buildings and walls in Nottingham are constructed. More recently, with the decline in the market for natural building stone, those quarries remaining open have worked the stone for ornamental purposes such as rockeries ('Bulwell Stone'). All quarries have now closed and most have been filled-in, although a few former faces remain. This locality is one such quarry remnant and is situated immediately to the west of St John's Church (itself built of Lower Magnesian Limestone). Other exposed faces partly surround the playground of the adjacent Rufford Primary School.

About 6m of the Lower Magnesian Limestone is exposed here, and is preserved as two distinct depositional units, separated by a slightly undulatory surface of **unconformity**. The lower unit is 4m thick and consists of reddish, rust-brown dolomitic limestone (dolostone) that, at first glance, resembles a very well sorted, coarse-grained sandstone. Closer examination reveals that the rock consists of yellowish-brown, rhombohedral crystals of dolomite about 1mm across. Bedding within the dolostone is typically 20 to 50cm thick, individual beds having a slightly irregular, lenticular shape. The beds are separated by thin partings of siltstone with scattered grains of quartz sand. Trough **cross-lamination** is visible in places

Figure 31. Brewhouse Yard, showing the lower entrance to the man-made cave Mortimer's Hole (entrance on the extreme right).

within beds, with **foresets** generally dipping towards the east, though a few dip in other directions. Larger scale, eastward-dipping, low angle cross-bedding occurs towards the top of the lower unit and is truncated by the erosion surface at the base of the upper unit. Access to this unit is difficult. It is up to 2m thick and appears decidedly more yellowish in colour than the beds below. Its bedding is generally thinner and more lenticular.

The Lower Magnesian Limestone was deposited as a carbonate sand bank in the clear, well-agitated coastal waters of the Permian **Zechstein** Sea. The cross-bedding indicates constant lateral shifting of the sand banks due to strong current activity. Deposition eventually ended when sea-level fell and coastal plain mudflats and sand dunes, now represented by the Edlington and Lenton Sandstone Formations respectively, advanced over the region. This allowed alkaline, magnesium-rich groundwaters to infiltrate the now-buried sand bank, and to chemically alter the original calcium carbonate ($CaCO_3$) sand grains to dolomite, a calcium-magnesium carbonate ($CaMg(CO_3)_2$). This process destroyed the original sedimentary grains and much of the primary depositional stratification in the rock.

Locality 2: Nottingham University campus (SK 5438). Both formations within the Sherwood Sandstone Group, the Lenton Sandstone and the Nottingham Castle Sandstone, are well exposed on the Nottingham University campus. The campus is best approached via the Derby Road (A52) entrance, which lies immediately to the west of the interchange with the Nottingham Ring Road (Clifton-Middleton Boulevard). Cars should be parked in the visitors' car park (pay and display), which is well signposted once inside the entrance (Figure 30). Several strategically placed map boards also assist with navigation around the campus.

Locality 2a: (SK 54403863) about 400m northeast of the visitors' car park (Figure 30). The Lenton Sandstone Formation is exposed in a low face adjacent to the Cripp's Computing Centre. The section consists of 6m of deep red, fine to medium-grained sandstone with both elliptical and irregularly shaped yellow-brown mottles. The sandstone is poorly cemented, the individual well-rounded sand grains being held weakly together by films of clay minerals and iron oxide (haematite), the latter producing the deep red colour. The sandstone is crumbly to the touch, but has an almost silky feel when rubbed between the fingers. This is due to the clay content and is one of the characteristic features of a good moulding sand. Beds range from a few centimetres to 1 metre thick, although individual bedding surfaces are poorly defined. The most obvious sedimentary structure is the extremely fine, often steeply inclined cross-lamination within some of the beds. The Lenton Sandstone was deposited by accumulation of wind-blown sand dunes, although some sand was probably redistributed by **flash floods** following rare but heavy rainstorms.

The Lenton Sandstone was formerly extensively quarried in Nottingham for use as moulding sand in iron foundries. The sandstone was ideal for this purpose because of its clay and iron oxide content, giving it naturally bonded properties that prevented the sand moulds from collapsing when the molten metal was poured. The Lenton Sandstone was once exported to many other countries worldwide for this purpose, but demand eventually declined with the development of a cheaper, synthetic substitute and all quarries in the Nottingham area are now closed.

Locality 2b: (SK 54323810) University Boating Lake below the Portland Building. The University Campus is crossed by two substantial faults with vertical displacements of 90m and 45m, trending roughly WNW to ESE (Figure 30). These bound a down-faulted block of Mercia Mudstone, which is exposed in a low cliff on the north side of the University Boating Lake. Here, 5m of mudstone, siltstone and very fine-grained sandstone display the typical, very thin lamination and pinkish-red hues of the Radcliffe Formation. This formation is, however, better examined at Locality 6 (see below).

Locality 2c: (SK 54103791) is situated on the northern side of the University Boating Lake at the foot of the slope below the imposing Trent Building, about 300m to the southwest of Locality 2b. At Locality 2c, a former quarry face exposes a 7m-thick section of the Nottingham Castle Sandstone. The sandstone is brownish grey in colour, medium to coarse-grained and contains pebbles. The latter are mainly rounded or sub-rounded in shape and are mostly composed of resistant **quartzite** and vein quartz eroded from the rocks of the **Variscan** mountains.

The sandstone was deposited by a major 'braided' river system (the Triassic River; see page 70) with numerous channels that branched, diverged and then rejoined around low sand bars. Both the channels and sand bars were constantly shifting, with sand being eroded from the upstream end of the bars and deposited on the downstream side. The bars thus migrated downstream, producing the characteristic, large-scale cross-bedding now seen. Cross-bedding occurs as sets up to 1.5m thick of inclined, planar or slightly trough-shaped laminae (**foresets**) bounded above and below by erosional, sub-horizontal bedding surfaces. Pebbles are strewn along these bounding surfaces or along foresets. The foresets are mostly inclined towards the ENE, indicating both the direction of sand bar migration and the local flow direction within the river system. Smaller scale cross-bedding, in sets 10-50cm thick, generally contains trough-shaped foresets and fewer pebbles, and was formed by the migration of smaller bedforms around the sides of the sand bars. Foresets within the trough cross-bedding are inclined in a greater variety of directions than in the larger scale cross-bedding.

As well as downstream migration of the sand bars, the channels also tended to migrate laterally, producing the sub-horizontal erosion surfaces separating the cross-bedded sets. This process also led to erosion of muddy sediments deposited in abandoned river channels or on the tops of sand bars. Remnants of these muds are preserved as eroded, pebble-sized flakes of mudstone. These are typically weathered to a yellow-brown colour at this locality but are usually reddish-brown or green in colour in less-weathered exposures elsewhere in Nottingham.

Locality 3: Nottingham City Centre (Figure 29). Numerous exposures of the Nottingham Castle Sandstone are found in the centre of Nottingham, but the best sections can be seen in the Park Tunnel (Locality 3a - see front cover) and in the spectacular cliffs of Castle Rock (Locality 3b). These excursions can be combined with visits to the Nottingham Castle and Brewhouse Yard Museums. Car parking is difficult in the city centre so public transport is recommended.

Locality 3a: The Park Tunnel. (SK 56523996). This is best approached via Upper College Street, off Derby Road, Nottingham. At the uphill end of Upper College Street, a small wrought iron gateway provides access to the tunnel via a spectacular, spiralling descent of stone steps. Excavation of the tunnel was commissioned in the mid-19th century by the Duke of Newcastle, owner of the Nottingham Park Estate. The tunnel was designed to provide access to Derby Road from the Estate, its considerable height being necessary to allow the horse-drawn coaches of the day to pass through. Unfortunately, it quickly became redundant when new surface roads were driven into the Estate. The Duke of Newcastle's folly is a splendid legacy to geologists because it allows an observer to get right inside the former bed of the Triassic river and observe the cross-bedding within the Nottingham Castle Sandstone in three dimensions.

The sandstone at this locality is virtually identical to that seen at Locality 2c. Near the base of the section, cross-bedding occurs in sets up to 2m thick, bounded above and below by sub-horizontal erosion surfaces. The trough shape of the thicker cross-bedded sets is evident when viewed in cross-section at the Park Estate (southwest) end of the tunnel and above the arched roof at the Derby Road end. Thinner sets of cross-bedding predominate towards the top of the section. As at Locality 2c, foresets mostly dip towards the ENE, indicating current flow in that direction during deposition of the sandstone.

From the lower, Park end of the tunnel, proceed on foot along Tunnel Road and turn left (southeastwards) into Tattershall Drive. After continuing for about 500m, Tattershall Drive merges into Peveril Drive, which runs along the southwest side of Castle Rock. On joining Castle Boulevard, turn into the Brewhouse Yard.

Locality 3b: Brewhouse Yard at the foot of Castle Rock (SK 56953938) (Figure 31). Castle Rock is a magnificent, 30m-high river bluff in Nottingham Castle Sandstone, showing all the features seen at Localities 2c and 3a. A display board at the foot of the cliff, produced by the British Geological Survey, describes the geological history of Castle Rock and the economic geology of the Nottingham Castle Sandstone. The Rock was probably carved initially when the Trent valley was excavated by glacial meltwaters at the end of the **Anglian** Ice Age about 450,000 years ago, but did not acquire its present form until the valley was deepened by further meltwater erosion at the end of the last (late Devensian) ice age about 13,000 years ago.

Brewhouse Yard is famous for its 'caves', notably Mortimer's Hole, which dates back to the 12th Century and linked the Yard with the former Norman Castle, providing a supply route for milled corn and ale (Figure 31). The Nottingham Castle Sandstone below Nottingham is riddled with numerous other man-made 'caves'. These were excavated for various purposes, including cellars, vaults, rock houses, access tunnels and sand mines. The weak, friable consistency of the sandstone made excavation relatively straightforward, and the lack of closely spaced joints within the rock enhanced the stability of the cave roofs. The weakness of the sandstone makes it useless as a building stone, but it is easily mined and disaggregated into sand and gravel for use by the building industry, and has been quarried for this purpose in many parts of Nottinghamshire. It is, however, as a source of potable groundwater that the Nottingham Castle Sandstone is of greatest economic importance. The rock is highly permeable due to the presence of pores between the sand grains. Groundwater extracted from the sandstone by boreholes and wells once supported the Nottingham brewing industry, but with the decline of water abstraction for this purpose over the past few decades, the water table is steadily rising below the city. Groundwater abstraction from the aquifer elsewhere in Nottinghamshire now meets about half of the county's demand for water and is rigorously managed to avoid over-exploitation and contamination.

Locality 4: (SK 59223970) (Figure 29). Former railway cutting, Colwick Road, Sneinton.

This locality exposes the boundary between the Sherwood Sandstone and Mercia Mudstone Groups. It is situated on the northern side of Colwick Road, Sneinton, and lies about 300m west of the level crossing, immediately opposite a large public house. The locality marks the northern end of a now demolished railway viaduct, where the former Great Northern Railway entered a shallow cutting in the river bluffs on the northern side of the Trent valley. Exposures occur in an amphitheatre-shaped face below the wooden railings at the southern end of the cutting, and on the steep slopes on the eastern side of the cutting itself.

The boundary between the Sherwood Sandstone and Mercia Mudstone Groups is exposed about 0.6m below the foot of the railings. The base of the Sneinton Formation, the lowest subdivision of the Mercia Mudstone Group, is marked by a 0.6m-thick bed of yellow, planar laminated, very fine-grained micaceous sandstone with a thin (2cm) conglomerate at its base. The conglomerate, which consists of small, subangular quartz pebbles in a matrix of red-brown siltstone, overlies about 2.5m of pale reddish and greenish brown, medium to coarse-grained, cross-bedded sandstone with scattered pebbles, typical of the Nottingham Castle Sandstone Formation of the Sherwood Sandstone Group.

Apart from the basal sandstone, the lowermost 10m of the Sneinton Formation is mainly argillaceous. These strata are exposed alongside the steep path leading up from the road and in the partly soil-covered face above. They consist mostly of dull reddish-brown or grey-green, micaceous siltstone and mudstone with thin beds of pale yellow, very fine-grained sandstone. Above this, thicker (20-70cm) beds of pale brown, very fine to fine-grained sandstone become much more common within the formation, though the proportion of interbedded siltstone and mudstone remains over 50 percent. These sandstone beds, which can be examined on the eastern side of the cutting, commonly display planar or **ripple lamination**, with abundant mica flakes on the lamina surfaces. Angular mudstone clasts are common at the bases of sandstone beds and indicate that deposition of the beds was preceded by erosion of the subjacent, cohesive beds of mudstone.

The conglomerate at the base of the Sneinton Formation is very thin here compared to elsewhere in the Nottingham area, where it is up to 80cm in thickness and has a strong calcareous cement. Pebbles within the conglomerate are often faceted ('**dreikanter**'), indicating prolonged exposure to wind erosion. Regionally, the base of the Sneinton Formation is demonstrably unconformable and correlates with the Hardegsen **Disconformity**, a widespread hiatus in deposition towards the end of the early Triassic, which has been recognised over much of Northwest Europe. It may represent a long period of non-deposition in the Nottingham region, during which time deposition of fluvial sediments by the Triassic river system was diverted elsewhere, probably towards northwest England. Sedimentation finally resumed on a muddy coastal plain with brackish water lakes. These teemed with fish, which have been found as fossils in the lower part of the Sneinton Formation at other exposures in Nottingham. Reptiles also wandered across the mudflats, leaving behind rare examples of fossil footprints. These early Triassic reptiles were distant ancestors of modern crocodiles and lizards and may have been fish-eaters. True dinosaurs were yet to evolve. As time progressed, shallow, gently meandering river channels once again started to flow northeastwards across the coastal plain, occasionally bursting their banks during heavy rainstorms. The resulting floods ripped up flakes of mudstone from the mudflat surface and then deposited sheet-like layers of sand, thus forming the sandstone beds in the upper part of the Sneinton Formation.

Locality 5: (SK 60063974). Colwick Park quarry, Nottingham. This section exposes the upper part of the Sneinton Formation. The disused quarry is heavily wooded and is best visited on a sunny, dry day in winter or early spring when more light can penetrate through the leafless canopy and undergrowth is low. Colwick Park is best accessed via Greenwood Road, Colwick. Follow the path, which leaves the roadside between the bowling green and mini-golf course, and descend along a pleasant, partially wooded valley to the lower slopes of the Park. The quarry lies at the southern end of the Park, in the woods on the eastern side of this valley, adjacent to the Nottingham to Newark railway line. The quarry face is unstable so a hard hat should be worn. **Do not trespass onto the railway**. The quarry and adjacent cutting is a Site of Special Scientific Interest and **must not be hammered**.

The quarry exposes about 9m of strata. The lower 7m consists of interbedded sandstone, siltstone and mudstone beds forming the upper part of the Sneinton Formation. The topmost 2m comprise the mudstone-dominated Radcliffe Formation. The sandstone beds, which can be examined as fallen blocks at the foot of the face, are typically 2-5cm thick and consist of pale brownish grey, very fine to fine-grained sandstone containing numerous pinhead-sized solution cavities. The sandstones commonly display well-preserved planar or ripple lamination and ripple marks are common on bed tops. Small **mud flakes** occur at the bases of many sandstone beds, where they commonly weather out to leave small pits. **Desiccation cracks** form large polygonal patterns on the basal or upper surfaces of sandstone blocks. The thinning of sandstone beds towards the top of the Sneinton Formation marks the gradual decline of the fluvially influenced depositional environments of the early part of the Triassic and the transition to the mainly lacustrine and saline mudflat environments of the Triassic Radcliffe and Gunthorpe Formations.

Locality 6: Radcliffe-on-Trent river cliffs. (SK 64613987). Radcliffe-on-Trent is named after the distinctive 'red cliffs', formed by exposures of the reddish brown mudstone and siltstone of the Mercia Mudstone Group. Sections of the Radcliffe and Gunthorpe Formations occur at the foot of the steep river cliffs abutting the river to the northwest of the town. They are best approached through the Rockley Memorial Park at the northwest end of Park Road, Radcliffe. On leaving the northwest exit from the Park through a low wooden gate, proceed down the stepped path to the foot of the cliffs. Continue southwestwards along the path for about 300m, where two closely adjacent rock faces expose about 7m of the Radcliffe Formation.

Locality 6a: (SK 64613987). The Radcliffe Formation is distinguished from other formations in the Mercia Mudstone Group by its extremely thin lamination and distinctive colours, which range from reddish brown to purplish or pinkish red. Vivid green-coloured beds also occur but are less common. The lamination is formed by alternation of red mudstone with pale grey laminae of siltstone. Siltstone laminae are commonly less than 1mm thick but may reach up to 3mm. Very thin beds of very fine sandstone 3 to 20mm thick also occur and commonly display current ripples, planar lamination and more rarely, convolute lamination. Desiccation cracks are abundant, ranging from 1 to 10mm wide and forming irregular polygonal patterns on bedding planes.

The fine lamination and current ripples indicate subaqueous deposition, perhaps in a brackish water lake bordered by mudflats. Each siltstone lamina or sandstone bed represents a single, rapid depositional event, usually accompanied by strong current activity, and was deposited when occasional rainstorms led to clouds of silt and fine sand being swept into the lake. Desiccation cracks formed when the lake dried out from time to time. The Radcliffe Formation occurs throughout the East Midlands with little variation in lithology, suggesting that the lake, though shallow, may have covered many hundreds of square kilometres.

Locality 6b: (SK 65074064). From Locality 6a, follow the riverside path about 700m downstream until Radcliffe Weir is reached. The Harlequin Fault is crossed en route but it is not exposed. The fault has a downthrow to the north of about 30m and juxtaposes the Radcliffe Formation against the younger strata of the Gunthorpe Formation. An 8m thick section of the middle part of the latter formation is exposed in the low rock face at the Weir.

The Gunthorpe Formation consists of interbedded reddish-brown, blocky mudstone with greenish grey, very fine-grained dolomitic sandstone. Gypsum is common, usually as veins of satin spar. Many of these veins intersect the bedding at high angles, and probably formed following recent dissolution of primary gypsum within the rock and its re-precipitation along joints. The mudstone is quite unlike that of the Radcliffe Formation, displaying little in the way of lamination. Some mudstone beds appear completely structureless, whereas others retain vestiges of lamination or thin bedding which was deformed and disrupted while the sediment was still soft. Sandstone occurs in units of between 5 and 20, closely spaced thin beds separated by mudstone partings. Individual sandstone beds are typically 2 to 30mm thick with ripple marked tops and internal planar or current ripple lamination. The bases of some sandstone beds are crowded with halite **pseudomorphs** - casts of large, cuboid salt crystals up to 15mm across. Each of the sandstone beds represents a single, short-lived depositional event separated by much longer periods of slow, mudstone accumulation. Desiccation cracks of various sizes penetrate the sandstones, often forming polygonal networks that are visible on both the bases and tops of beds. Sandstone beds and laminae are commonly curled upwards towards the cracks, a feature which can often be observed on dried-out mudflats at the present day.

The Gunthorpe Formation was probably deposited on saline mudflats in an arid or semi-arid, continental drainage basin. The thin layers of sand were laid down by flash floods following infrequent but heavy rainstorms. Fluctuating water tables led to alternate wetting and drying of the mudflat sediments, resulting in desiccation cracking, **fluidisation** and deformation to form the characteristic disrupted texture of some of the mudstones. Other, structureless mudstones accumulated when the mudflats were damp and wind-blown dust and mud pellets adhered to the surface. The halite pseudomorphs were formed when large salt crystals grew from evaporating saline water to form a crust on the mudflat surface. As sheet floods flowed across the mudflats, the salt was quickly dissolved, leaving behind crystal-shaped moulds in the mud surface. Simultaneously, these moulds were filled with the fine sand washed in by the flood, to form casts on the base of the resulting sandstone bed.

When the level of the Trent is low, the top of a thick bed of very fine sandstone is exposed by the water's edge at the downstream end of the locality. This is the 'Plains Skerry', named after Mapperley Plains in Nottingham, and is one of a series of resistant sandstone beds that cap the steep-sided plateau in that area. The sedimentary lamination within the Plains Skerry has been extensively convoluted, accounting for the irregular, hummocky appearance of the top of the bed. Similar, isolated beds of slumped sandstone occur within mudstone-dominated successions in many parts of the geological record. Such **slumping** is thought to have been triggered by seismic shock waves generated by earth tremors, which must have taken place soon after deposition when the sediments were still soft. Curiously in such cases, the resulting deformation is usually confined to the sandstone beds, leaving the adjacent mudstones untouched.

Most formations within the Mercia Mudstone Group have been quarried for brick clay in the Nottingham region, but the Gunthorpe Formation has been the most extensively exploited, notably in the Mapperley Plains district of the city. Local bricks helped to sustain the construction boom in 19th century Nottingham. At this time, the local brick-making industry achieved national importance, providing bricks for some Britain's most famous buildings, such as the magnificent facade of London's St. Pancras Station. The opening up of new quarries in the Oxford Clay of the south Midlands, however, led to the demise of the Nottingham brick industry. Only the Dorket Head quarry, near Arnold, remains open today. The Mercia Mudstone is of greater economic importance nowadays for its valuable gypsum deposits. A seam of gypsum within the Gunthorpe Formation was once mined on a small scale in East Bridgford and used for ornamental carving, but the best gypsum deposits occur at a higher stratigraphical level within the Group. These are of national importance and are mined at East Leake, Barrow-on Soar and Newark, mainly as the raw material for plasterboard manufacture.

EXCURSION 10. LIASSIC OF THE VALE OF BELVOIR

Alan Brandon, British Geological Survey, Keyworth, Nottingham

Objectives

The objectives of this excursion are to examine the stratigraphy and geomorphology of the Lower Jurassic strata of the Vale of Belvoir. Firstly, it provides a down-dip transect through the stratigraphy of the Scunthorpe and Brant Mudstone Formations of the Lower Jurassic Lias Group. Secondly, the walk provides an opportunity to relate the Lias stratigraphy to the geomorphology of the Vale.

Logistics

This walk (Figure 32) follows a fairly direct footpath transect in unfaulted ground across the Vale of Belvoir. The walk starts at the Rhaetic escarpment at Sutton (SK 75933725), near Granby (accessed from the A52), and ends just below the Marlstone Formation at Belvoir Castle (SK 81703373), a distance of about 8km.

It crosses pastureland and ploughed fields and boots are recommended, particularly wellington boots in the winter, as the soil is very heavy clay. The use of two cars, one left at either end, is the most convenient way of completing the walk. Otherwise, a return along an approximately parallel route could be planned. Alternatively, the walk can be divided into two parts, broken at Barkestone-le-Vale. Unfortunately, there is no public house at Barkestone! The walk should be taken between late September and April when most fields have been ploughed and there is minimal vegetation.

The geology north of Barkestone-le-Vale is shown on British Geological Survey 1:10,000 Sheet SK 73 NE. This part of the walk is depicted on the new BGS 1:50,000 Sheet 126 (Nottingham). The area south of Barkestone is included in BGS 1:50,000 Sheet 142 (Melton Mowbray).

Geological Background

The Scunthorpe and Brant Mudstone Formations of the Lower Jurassic Lias Group, are approximately 120m and 110m thick respectively (Figure 33). Together, these formations equate to the former 'Lower Lias' and basal part of the 'Middle Lias' and consist of marine grey mudstones and siltstones with thin beds of shelly limestone, a few sandstones and various nodular beds. Natural exposures are rare and the walk allows the various strata and their fossil content to be examined as **brash** in ploughed fields and ditch dredgings. Fossils are commonly found within slabs of limestone or as discrete specimens. The Lias mostly comprises readily weathered mudstones and siltstones, which give rise to a featureless topography. The thin harder beds composed mainly of limestone form a series of dip and scarp ridges or **cuestas**; some of which are many metres in height whereas others are less

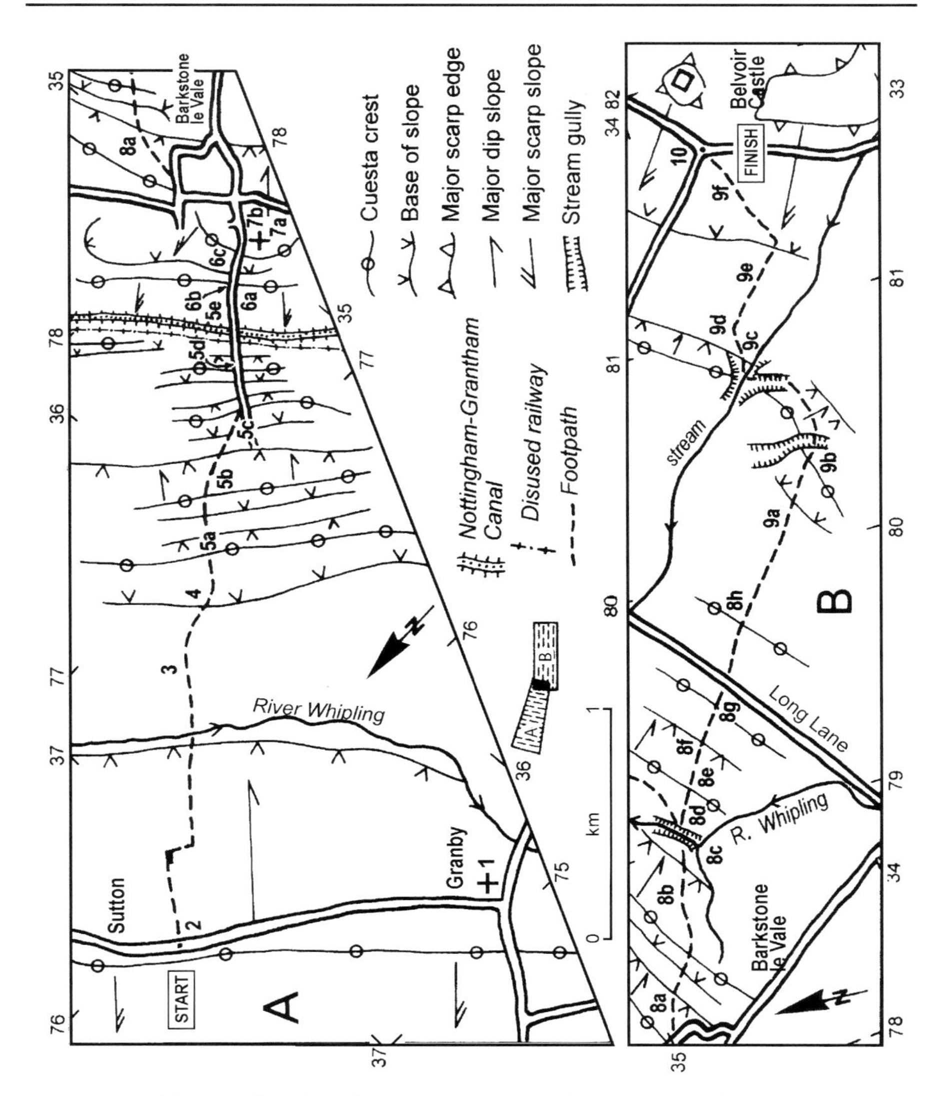

Figure 32. Vale of Belvoir excursion showing the localities visited and the relationship between geomorphological features and the geology.

than a metre high. However, each one can be traced along the Lias outcrop from the Newark area. Along the traverse, the strata dip at 1° to 1.5° to the southeast so that each cuesta consists of a steep convex escarpment facing northwest and a wider, gently sloping southeast facing dip slope. The base of each hard bed generally crops out near the crest of the feature and the top of the hard bed crops out at the lower end of the dip slope. However, the feature-forming hard unit commonly comprises a closely spaced group of limestones or sandstones with interbedded mudstones, so that the dip slope is slightly less steep than the true dip of the strata. Because the stratigraphy is so uniform over wide areas, all the feature-forming beds have been named (Figure 33). Detailed mapping of these features and examination of the field debris has resulted in a high degree of stratigraphical and structural resolution in the neighbouring Bottesford area.

This Lias outcrop perfectly illustrates the detailed relationship between lithology and landform. The main reason is that the East Midlands was last glaciated during the **Anglian** Stage some 450,000 years ago and since then, during several cycles of alternating temperate and **periglacial** climate, the topography has reached geomorphological maturity. The absence of glacial deposits enables the field brash and drainage ditch debris to be related directly to the underlying geology.

The Vale of Belvoir is the generally low-lying ground, some 6km wide, lying between the prominent Rhaetic and Marlstone escarpments. Towards the northeast, the Vale passes imperceptibly into the 'Lower Lias' outcrop extending northeastwards beyond Newark. However, the southwestern limit of the Vale is sharply defined by a till-capped escarpment at Upper Broughton. Were it not for this escarpment closure, the Vale's geomorphology would be similar to that produced elsewhere by the 'Lower Lias'.

The floor of the Vale is roughly planar, sloping gently northwestwards from about 60m to 30m above O.D., and is broken by many small escarpments. The four main cuestas are associated with the Holme Farm Limestone, the Dry Doddington Nodule Bed and Stubton Limestone, Littlegate Limestone and the Brandon Sandstone.

The previously accepted model for the origin of the Vale is that of glacial scouring by 'cleaner' ice during the older glaciation. A lobe of slowly melting, stagnant ice is thought to have remained in the Vale, and prevented the Trent from regaining its assumed ancestral, pre-glacial course across the Vale towards the Ancaster Gap in the Lincolnshire Limestone escarpment east of Grantham, instead directing the river northward creating the Trent Trench.

Undoubtedly, much Lower Lias strata was glacially eroded and incorporated into the basal Lias-rich Oadby Till of the Wreake Valley area. But this itself was insufficient to create the present Vale.

The author considers that the Ancaster Gap was initiated by meltwaters during the melting of the Anglian ice sheet. This drainage evolved into the River Witham, although subsequently this river abandoned the Ancaster Gap in favour of a more westerly course. Similarly, the glacial melt waters that initiated the Trent are thought to have drained through the Lincoln Gap. Given the Vale's geomorphological maturity, the lack of glacial deposits on its floor, and the absence of filled depressions below base-level, it seems reasonable that it formed as a result of periglacial mass wasting and removal of incompetent **argillaceous** strata during

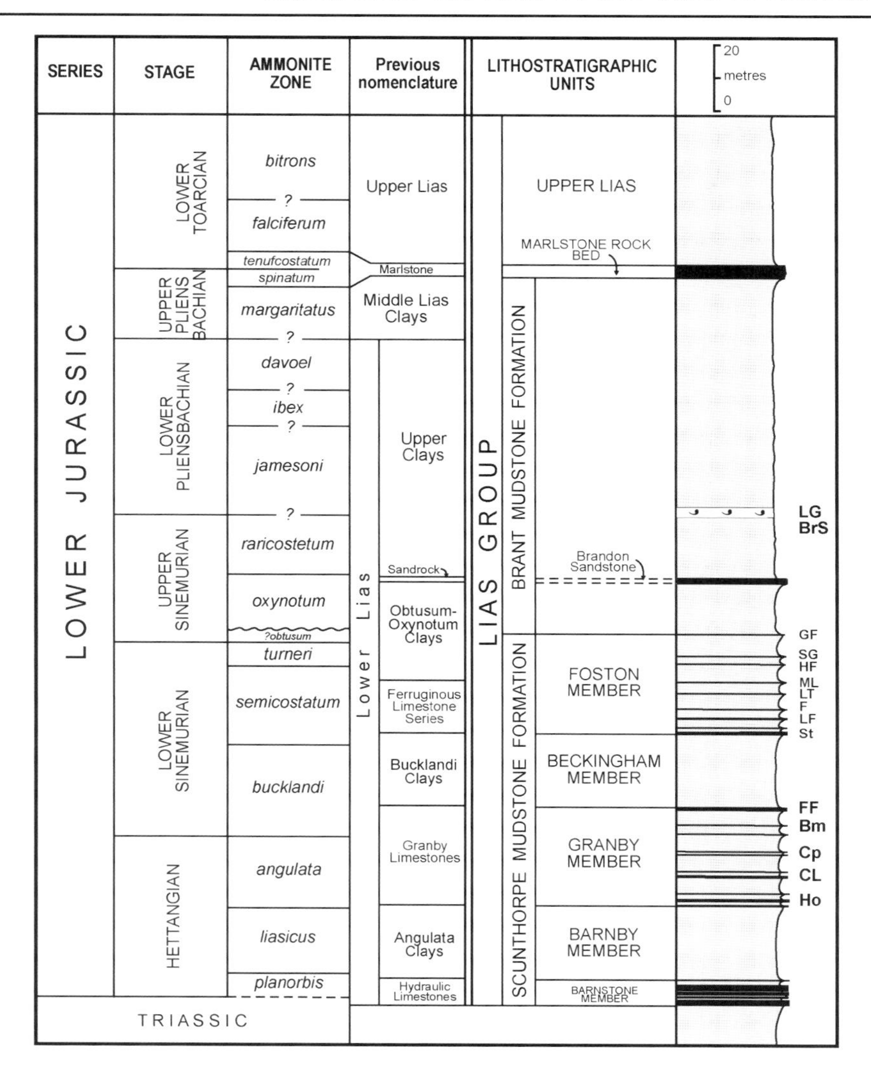

Figure 33. Stratigraphy of the Lias Group in the excursion area. (Abbreviations in the text and Figure 33 are Bm = Blackmires Limestone, BrS = Brandon Sandstone, CL = Cross Lane Limestone, Cp = Claypole Limestone, F = Fenton Limestone, FF = Fen Farm Limestone, GF = Glebe Farm Bed, Ho = Holme Farm Limestone, HF = Highfield Farm Limestone, LT = Littlegate Limestones, LF = Lodge Farm Limestone, LG = Loveden Gryphaea Bed, ML = Mill Lane Limestones, SG = Stragglethorpe Grange Limestones, ST = Stubton Limestone.)

successive cold periods since Anglian times. Such erosion lowered the general land level, in response to a falling base-level within the Trent Basin.

The Trent drainage initially developed on an overburden of till and other glacigenic sediments left behind at the end of the Anglian. This higher level till cover on Lias strata is now only present at the Vale's southwestern end, at the edge of the higher ground of the Nottinghamshire Wolds. Here, the base of the drift falls northwards from approximately 120m above O.D. at Old Dalby, to approximately 80m above O.D. around Kinoulton and Owthorpe. The floor of the Vale, between Harby and Old Dalby, also contains residual stony **head** deposits.

Erosion during these cold **Pleistocene** phases did not widen the Vale because of the constraining Rhaetic and Marlstone escarpments. However, the till-capped western escarpment was susceptible to freeze-thaw and related processes and must have retreated more to the southwest during successive cold periods.

The geological maps show till infilling two channels incised into the Marlstone scarp, above Long Clawson and Stathern respectively. These channels, whose floors fall generally southeastwards, were probably cut by left bank tributaries of the region's major easterly flowing pre-glacial river (Figure 32). Due to post-glacial erosion, the channel floors, at about 105m above O.D., are now 'hanging' some 45m above the neighbouring floor of the Vale. This testifies to the significant amount of down cutting that must have take place subsequent to the channels being filled with till, but indicates minimal scarp retreat.

Several small streams in the Vale cut across upstanding, unfaulted cuestas, for example the River Whipling, which will be encountered on the walk. These may have originated as superimposed meltwater streams from a former till cover. Because of the uniform stratigraphy of the 'Lower Lias', virtually any walk across the outcrop will demonstrate a similar sequence of landform features and field brash. However, certain features and brash will be better represented along some footpath transects than others. **Faulting** greatly complicates the disposition of landform features in some areas.

Locality Details

From the A52 near Bingham, take the Granby road (SK 725393) for about 5km, passing through red clay fields underlain by the gypsiferous Cropwell Bishop Formation of the Triassic Mercia Mudstone Group. On approaching Granby, there is a steep rise which is the 'Rhaetic' escarpment formed of greenish grey mudstones of the Blue Anchor Formation, overlain by the grey Penarth Group, all of late Triassic age and capped by the Barnstone Member, the lowest strata of the Lias Group. Drive over the crest of the cuesta feature and Granby is situated on the upper part of the dip slope of the Barnstone Member.

Locality 1: Granby Church (SK 751362) An option is an inspection of the building stones of the village church. Although mostly constructed of limestones of the Barnstone Member, the quoins and buttresses are of Middle Jurassic Lincolnshire Limestone and there are minor amounts of 'Sandrock' from beneath the Marlstone Formation. Note the difference in the weathered appearance of the blocks of Barnstone Member used at different times. There are two main periods represented in the tower and the most recent is in the south extension. The perimeter walls are built of Barnstone Member capped by Permian 'Bulwell Stone' (dolomite) from Nottinghamshire.

Locality 2: Start of the walk at Sutton and Barnstone Member (SK 75933725) Drive the car along the left turn on the north side of the church for 1.3km and park at the start of the footpath just before reaching the first houses of Sutton village. The crest of the Barnstone Member feature is marked by a pylon on the north side of the road. Shallow degraded workings in the Barnstone Member occur in the field. Looking to the southeast across the Vale, Belvoir Castle at the far end of the walk can be seen on the wooded Marlstone escarpment. Follow the footpath along the south side of the field boundary and down the dip slope of the Barnstone Member that comprises closely spaced limestone and mudstone beds. The wide dip slope is covered by brash of pale grey, often laminated, generally sparsely fossiliferous, fine-grained, argillaceous limestone or **calcilutite** with less common lumps of shelly bioclastic limestone. Typical fossils are the **bivalves** *Liostrea liassica* and *Modiolus minimus*, and the **ammonite** *Psiloceras*.

The Barnstone Member was formerly called the 'Hydraulic Limestone' because it was used to make cement that set under water. It was once worked on a large scale for this purpose at Barnstone. Hereabouts, the small shallow degraded workings in the fields to the east were probably for wallstone or for making lime.

Cross the stile near the old farm building, turn right along the far side of the field boundary and then turn left at the next field boundary to continue down the dip slope. Abundant slabs of fawn-weathering, grey limestone have been dug out of the ditch. Cross the ditch and proceed across the corner of the adjoining field. Notice the site of another former limestone working, now a shallow hollow with hawthorns.

Locality 3: Is the field immediately after a small wooden bridge over the canalised River Whipling, situated at the foot of the Barnstone Member dip slope (SK 76603650). Continue southeastwards along the field boundary for 0.5km across flattish clay fields with no rock brash. This is typical of the outcrop of the Barnby Member, composed entirely of grey mudstones with no feature-forming beds. Fairly common fossils include the bivalve *Cardinia* and the ammonite *Caloceras*. The flat is covered in places by thin alluvial clay. Cut across the bottom of the field to the right side of the wood. Looking back towards the northwest, the broad flattish outcrop of the Barnby Member can be seen in the foreground, beyond which is the rising dip slope of the Barnstone Member with the pylon marking the crest on the horizon. Note that both Sutton and Granby villages are situated on the crest and upper part of the dip slope.

Locality 4: Jericho Covert (SK 769361), climb the marked scarp face of the Holme Farm Limestone feature (Ho). Most of the scarp is underlain by the upper part of the Barnby Member, and weathered grey mudstone may be seen in a 1m deep ditch.

Localities 5: This demonstrates the outcrop of the Granby Member between Jericho Covert and the Grantham Canal. The Granby Member is an interbedded sequence of grey mudstones and groups of limestones. Each limestone group comprises closely spaced argillaceous calcilutite and shelly bioclastic limestones, thinly interbedded with mudstone. Each group forms a separate feature but some of the associated cuesta features are weak along this transect. The most common fossils are bivalves; *Liostrea irregularis* is characteristic of the lower two beds and is replaced by *Gryphaea arcuata* and *G. arcuata incurva* in the higher limestones. *Cardinia* and *Plagiostoma giganteum* are also common throughout. The nautiloid *Cenoceras* is found in the Holme Farm Limestone. The Claypole Limestone (Cp) contains the bivalve *Mactromya* and rhynchonellid **brachiopods**. The Blackmires (Bm) and Fen Farm (FF) Limestones contain the coral *Montlivaltia haimei* and abundant pentacrinoid columnals. Schlotheimiid ammonites occur in all but the higher two limestones. The **trace fossil** *Kulindrichnus*, termed 'turnip stones' by the farmers, is fairly common in the ploughed limestone dip slopes. These are conical burrow infills of bioclastic limestone commonly up to 10cm in diameter.

Locality 5a: (SK 76953600). The Holme Farm Limestone comprises three groups of closely spaced limestones that give rise to a strong feature with a broad crest and narrow dip slope of brown-weathering grey clay. There are some slabs of both fine-grained limestone and shelly bioclastic limestone lying around. Many of the larger blocks around have been brought in from the 'Sandrock' at the base of the Marlstone Rock.

Locality 5b: Cross the field to the southwestern corner, keeping Jericho Lodge farmhouse on your right, where there is the crest of a moderate feature formed by the Cross Lane Limestone (CL) (SK 77203580). The sparse brash on the dip slope is pale brown-weathering bioclastic limestone. Cross the next field diagonally over a weak feature on the composite Cross Lane Limestone dip slope. Both bioclastic and argillaceous limestone brash occurs on this lower part of the dip slope, particularly along the ditch at the bottom of the feature.

Locality 5c: (SK 77303545). Cross the small bridge over a ditch onto a clay flat and proceed diagonally towards Jericho Lane. The next cuesta, formed by the Claypole Limestone (Cp) is very indefinite and there is only sparse limestone brash on the crest and dip slope.

Locality 5d: (SK 77453450). The Blackmires Limestone (Bm) forms a moderate, 1m-high feature crossing, Jericho Lane a short distance below the canal. The brash contains abundant pentacrinoid debris. Pause at the old railway bridge for a good view of most of the topographical features we have so far crossed over. The weak Granby Limestone cuesta is most easily discernable as slight undulating rises in the trackway and adjoining hedge.

Locality 5e: (SK 77553525). The cuesta of the Fen Farm Limestone (FF), the highest of the limestones in the Granby Member, has been obliterated by railway and canal construction. It comprises bioclastic limestones with pentacrinoid columnals.

Localities 6: Demonstrate the outcrop of the Beckingham Member between the Grantham Canal and Barkestone-le-Vale. The Beckingham Member comprises principally grey mudstone. The member generally crops out on the steep scarp (**Locality 6a:** SK 77653520) to the south of the canal capped by the Dry Doddington Nodule Bed and adjacent shelly limestones. This is probably the strongest feature of the 'Lower Lias' outcrop. Looking northeastwards, the same feature forms the hill behind Bottesford Church spire. The nodule bed at the crest of the feature (**Locality 6b**: SK 77703515) contains large nodules (0.1-0.3m across) of brown weathering, fine-grained limestone, commonly with the abundant small bivalve *Modiolus*. The outcrop of the Lincoln Hill Limestone above the Dry Doddington Nodule Bed forms a small shelf, which in ploughed land would be marked by abundant well-preserved *Gryphaea arcuata* in the field brash.

The highest mudstone beds of the Beckingham Member underlie another steep scarp, which culminates in a crest (**Locality 6c:** SK 77703510) about 100m north of Barkestone-le-Vale Church. This is formed of grey mudstone containing abundant phosphate nodules similar to those described from the overlying Foston Member (See Localities 8, below).

Localities 7: Barkestone-le-Vale village and the church. The base of the perimeter wall of Barkestone Church (**Locality 7a:** SK 77753490) is built of 'Sandrock', the brown, ferruginous sandstone immediately underlying the Marlstone Formation. The top part is formed of Lincolnshire Limestone capped by brick. The old part of the church, including the tower, is of 'Sandrock'. The buttresses, plinths, spire and newer parts of the church, including repair work, are made of Lincolnshire Limestone. The latter is the 'Ancaster Stone' that takes on a banded appearance on weathering.

Continue the walk into the village, down the dip slope of the phosphate nodule bed. Most of the rock utilised in the village is 'Sandrock' although there is also some Lincolnshire Limestone (**Locality 7b:** SK 77753485). Turn left along New Causeway at the first crossroads in the village, sign-posted to Redmile. This takes you along the **strike** of the beds. Turn right at Fishpond Lane and take the footpath to the left at a distance of about 50m. Enjoy the good view of Belvoir Castle on the wooded Marlstone Formation scarp.

Localities 8: Demonstrates the outcrop of the Foston Member between Barkestone-le-Vale and just beyond Long Lane. The Foston Member, like the Granby Member, consists of groups of closely spaced limestone beds separated by mudstone, each of which forms a distinct cuesta. Unlike those of the Granby Member, the named limestones of the Foston Member are lithologically distinctive and many of the beds are ferruginous or sandy. Mudstone with small grey, weathering brown, peanut-sized (2-3cm) calcium phosphate nodules commonly occur beneath the limestones at the crest of the cuesta features. The commonest fossils are bivalves including *Pseudopecten* and various species of *Cardinia*. *Gryphaea arcuata* is abundant in the lower two beds and is replaced by *G. maccullochii* in higher beds. *Pholadomya* and *Hippopodium* occur in the sandy Mill Lane Limestone (ML) and Stragglethorpe Grange Limestones (SG) respectively. Rhynchonellid brachiopods are common in the Fenton Limestone (F). **Belemnites** enter the local stratigraphical column at the Littlegate Limestones. Ammonites of the *semicostatum* zone, particularly *Arnioceras*, occur up to the Highfield Farm Limestone. The most ammonite-rich bed is the Fenton Limestone, followed by the Littlegate Limestone (LT).

Locality 8a: The crest of the Stubton Limestone cuesta, the same one seen north of Barkestone Church, occurs where the footpath leaves Fishpond Lane (SK 78303500). Walk diagonally across the field, formed of the dip slope with abundant field brash of ferruginous shelly limestone in rusty brown silty soil. The limestone contains concentrations of shiny goethitic sideritic **ooids** and the rock was formerly named the Plungar Ironstone. Fossils, particularly *Gryphaea arcuata*, are abundant. At the stile at the foot of the Stubton Limestone (St) dip slope, take the right-hand route towards the southeast.

Locality 8b: (SK 78703480). Continue across the field at right angles to the strike of the beds. A weak **cuesta** in the ridge and furrow field is formed by the Lodge Farm Limestone. Cross the stile or gate and turn left into a field on the dip slope. Then proceed diagonally towards Belvoir Castle. Characteristic grey bioclastic limestone with abundant bivalves *Gryphaea arcuata* and *Pseudopecten* occur as brash in the grey clay soil.

Locality 8c: The footpath crosses the River Whipling (locally called The Grimmer), a canalised stream that probably cuts through grey mudstone into the Lodge Farm Limestone (SK 78903465). Two prominent scarp features can be seen on either side of a narrow, flat alluvial strip. Follow the footpath southeastwards towards the castle.

Locality 8d: (SK 79103465). The Fenton Limestone (F) is a single bed of sandy limestone low down on the scarp slope to the southeast. It forms a very subtle feature and little brash is seen. Elsewhere, it contains abundant ammonites of the *scipionianum* Subzone, which is part of the *semicostatum* Zone.

Locality 8e: (SK 79153460). A phosphate nodule bed underlying the Littlegate Limestone (LT) forms the crest of the steep scarp that contains small, brown-weathered, commonly bored ovoid nodules. This is the secondmost prominent cuesta in the Vale.

Locality 8f: (SK 79353420). A little brash of the Littlegate Limestones occurs in the upper part of the dip slope of the cuesta. Sporadic slabs of tough, ferruginous bioclastic limestone are present, particularly on the lower part of the dip slope. Bivalves are abundant in the limestone and well-preserved ammonites can be found.

Locality 8g: (SK 79503435). The Mill Lane Limestones (ML) form a very subtle feature, about 100m short of the main road. The greyish brown, finely sandy loam of the dip slope is an indication of the sandy nature of the limestone beds. Only sporadic brash of sandy bioclastic limestone can be seen. Cross over the road (Long Lane) and continue southeastwards along the footpath across a nearly flat clay field.

Locality 8h: (SK 79753420). A slight rise formed by the Highfield Farm Limestone (HF) occurs at the far side of the field. This limestone is grey, shelly, bioclastic and platy, and is pyritous when fresh. The bivalves *Gryphaea maccullochii* and *Pseudopecten* are abundant in the limestone and phosphatised ammonites, especially *Arnioceras*, and bored phosphate nodules are common in the underlying mudstone. A few pieces of the oxidised limestone with brown-lined cavities were found in the field to the southeast of the feature crest. Continue the walk in a southeasterly direction.

Localities 9: Demonstrates the outcrop of the Brant Mudstone Formation. The formation is composed of grey mudstones and siltstones with very few limestone beds. It contains distinct beds with nodules of calcium phosphate, **siderite** or fine-grained, argillaceous calcilutite.

Locality 9a: (SK 80103390). This part of the walk is currently pastured and hence no direct lithological evidence can be seen. The Glebe Farm Bed (GF) at the base of this formation is a ferruginous **oolite**, marking a non-sequence at the base of strata of the oxynotum zone. It generally contains the bivalve *Hippopodium*, belemnites and the ammonites *Oxynoticeras* and *Gagaticeras*. The succeeding Sand Beck Nodule Bed crops out on flat ground to the northwest of the next scarp feature. It comprises grey shaly mudstone with-numerous chocolate-brown-weathering siderite mudstone nodules containing abundant *Gagaticeras* ammonites.

Locality 9b: This is the Bradon Sandstone and the only bed of the Brant Formation that forms a cuesta (SK 80403370). The crest is typically broad and ill-defined. The dip slope carries a finely sandy loam with only sporadic buff-weathered, calcareous, fine-grained sandstone brash and fossils which can be collected from ditch dredgings. Bivalves are the most abundant fossils, particularly *Pholadomya*, though ammonites are also common. The cuesta feature is cut locally by three stream gullies along each of which it may be slightly offset by faulting. At this point the footpath assumes a northeasterly course to cross a small stream with a thin strip of alluvium along the largest, eastern-most gully.

Locality 9c: (SK 80803385): The path crosses a second bridge over a tributary stream. The crest of the Brandon Sandstone (BrS) can be seen a short distance to the northwest. In the bank of the steam gully, at the northeastern side of the bridge, the basal part of the Brandon Sandstone is exposed, comprising 0.6m of hard, brown, fine-grained calcareous sandstone, very broken and rubbly. It overlies 1.2m of soft, weathered, greyish brown siltstone overlying 0.4m medium grey, shaly mudstone.

Locality 9d: Oil borehole site (SK 80803390). A short distance to the northeast of the bridge, a small enclosure is the site of an unexploited deep borehole for oil.

Locality 9e: (SK 81103370). Cross over the bridge into a field that slopes initially gently to the northwest away from the steeper Marlstone scarp. This gentle slope is a **solifluxion** terrace underlain by head deposits derived by solifluxion and downslope wash of clay and silt from the steeper scarp. The deposit conceals grey mudstones containing several horizons of ammonite-bearing calcilutite limestone nodules commonly associated with impersistent bioclastic limestones.

Locality 9f: (SK 81553370). Turn left along the small track crossing the scarp slope obliquely. Beds above the Brandon Sandstone (BrS) comprise grey mudstones and siltstones with some beds characterised by phosphate, siderite mudstone and nodules of fine-grained limestone with the bivalve *Gryphaea*. These limestones do not form features but several can be identified and traced along the outcrop by their distinctive lithology. The Loveden Gryphaea Bed (LG) is the easiest to trace and contains abundant large *Gryphaea maccullochii*. Scattered fragmentary *Gryphaea* suggests that it crops out at this locality.

Locality 10: (SK 81703373). The walk ends at the junction of Belvoir Lane and Jubilee Way below the Castle. From here, look back across the Vale to Granby Church. The Castle stands on a small hill, which is a small outlier of 'Sandrock' beneath the Marlstone.

EXCURSION 11. MIDDLE JURASSIC OF SOUTH LINCOLNSHIRE, LEICESTERSHIRE AND NORTHAMPTONSHIRE

Alan Dawn, Stamford

Objectives

To examine sequences in the Middle Jurassic, which provide an opportunity to compare sediments deposited in marine and non-marine environments.

Logistics

The strata are exposed in quarries, most of which are currently being worked. Permission must be obtained in writing in advance from the quarry managers as specified before visiting a quarry. The sites are in isolated localities so that private transport is essential. Protective clothing including boots and helmets is obligatory. A reflective, brightly coloured "jacket" is demanded by many quarry managers, and some also insist on eye protection.

The two itineraries (Figures 34 and 38) cover a total of 11 sites of interest that are in easy reach of the A1 between Wansford in the south and Stretton in the north on OS 1:50,000 sheets 130 (Grantham), 141 (Kettering and Corby) and 142 (Peterborough). The area is shown on the British Geological Survey 1:50,000 sheets 143 (Stamford) and 171 (Kettering). Larger scale maps at six-inch or 1:10,000 scale may be examined at the BGS Keyworth Office, Nottingham.

Clay beds readily weather and degrade becoming extremely sticky in wet months. Extreme caution should be exercised when crossing clay scree, particularly where flowing water is present. It is extremely difficult to escape once you are trapped, even with the loss of wellingtons. In addition, the limestone faces and blasted areas are unstable. Great care must be taken when approaching in order to avoid falling blocks.

Geological Background

The sequences comprise alternating beds of limestone, ironstone, clay and sand (Figure 35). Lying above the Upper Lias Clay is the Northamptonshire Sand Ironstone, formerly extensively worked for its iron content and largely processed at the Corby Iron and Steelworks in Northamptonshire. Next comes the Grantham Formation, formerly known as the Lower Estuarine Series. In places it consists of pure white silica sand, used in the making of high temperature refractory products. Above the Grantham Formation the sands are calcite-cemented and pass up into the Inferior Oolite, the Lincolnshire Limestone. Overlying the Lincolnshire Limestone and following a **discontinuity** is the Rutland Formation, a series of clay cycles each showing shelly clays followed by root beds. The Blisworth Limestone above this is highly fossiliferous. It is overlain by the Blisworth Clay and this in turn gives way

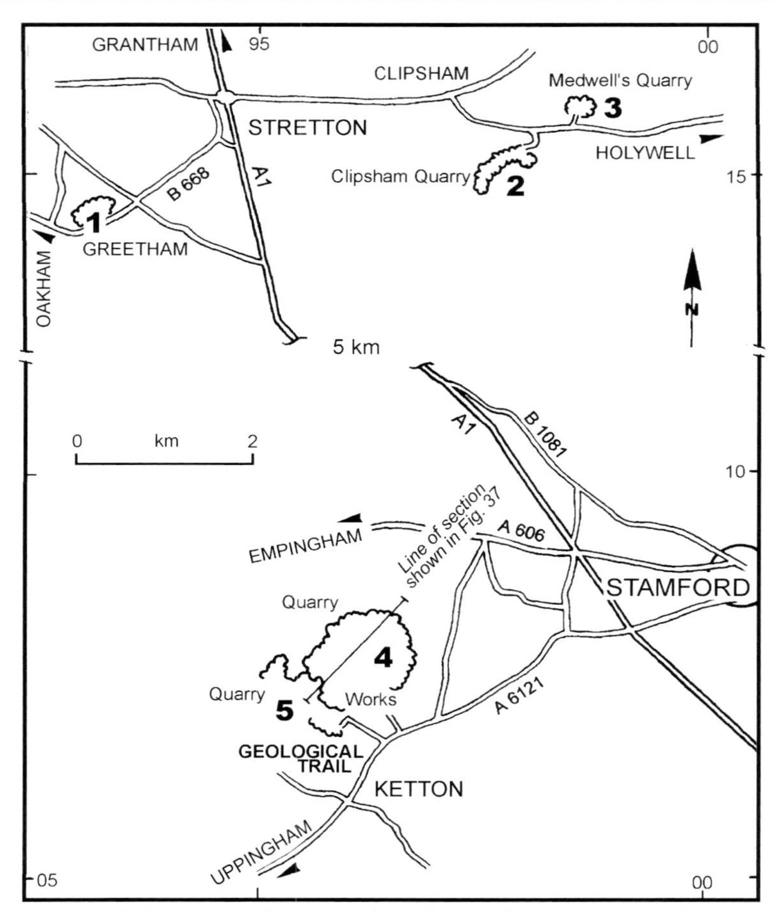

Figure 34. Map showing localities for excursion 1.

to the Cornbrash Limestone that in places is highly fossiliferous. The Cornbrash often yields a diagnostic **ammonite** *Macrocephalites*. The Cornbrash is the uppermost of the Middle Jurassic Limestones and is overlain by the Kellaways Beds that finally give way to the Oxford Clay.

Itinerary 1 (Figure 34): Locality Details

Locality 1: Greetham Quarry (SK 931145). The quarry is situated about 400m east of Greetham on the north side of the B668. Lincolnshire Limestone is extracted, largely for road aggregate, though smaller quantities are quarried for building stone.

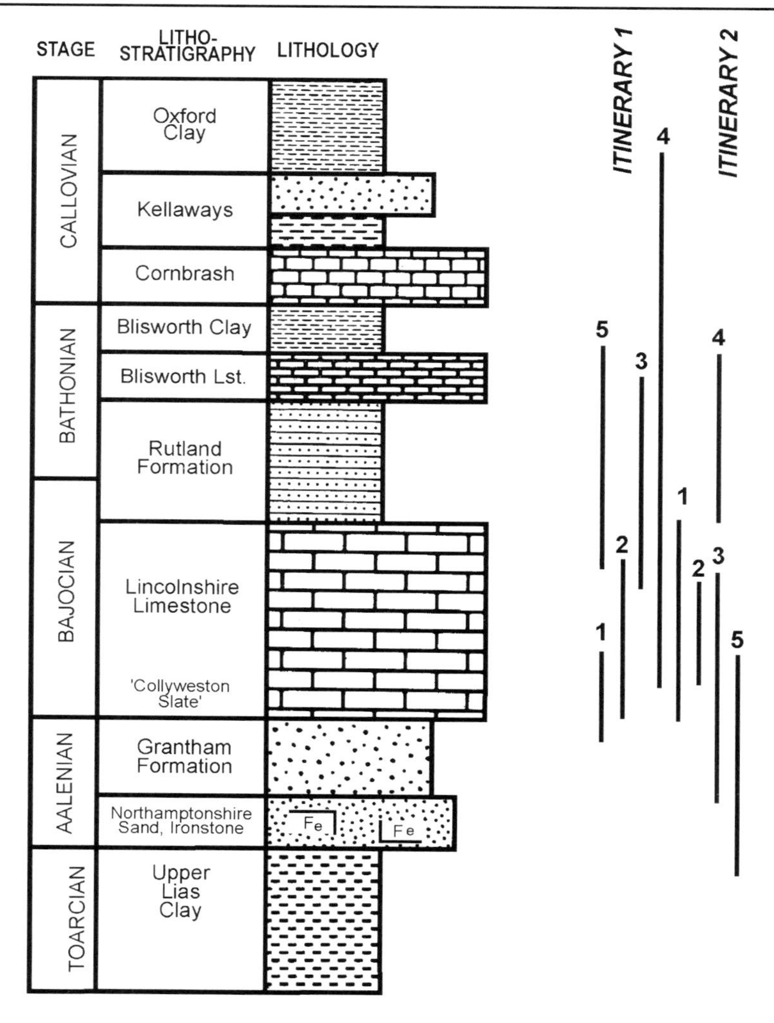

Figure 35. The Middle Jurassic succession in the excursion area.

The Grantham Formation, which can be seen in a drainage sump in the south-eastern corner of the quarry, is creamy white sand that passes upwards into clay. The basal beds of the Lincolnshire Limestone occur in the quarry face and comprise thin bands of limestone interbedded with clay or sandy bands. The bands of clay or sand are less common and thinner upward. In the higher limestones horizontal bedding and vertical **jointing** is prominent and current bedding can be seen in some beds.

Figure 36. Clipsham Quarry. Cross-bedded oolitic Upper Lincolnshire Limestone overlain unconformably by the freshwater Stamford Member and the cyclic Rutland Formation (top).

The lower limestones are typically micritic with variable quantities of **ooids**. However, the uppermost beds are cemented by calcite **spar** and are made up almost entirely of ooids. The oolitic limestone is used as a high quality building stone and called a freestone by stonemasons. At certain stages of quarrying channelling may be seen within the limestone. The lower fine-grained limestones are sporadically fossiliferous with shell debris and beds with high-spired nerineid gastropods are present. The oolitic freestones are almost entirely devoid of fossil material.

Permission to enter this quarry must be obtained in advance in writing from Bullimore's Sand and Gravel, Head Office, South Witham, Grantham, NG33 5QE.

Locality 2: Clipsham Quarry (SK 982156). Return to the A1 from Greetham along the B668, pass through Stretton after passing under the A1, and follow the road to Clipsham. At the eastern end of the village turn right on the road signed Holywell and Pickworth. After about 1km the quarry entrance will be seen on the south side of the road. A short lane leads to the quarry.

The quarry exposes an almost complete section of the Lincolnshire Limestone with intermittent covering of the Rutland Formation (Figure 36). The lower part of the Lincolnshire Limestone is exposed in a branch of the quarry to the left and beyond the weighbridge. It consists of fine-grained **micritic** limestones that in parts are highly fossiliferous with **bivalves**, corals, nerineid gastropods and occasional sharks' teeth.

These beds become increasingly oolitic upwards. An upper unit contains abundant shell debris in an oolitic matrix. This is the famed Clipsham Stone. This

Figure 37. Faulting (Lincolnshire Limestone and Kellaways Beds) at Ketton Quarry - line of section on Figure 34.

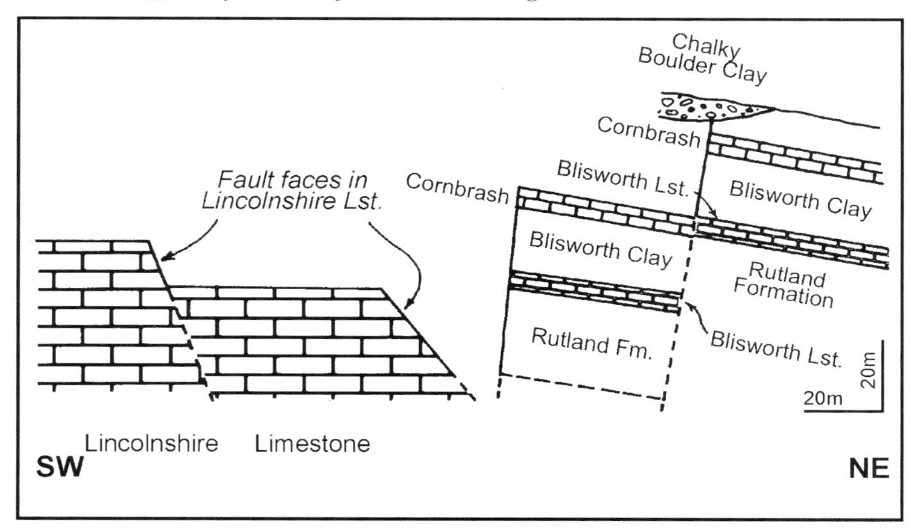

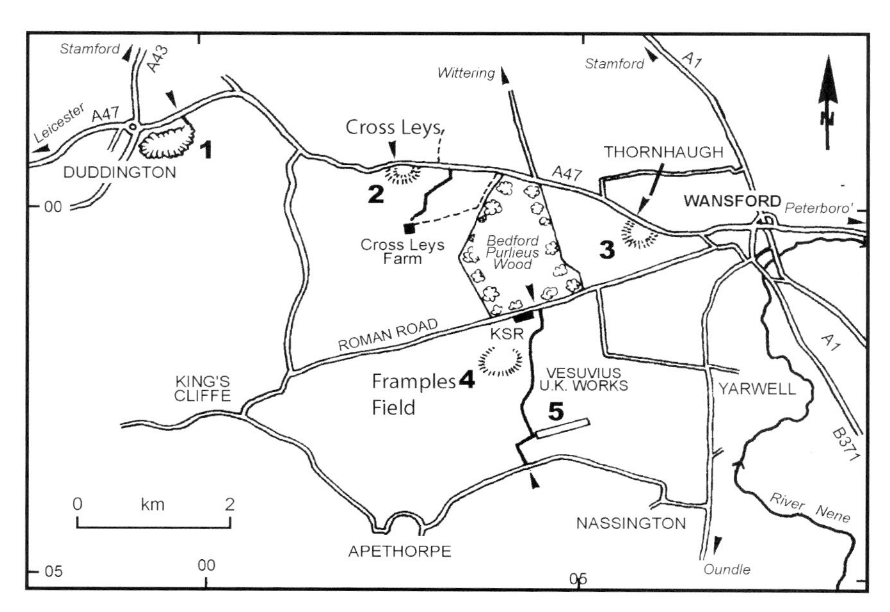

Figure 38. Map showing localities for itinerary 2.

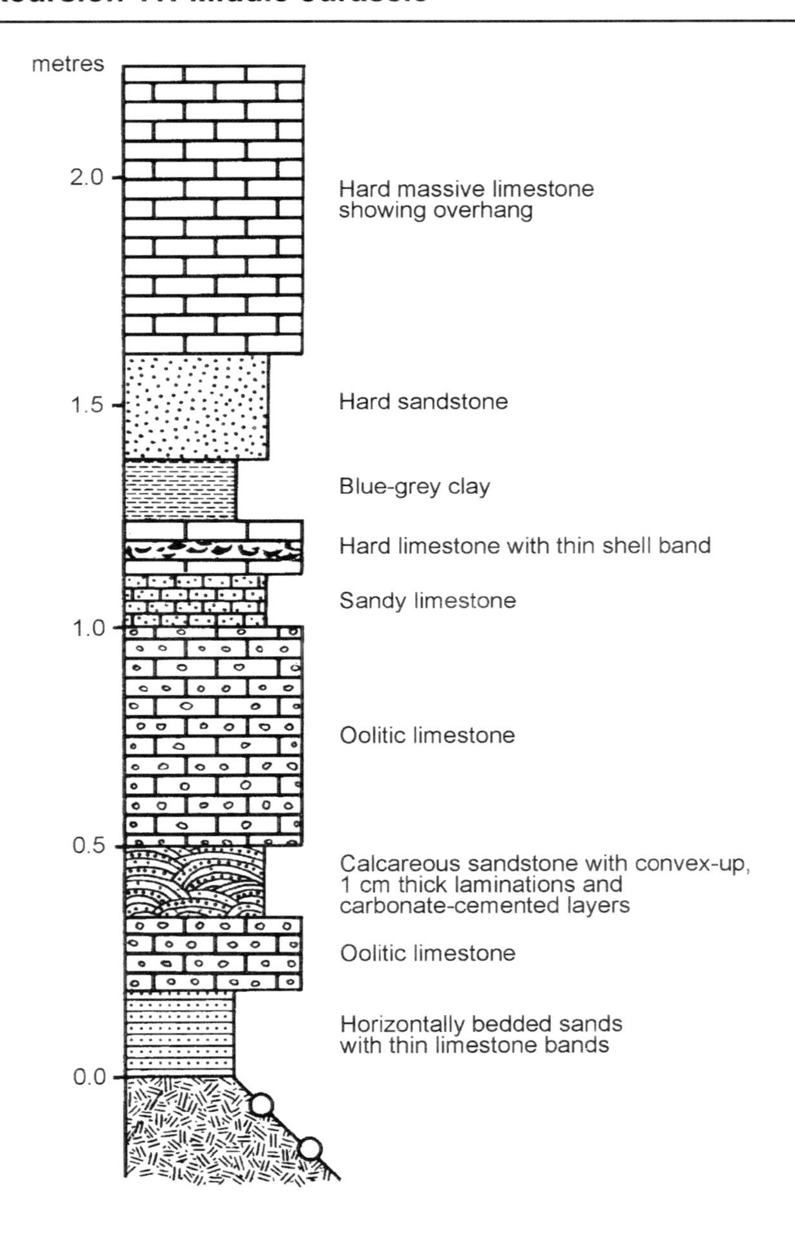

Figure 39. Succession at Cross Leys Quarry near Wittering.

is horizontally bedded and vertically jointed. It has been much used as a building stone both locally and countrywide. For example, it is widely used in Oxford colleges. Undressed blocks of this stone can be seen on the quarry floor.

In the main part of the quarry all the limestone is being extracted for aggregate, crushed and sorted into various sizes. Horizontal bedding and vertical jointing are prominent in the vertical faces. Brachiopods and bivalve fossils can often be found on the quarry floor and in the fallen blocks.

The southwestern face of the quarry reveals a channel eroded into the top of the Lincolnshire Limestone beds. The channel appears to be infilled by the Stamford Member of the Rutland Formation, but is currently inaccessible at the top of a vertical face.

Permission to enter this quarry must be obtained in advance in writing from Bullimore's Sand and Gravel, Head Office, South Witham, Grantham NG33 5QE

Locality 3: Medwell's Quarry (SK 987160). Proceed about 400m further towards Holywell until you come to farms on either side of the road. A track towards the north (left) is marked Rattee and Kett Quarry. The quarry is about 100m off the road, and is hidden by trees. Rattee and Kett, a branch of Mowlem, extract the Clipsham **ragstone** at the top of the Lincolnshire Limestone for use as a building or decorative stone. The stone is worked from beneath a thick overburden of Rutland Formation and basal Blisworth Limestone, neither of which is easily accessible. The ragstone consists of shell debris with ooids in thick beds with widely

Figure 40. Framples Field Quarry. Freshwater Stamford Member (base) overlain by cyclic clay-dominated Rutland Formation.

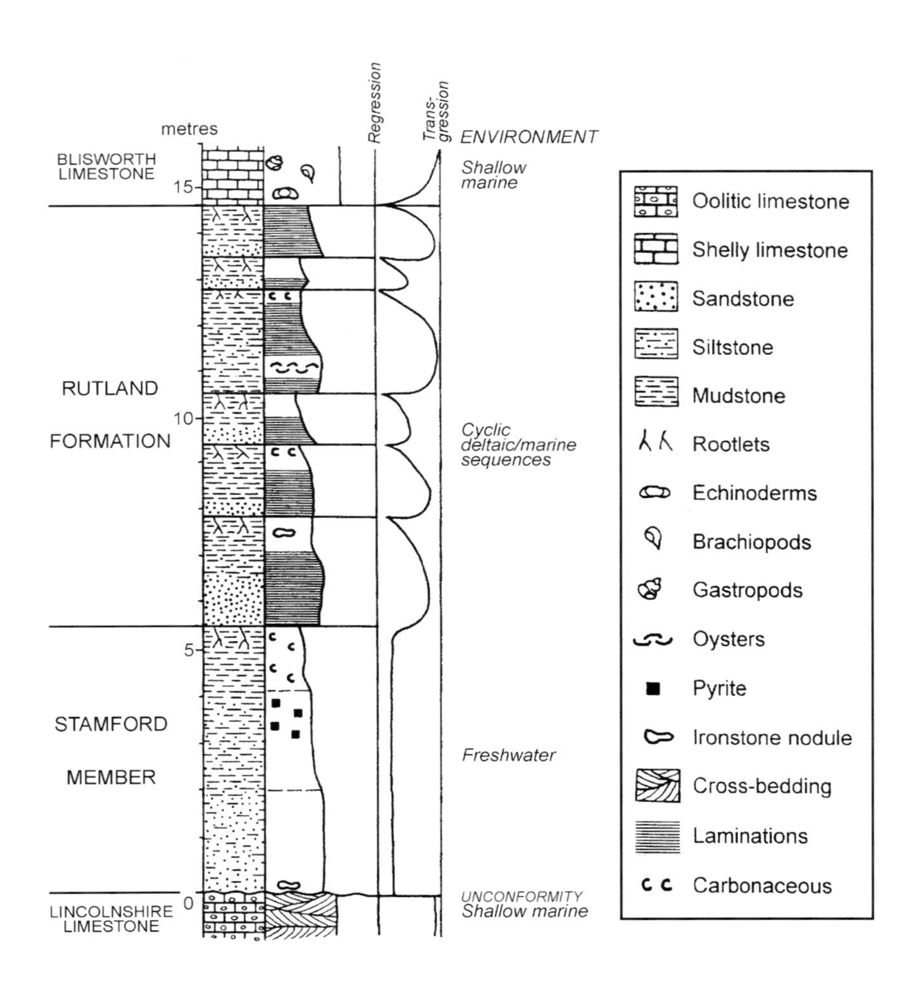

Figure 41. Section through the Rutland Formation showing the cyclicity of depositional environments. The unconformity between the Lincolnshire Limestone and the overlying Stamford Member represents a time gap of 4 to 6 million years.

spaced vertical joints. Note that the Limestone is strongly **cross-stratified** indicating current flow towards the southeast at the time of deposition. The total thickness of ragstone worked here is about 6m.

The method of extracting the stone is of interest. It is cut into blocks of about one or two metre cubes by drilling two sets of closely spread holes in lines at right angles. Steel wedges are driven into the holes to split away the blocks, which are then lifted by crane. After additional dressing they are sent, if necessary, to the stonemason's yards for final preparation as ornamental or building stone.

Permission to enter the quarry must be obtained in advance from Messrs Rattee and Kett, Purbeck Road, Cambridge CB2 2PG. Telephone 01223-248061.

Locality 4: Ketton Quarry Castle Cement (SK 980060). From Clipsham return to the A1 and travel south to the Stamford by-pass. Leave the A1 by the A 6121. The cement works can be clearly seen some 3km to the west. Enter the quarry via Pit Lane at the junction with A6121 at SK 983051. Drive to the quarry office. This is a very large quarry, requiring a total walk of about 3km. Three to four hours are required to see all the features. Hard hats and strong boots are essential, and the floor of the quarry is muddy in wet weather.

The quarry exposes the Lincolnshire Limestone, Upper Estuarine Clays and Blisworth Limestone. Faulting to the north has preserved Blisworth Clay, Upper Cornbrash Limestone and Kellaways Clay and Sand, overlain by thick **Pleistocene** deposits. The exposures range from Middle Bajocian to Lower Callovian stages.

From the quarry top you can see the valleys of the River Welland to the south, and the Gwash to the north. Both of these rivers have cut down to the Upper Lias clays.

Starting from the quarry office car park walk northeastwards to the limestone face. This is of unreliable stability. Fallen blocks from the blasting operation may be examined. Note the brown ironstone bed at the top of the face. This contains shells and fossilized wood. Beneath is the oolitic freestone; blocks are often blue-hearted. The blue core of these blocks is caused by the presence of disseminated pyrite. This decomposes on **weathering** to give the outer creamy brown stained limestone together with gypsum as a by-product. Vugs of gypsum, lined by calcite cement are sometimes found in the limestone. This deposit is part of a **diachronous** prograding offshore barrier, which overlies a back-reef **facies** of more muddy limestones in the lower part of the face. High-spired nerineid gastropods occur at the two horizons and occasional bivalve and other shells may be found in the fallen blocks.

The nerineid beds are often heavily cemented and can be brought to a dull polish. They have been used in decorative building work under the name of Stamford Marble. Note the horizontal bedding and vertical jointing as in the earlier quarries. Note also the occurrence of intermittent blue-hearted limestones.

Prominent ramps lead from the quarry floor to the top of the limestones. Walk (or drive if permitted) up one of these ramps to the limestone surface. This surface is an erosion surface (**unconformity**) that represents an estimated time gap of four to six million years.

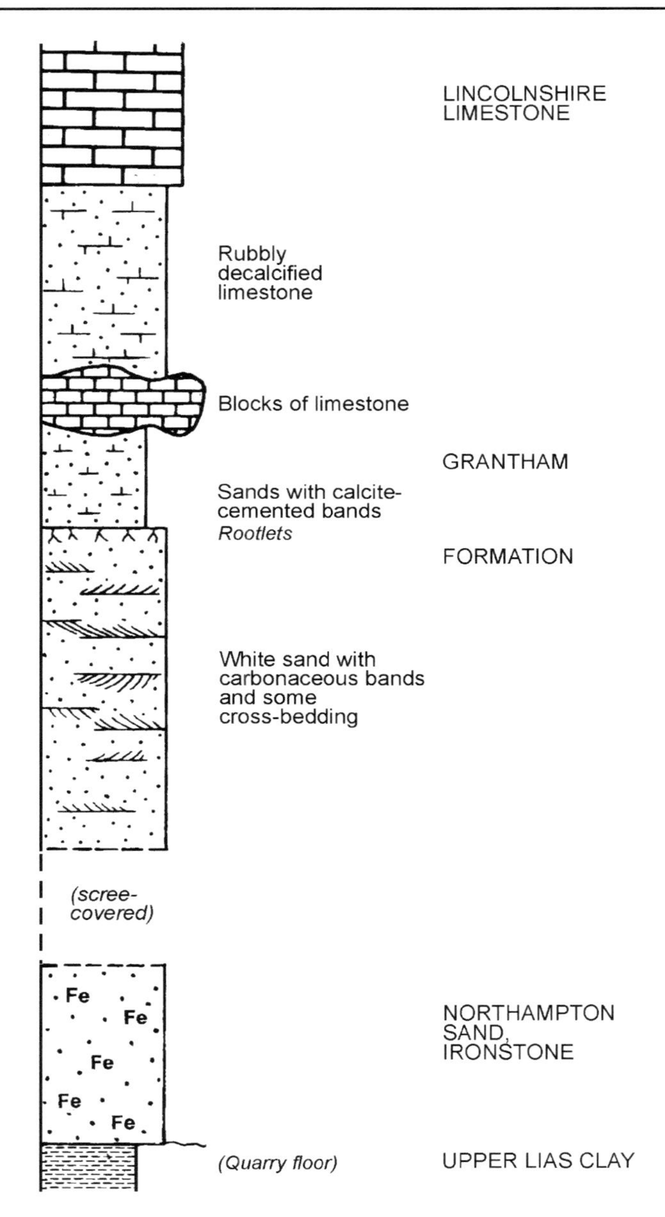

Figure 42. Succession through Northamptonshire Sand Ironstone, Grantham Formation and basal Lincolnshire Limestone at Ring Haw strip mine.

A search of this surface will yield gypsum in the form of satin spar and **siderite** ironstone nodules of golf ball size. Watch out for deep fissures and vertical joints.

Walk across to the clay face. This is the Upper Estuarine Clay, now called the Rutland Formation. The bottom bed is a freshwater bed with bands of ironstone at the base. Above is a **cyclic** sequence of beds deposited in brackish water. Examine one of the cycles and note the progression from abundant shell remains at the bottom. These shells indicate shallow brackish water where these animals could survive. The gradual deposition of mud caused a progressive shallowing until reed beds could root, probably forming intertidal flats. The beds with roots are truncated at the top of the sequence and shells reappear indicating a deepening of the water. There are at least seven of these cycles.

Above the clays you see the buff-coloured Blisworth Limestone. The Blisworth Limestone is fossiliferous and yields the bivalves *Modiolus*, *Pleuromya*, *Pholadomya* and *Protocardia*, the echinoid *Clypeus*; occasional corals, brachiopods and gastropods are also present.

A fault can be seen in the clay face. This has down-thrown the Cornbrash Limestone to the same horizon level as the Blisworth Limestone. The fault system can be examined by ascending the next ramp and walking along the surfaces of the Blisworth and Cornbrash Limestones (Figure 37). The faulting appears to be a **graben** subsidence along a shallow **anticline**, and this becomes obvious towards the western end of the system. A search of the Cornbrash will sometimes reveal the fossil ammonite *Macrocephalites*. Above the Cornbrash there is a deposit of Kellaways Clay and Sand that yields *Gryphea* and belemnites.

Pleistocene deposits overlying these clays contain various erratics, including chalk and flint. This suggests an early ice advance possibly during the **Anglian** or possibly **Wolstonian**.

The Lincolnshire Limestone and Upper Estuarine Clays are quarried for the manufacture of cement. Some of the freestone is used in monumental work at the nearby Ketton Stone Works. The worked out quarry is now backfilled and restored to agriculture.

Permission to enter the quarry should be sought in writing from the Quarry Manager, Castle Cement, Ketton, near Stamford.

Locality 5: Grange Quarry (SK 978054). A Geological Trail in the quarry, adjacent to Ketton Quarry. Enter via a small industrial complex on the western side of Pit Lane. There is a car park and access is free and requires no permit.

This is a Regionally Important Geological Site (RIGS) exposing sediments of Bajocian and Bathonian Age. The Stamford and District Geological Society have developed the site as a Geology Trail. It displays the freestone (oolitic limestone) of the Upper Lincolnshire Limestone, the Upper Estuarine Clays of the Rutland Formation, and the Blisworth Limestone, together with a fault. Easy access by steps allows close inspection of the faces in safety. Wheelchair access is made possible by a concrete pathway from the car park to the face one hundred metres away.

The site is open to the public and an explanatory leaflet is available from The Secretary, Stamford and District Geological Society, 26 Sutherland Way, Stamford, Lincs, PE9 2TB price 50p plus postage. Except in very wet weather ordinary walking shoes are adequate. No hammering on the faces is allowed, but there are many fallen blocks available for specimen collectors. Allow about one hour to walk round the trail.

Itinerary 2 (Figure 38): Locality Details

Locality 1: Duddington Quarry (SK 995013). The quarry is on the A47 road, a short distance east of the roundabout where the A47 crosses the A43 at Duddington. The Bajocian age Lincolnshire Limestone is extracted chiefly for roadstone. Some Collyweston Slate is also used for roofing by David Ellis, of Ryhall, near Stamford.

This quarry exposes the lower beds of the Lincolnshire Limestone. The deepest part of the quarry in the southwest corner exposes the Collyweston Slate beds. These are not true slates but have been so-called by the local roofing industry. They are thinly bedded calcite-cemented sands which split along micaceous bedding planes when exposed wet to the effects of frost. Once dried they will split no further.

The beds lie immediately over the Lower Estuarine Beds, now termed the Grantham Formation, and are overlain by thinly bedded, fossiliferous limestones, followed by more blocky stone above. The rare gastropod *Phyllocheilus bentleyi* is occasionally found here.

Permission to enter should be sought in writing from Bullimore Sand and Gravel, Head Office, South Witham, Grantham, Lincolnshire NG33 5QE. Hard hats and boots are required.

Locality 2: Cross Leys Quarry (TF 032005). Proceed eastwards along the A47 towards Peterborough for approximately 3.6km. The quarry entrance is at TF 032005 on the south side of the A47. It is indicated by a large notice board, slightly set back from the road.

Allow one to two hours to see all the features of the quarry. Car parking is limited to the entrance of the quarry and will take no more than six or seven cars. Hard hats and boots are required. There are flooded areas that might present a danger to the incautious. About 200m into the quarry several large concrete beams will be seen. Examine the quarry face here (Care! falling blocks). The limestones **dip** gently to the south. A measured section is shown for one part of the quarry by Figure 39. However, there is some lateral variation in the succession. Blue-hearted sandy limestones can be seen at the base of the sequence, followed by alternating bands of clay and limestone. The lower beds are often hidden by fallen scree.

Of particular interest are the banded units that are quite prominent. Each consists of alternate thin layers of strongly cemented sandy limestone and yellow/brown decalcified sand up to 2cm thick. In places these bands are horizontal, in others they have been deformed into convex-up or dome-like structures. In a few places this banding is interrupted by narrow vertical **decalcified** sand pipes. The structures may be the result of dewatering of rapidly deposited sediment followed by patchy cementation of the sandstone.

Elsewhere one sees both on the vertical faces and the undersides of overhanging rock a series of concentric circle and ovoid patterns. These are superimposed on the original horizontal bedding and cross-stratification. This may represent spheroidal weathering of the rectangularly jointed limestone beds. Locally the clay beds have been squeezed upwards and occasionally downwards into the vertical joints in the limestones. Burrows can be seen on the surface of many of the fallen blocks and nerineid gastropods can be found in some horizons in the limestones.

Permission to enter this and Thornhaugh quarries must be sought from the quarry manager.

Locality 3: Thornhaugh Quarry (TL 058998). From Cross Leys Quarry follow the A47 eastwards towards Wansford and Peterborough. After about 3km Thornhaugh quarry is on the right, south of the A47. Drive past the weighbridge and into the quarry to the office blocks in the bottom to park. Watch out for moving machinery and vehicles.

The floor of the quarry exposes the White Sands of the Grantham Formation. These are quartz-rich (silica) sands with cross-stratification and some root beds, indicating shallow water deposition. The Lincolnshire Limestone is exposed in a face some 6m high, capped by the clays of the Rutland Formation on the south-eastern side of the quarry.

The quarry manager will usually indicate which areas are safe to approach.

Locality 4: Framples Field Quarry (TL 042978) (Figure 40). From Thornhaugh Quarry, proceed along the A47 towards Wansford. After about 1km take the road to the right for Wansford and in a further 200m turn right along the old Roman Road towards King's Cliffe. The quarry offices are about 2 km further on the south side of the road at TL 045988, opposite Bedford Purlieus Wood. The works are now called Vesuvius UK; visitors should report to the office before proceeding to Framples Field Quarry. The entrance to the quarry is through the works, following the track to Great Byards Sale Wood at TL 042978.

The quarry exposes the complete Rutland and Blisworth Limestone Formations and the lower part of the Blisworth Clay. The floor of the quarry reveals the basal ironstone nodule bed of the Stamford Member. This rests on the Lincolnshire Limestone (as seen at Ketton Quarry). Above is a bed of white fine-grained quartz sand that persists through the quarry, and in fact is found in several other quarries in the area. It is overlain by pale grey blocky silty mudstone that shows some channelling infilled by the overlying dark purplish grey silty mudstone. This contains plant debris and rootlets, some of which have been pyritized. The youngest bed of the Stamford Member is a very dark grey blocky mudstone with superb rootlets. This is reminiscent of a Coal Measures **seatearth**. These beds were formerly called the Freshwater Beds. The white sands represent river channel infill with the overlying silty clays perhaps forming in marginal lake basins. The final bed represents a more distal swamp environment.

A marine **transgression** preceded the deposition of the upper part of the Rutland Formation. The rhythmic sequence above indicates the cyclic nature of the sedimentation (Figure 41). Each cycle starts with a transgression and the deposition of calcareous silts with numerous bivalves and gastropods. The silts fine upwards into black carbonaceous clay with prominent vertical roots. These are then abruptly truncated by overlying sediments deposited during the next marine transgression.

The cyclic sequences are remarkably consistent between several quarries in the area and can be compared with those seen at Ketton Quarry. The planar bedding and lateral persistence of these beds is evidence of deposition on a low-lying very mature coastal plain subjected to repeated relative changes of sea-level.

The overlying Blisworth Limestone was deposited following a major marine transgression. The lower beds contain clay galls, burrows and numerous oysters (*Liostrea*) that usually extend into the upper parts of the Rutland Formation. The limestone is coarse with shells and **ooids**. The proportion of **micrite** and **sparry** calcite varies from bed to bed, resulting in the alternation of soft **marls** with harder and more resistant limestone. The abundant fauna is restricted in species but yields numerous bivalves (*Modiolus*, *Pleuromya*, *Pholadomya*, *Liostrea*, *Radulopecten*), brachiopods (*Kallirhynchia*, *Epithyris*), echinoids (*Clypeus*, *Nucleolites*), gastropods and occasional corals (*Isastrea* and a small button coral). This limestone formed in a much lower energy environment than the older Lincolnshire Limestone.

Permission to enter this quarry must be obtained in advance from the Manager, Vesuvius UK, Kings Cliffe Works, King's Cliffe, Peterborough.

Locality 5: Ring Haw Quarry (TL 045972). The former ironstone strip mine, the Nassington pit, was last worked in 1967. Methods of working can still be traced. The pit is under the control of Vesuvius UK who should be approached for permission to enter.

From the Vesuvius UK offices, proceed to King's Cliffe. Turn left at the village, and then left again to Apethorpe. About 400m beyond Apethorpe take the road on the left towards Nassington. In about 1.1km find the wood at Little Morton Sale. Enter by a gate at the western side of the wood. The gate is numbered 25 and is painted green, with a red sidegate. Walk along the track for about 270m until you reach a junction near the old railway bridge. The strip mine is on the right. Approach via a side gate that leads into a field on the back-filled land. Walk along the fence for about 130m until you reach an iron five-barred gate. Go through and descend by the rope handrail to the bottom of the quarry. You can see all the relevant geology from this point (Figure 42).

The somewhat overgrown face reveals the section from the Lincolnshire Limestone down through the Grantham Formation to the Northamptonshire Sand Ironstone. In dry conditions the ironstone can be examined. It is composed largely of sideritic limestones and **chamosite** ooids. Weathering by oxidation of the original iron minerals has created box-like structures in the deposit with parallel bands of limonite and goethite. Any fossil shells are largely destroyed in this process.

Above the ironstone are some 6m of white sand of the Grantham Formation. The sands are inter-layered with thin black carbonaceous beds, and the top of the beds is thickly penetrated by rootlets. Above the sands there is a sharp contact with buff-coloured sand which grades up into a decalcified limestone. Here you see the contorted banded units similar to those seen in the Cross Leys Quarry, and which must be the lateral equivalent of the Collyweston Slate Beds. These beds are some three metres in thickness and grade into first rubbly and then more solidly cemented blocky Lincolnshire Limestone, of which some 2m is visible.

A walk along the field allows a view of the lateral extent of the quarry workings. The quarry was worked by two excavators; a very large dragline worked areas to the north and a second smaller dragline then lifted the ironstone to a temporary railway laid on top of the ironstone bed. Discarded railway sleepers can be seen here and there.

GLOSSARY

This is not intended to be a comprehensive geological glossary but includes the terms used in this account of the geology of the East Midlands highlighted in the text. Terms highlighted in the definitions are cross-referenced with other terms in the glossary.

Agglomerate: a volcanic rock formed of subangular and rounded fragments more than 64 mm in diameter set in a matrix of ash.
Alluvium: Deposits laid down by rivers.
Ammonoid: a free-swimming marine mollusc (**cephalopod**) with a coiled, chambered shell; the Nautilus is a similar living example. See also **goniatite** and **ammonite.**
Ammonite: a Mesozoic **ammonoid** with a highly ornamented suture.
Andesite: lava of intermediate composition with dominant sodium/calcium plagioclase **feldspar**.
Anglian: The second of the four main glacial episodes during the **Pleistocene**.
Anticline: upfolded strata with the oldest rocks in the core of the fold.
Argillaceous: applied to sediments with clay-sized particles commonly clay minerals.
Arkose: sandstone with more than 25% detrital **feldspar** grains. A sub-arkose contains between 5-25% detrital feldspar.
Asbian: The second youngest stage (D1) of the **Dinantian**; comes before the **Brigantian**.
Auto-brecciation: Lava forms a brittle crust as it cools. Flowing molten lava causes the crust to break up into angular blocks that are incorporated into the flow.
Ball and pillow: A dewatering structure (pseudo-nodule) seen in sandstones in which a segment has foundered into the underlying waterlogged sediment.
Basalt: Lava that contains calcium-rich plagioclase **feldspars**, pyroxenes and iron ores.
Basement: Deformed and metamorphosed Precambrian to Lower Palaeozoic rocks that underlie Carboniferous and Mesozoic sediments in the East Midlands area.
Belemnite: A cigar-shaped calcareous fossil forming part of a **cephalopod** that resembled the modern squid.
Bivalve: a marine or freshwater mollusc with a shell consisting of two hinged valves. The hinge normally forms the plane of symmetry. Mussels are living and fossil bivalves.
Boulder clay: till deposited by glaciers comprising a mixture of boulders and clay.
Brachiopod: a marine animal with a hinged two-valved calcite shell. The plane of symmetry is perpendicular to the hinge. Gigantoproductids are a large (up to 20cm across) brachiopod commonly found in the Carboniferous Limestone.

Brash: Fragments of the bedrock or fossils in soil; a useful indicator of the underlying bedrock in areas of no exposure.
Breccia: A coarse-grained sedimentary rock dominantly made of angular fragments.
Brigantian: The youngest **Dinantian** stage (D2-P2) of the Carboniferous period; following the **Asbian**.
Bryozoans: Colonial animals with a calcareous skeleton attached to the seabed. Fenestellids were large fan-like bryozoans.
Bullion: an egg- or disc-shaped **concretion** typically found in mudstones or coal. Formed by the precipitation of calcareous or ferruginous minerals in the sediment.
Calcarenite: detrital limestone composed mainly of sand-sized carbonate grains.
Calcilutite: very fine-grained detrital limestone composed mainly of **micrite**.
Calcirudite: detrital limestone composed mainly of pebble-sized carbonate fragments.
Caldera: a large volcanic depression, completely or partly walled, more or less circular in plan.
Caledonian Orogeny: Mountain building during the Ordovician to Devonian mainly affecting northern Britain and also the **basement** rocks of the Midlands.
Carbonate mud mounds: lenticular reef-like build-ups of fine-grained limestone formed by algal-bacterial communities during the early Carboniferous.
Carbonate platform: an area of shallow marine carbonate sedimentation.
Cement/cementation: Minerals including calcite that have been chemically precipitated between grains in sedimentary rocks.
Cephalopod: a free-swimming marine mollusc with a chambered shell that is usually coiled; see also **ammonoid**, **goniatite** and **ammonite**.
Chamosite: an iron silicate mineral that sometimes forms oolitic coatings around sediment grains.
Chert: finely crystalline silica that often forms **concretions** in limestone or mudstone.
Clay wayboard: Volcanic-derived mudstone developed by weathering in a soil profile on **palaeokarsts** in Dinantian limestones.
Cleavage refraction: is the variation of angle between cleavage and bedding through a succession of interbedded fine and coarse-grained sediments.
Concretion: a hard compact mass or aggregate of minerals formed by the localized precipitation of calcareous, siliceous or ferruginous minerals in a sediment.
Crinoid: a marine invertebrate known as sea lilies. Consists of plated cup-bearing feeding arms supported by a stalk of disc-shaped ossicles or columnals, which are commonly preserved as fossils. Closely related to starfish and sea urchins.
Cross-stratification/bedding/lamination: inclined layering (**foresets**), usually seen in sandstone or **calcarenite**, deposited at an angle to bedding formed by the downstream migration of ripples or sand dunes deposited by water or wind action. The dip direction of cross-bedding indicates the former current or wind direction.
Cuesta: A hill or ridge consisting of a steep scarp slope and a less steep dip slope.
Cyclic sedimentation: A succession made up of numerous **cycles** or **cyclothems** each of which repeats a similar sequence of sedimentary rock types.

Cyclothem/Cycle: One of the sedimentary units that make up a cyclic succession. For example deltas often deposit sedimentary cycles with a marine shale at the base passing upwards into progressively coarser sediments. This represents a delta building out into the sea culminating in the deposition of a fluvial sandstone.
Dacite: "acidic" lava consisting of plagioclase **feldspar** plus quartz, hornblende, biotite or pyroxene.
Decalcified: an originally calcareous rock from which the calcium carbonate has been leached, or replaced by another mineral.
Delta/deltaic: a large accumulation of sediment at the mouth of a river where the rate of sedimentation exceeds that of the rate of sediment removal by erosional processes.
Delta slope: the region beyond the mouth bar of a delta distributary channel where sediment is deposited on a slope leading down to deeper water.
Derbyshire Massif: Western part of the East Midlands Block upon which shallow water sediments were deposited during the early Carboniferous.
Desiccation cracks: Polygonal shrinkage fractures in mud usually formed by drying.
Devensian: The British name for the last period of glaciation during the **Pleistocene**. Devensian glaciation features are largely absent in central England.
Devitrification: Recrystallisation of glassy igneous rock into very fine crystals.
Diachronous: A diachronous body of sediment is a continuous bed that was deposited at different times in different places, e.g. a deltaic sandstone progressively building out into the sea.
Diagenesis: All processes affecting a sediment after deposition, during and after lithification excluding weathering and metamorphism.
Dinantian: Oldest division of the Carboniferous System. This was a time of limestone deposition over much of central England.
Diorite: an intermediate intrusive coarse-grained igneous rock containing 55-65% silica and a variable mixture of sodium/calcium plagioclase **feldspar** and common hornblende. (Microdiorite is medium-grained diorite.)
Dip: The inclination of a bedding plane, measured perpendicular to **strike**.
Disconformity/discontinuity: A break within a sedimentary succession that represents a significant time gap; the term is applied to an **unconformity** where there is little or no discordance between the strata above and below.
Dolomite/dolomitization: A process whereby original aragonite and calcite in a sediment is converted by magnesium-rich fluids into the mineral dolomite. The rock name is also dolomite or dolostone.
Dreikanter: A pebble faceted by wind action; indicative of desert conditions.
Epiclastic: sandstones of non-volcanic origin.
Eustasy: Global sea-level variations caused by changes in the volume of the oceans or sea water.
Evaporite: a mineral or sediment deposited as a result of the evaporation of water. Evaporites include halite (rock salt), gypsum and anhydrite.

Facies: the facies of a sedimentary rock are its characteristics including its fossil content, sedimentary structures and grain-size from which the environment of deposition can be deduced. The facies of a metamorphic rock refers to the intensity of metamorphism indicated by the mineral assemblage.
Fault: a fracture in the bedrock, usually steeply inclined; along which one side has moved relative to the other. The direction of movement may be vertical (dip-slip), horizontal (strike-slip) or a combination of both. The throw is the amount of relative vertical movement of strata across a fault. The most common type of fault is the normal fault that has a fault plane that dips steeply towards the downthrown side. Faults are often marked by a zone of fault **breccia** that comprises angular fragments of rock formed by movement of the fault.
Feldspar: a group of common alumino-silicate rock-forming minerals found in igneous and metamorphic rocks and in sandstones as detrital grains. **Plagioclase** is a sodium-calcium feldspar; **Orthoclase** is a potassium-rich feldspar.
Felsite: a finely-crystalline lava or shallow intrusive igneous rock of granitic composition composed almost entirely of feldspar and quartz.
Fenestellid: bryozoan with a lattice-like framework.
Fireclay: fossil clay soil with refractory properties found beneath coal seams especially in the Coal Measures.
Flame structure: Flame-shaped bodies of mud produced by the upward injection of waterlogged sediment into overlying sediment resulting from loading, rapid deposition or vibrations of the sediment.
Flash flood: a sudden catastrophic flood produced by infrequent, heavy rainfall.
Flowstone: calcium carbonate precipitated by water flowing over cave walls.
Fluidisation: sediment that becomes fluid as a result of vibration or sudden loading.
Foresets: inclined layers, usually seen in sandstone or **calcarenite**, deposited at an angle to bedding representing the down-stream migration of ripples or sand dunes deposited by water or wind action. The dip direction of the foresets indicates the former current or wind direction.
Frost heave: sediment disturbance by freeze-thaw action in **periglacial** conditions. See also **solifluxion**.
Ganister: a silica-rich fossil soil (**seatearth**) commonly found in the Coal Measures.
Gastropod: a mollusc with a coiled, non-chambered calcareous shell e.g. a snail.
Glacio-lacustrine: sediment deposited in lakes in front of melting glaciers.
Goniatite: a Palaeozoic **ammonoid**.
Graben: a down-faulted trough between parallel normal faults.
Granite: a coarse-grained intrusive igneous rock that contains 20-40% quartz and **feldspar** and typically not more than 5-10% of mica and/or amphibole.
Granophyric: Fine-scale intergrowth of quartz and alkali feldspar in medium and fine-grained igneous rocks of granitic composition.
Greenschist facies: Rocks that have undergone low to medium grade regional metamorphism, commonly containing chlorite and epidote.
Greywacke: a poorly sorted muddy sandstone; often, but not always deposited by a

turbidity current.
Head: a loose superficial deposit with angular fragments resulting from **solifluxion.**
Hornfels: metamorphic rock produced by heating of the country rock in contact with an igneous intrusion.
Hydrothermal: Deposition of minerals such as fluorite and galena from hot aqueous solutions.
Ignimbrite: A welded volcanic tuff deposited by a hot turbulent incandescent ash flow from a volcano.
Inlier: An outcrop of older strata, surrounded by younger strata.
Interfluve: the terrain between two river or stream valleys.
Inselberg: A prominent isolated residual hill rising abruptly from a surrounding extensive lowland erosion surface in a desert or semi-arid environment.
Island arc: A line of oceanic volcanic islands associated with a **subduction zone**.
Joint: A rock fracture along which no relative movement has taken place.
K-bentonite: Potassium-rich volcanic soil on **palaeokarsts** in Dinantian limestones.
Karst: Landforms formed by the action of water on limestone such as sinkholes, caves and limestone pavements.
Laccolith: a mushroom-shaped igneous intrusion.
Lapilli: volcaniclastic particles between 2 mm and 64 mm in size.
Listric fault: A normal fault where the fault plane flattens off at depth.
Load casts: rounded protuberant bodies of sediment that have foundered into waterlogged fine-grained sediment as a result of **fluidisation**.
Loess: fine-grained unstratified wind-blown silty clay commonly found in periglacial areas.
Marine band: A mudstone with marine fossils dominated by a few species.
Marl: a calcareous or dolomitic mudstone.
Mesozoic: a period of geological time lasting from the beginning of the Triassic 248 million years ago to the end of the Cretaceous 60 million years ago.
Mica: silicate mineral characterised by very thin flake-like crystals. Found in **granite** and metamorphic rocks and as detrital grains in sandstone and siltstone.
Micrite: Mud-sized carbonate particles.
Monocline: A fold with one inclined and one horizontal limb.
Mud flakes: clasts of mudstone formed by desiccation or erosion of weakly consolidated clay beds.
Muschelkalk: A sea occupying central Europe and Germany during the Middle Triassic. The North Sea Basin and the East Midlands area were located at its margins.
Namurian: The period following the **Dinantian** in the Carboniferous System. This was a time of **deltaic** sedimentation over much of central England.
Ooid: rounded grain made up of calcium carbonate or **chamosite** precipitated around another grain. An **oolite** is a limestone made up of ooids.
Palaeogeography: Ancient geography, e.g. the distribution of rivers, deltas, seas

and land etc. through geological history.
Palaeokarst: An ancient subaerial erosion surface formed by the action of water on lithified limestone, including such features as sinkholes, caves or limestone pavements.
Palaeosol: a fossil soil horizon.
Palaeozoic: a period of geological time lasting from the beginning of the Cambrian approximately 590 million years ago to the end of the Permian 248 million years ago.
Pangaea: A late Palaeozoic supercontinent that broke up during the Mesozoic.
Pelite/pelitic: metamorphosed shale or mudstone.
Periglacial: relating to structures or processes associated with ice sheets.
Phenocrysts: large crystals enclosed by finely crystalline groundmass minerals in an igneous rock.
Playa lake: temporary lake in a desert, evaporating to form mud flats and **evaporites.**
Pleistocene: a geological epoch commencing 1.8 million years ago and ending around 10 thousand years ago. The Pleistocene was dominated by climatic fluctuations, resulting in several Ice Ages during the latter half of the epoch.
Plunge/plunging: The inclination of a fold axis (a line along the crest of the fold).
Porphyry/Porphyritic: an igneous rock containing **phenocrysts**.
Pseudomorphs: Minerals or structures that mimic the shape of a pre-existing crystalline mineral. E.g. cubic moulds in mudstone mimicking former salt crystals.
Quartzite: a sandstone composed entirely of detrital quartz grains.
Quaternary: The latest period of geological time starting 1.8 million years ago, up to and including the present day.
Ragstone: an informal term for a shelly limestone.
Reduction spots: An elliptical patch of paler colour found in slates, red sandstones and mudstones caused by the local reduction of iron oxide during **diagenesis.**
Refracted cleavage: variation in cleavage plane orientation seen in a succession of interbedded fine and coarse-grained sediments.
Regression: Relative sea-level fall caused by a decrease in the volume of the ocean by ice cap accretion, local uplift, evaporation or increased sediment deposition.
Rhyolite: acidic lava with more than 65% silica, and orthoclase the dominant feldspar.
Ripple lamination: small-scale cross-stratification produced by migration of ripple marks
Rollover: A gentle reversal of stratal dip found on the downthrow side of a **listric** fault.
Saccharoidal: Sugary appearance commonly displayed by dolomite.
Scrins: minor mineral veins in joints or small faults.
Seatearth: Soil horizon underlying a coal seam, often contains fossilised plant roots.
Siderite: Iron carbonate mineral; often forms concretions within sandstone and shale.

Siliciclastic: Sediment comprising detrital silicate minerals, includes conglomerate, sandstone, siltstone and mudstone.
Skerry: harder, cemented patch or bed within friable sandstone or mudstone.
Slaty cleavage: A pervasive planar fabric found in slate that allows the rock to split.
Slickensides: Linear grooves on a fault plane showing the most recent direction of fault movement.
Slumping: Mass movement of sediment caused by slope failure.
Smectite: An expandable clay mineral that absorbs and releases water.
Solifluxion: Slow downhill transport of soil or scree by freeze-thaw action. See also **frost heave**.
Spar: Crystalline calcite precipitated in pore spaces within sedimentary rocks.
Strike: Direction of a horizontal line on an inclined plane, perpendicular to the dip.
Stromatactis: irregular cavities in **carbonate mud mounds** formed by various depositional and **diagenetic** processes; may represent decayed soft-bodied organisms.
Stylolite: irregular boundaries formed by dissolution of the limestone under pressure. Insoluble residues such as clay are concentrated along stylolites.
Subduction zone: A linear zone where a tectonic plate passes beneath another plate; **granite** intrusions and volcanism at the margin of the overlying plate are associated with subduction zones. See **Island Arc**.
Syncline: trough-like fold with the youngest rocks in the core of the fold.
Syn-sedimentary fault: A fault that was active during sedimentation; recognized by a change of sediment thickness across the fault.
Tephra: a general term for all types of pyroclastic particles erupted by volcanoes.
Trace fossil: Animal tracks, trails and burrows preserved in sedimentary rocks.
Transgression: Relative sea-level rise resulting in flooding of the land; caused by increase in the volume of the ocean by melting ice caps or by local subsidence.
Trilobite: An extinct marine arthropod with a head-shield, thorax and tail-shield.
Tuff: consolidated volcanic ash.
Turbidite/turbidity current: a graded (grain size decreases upwards) sandstone bed deposited from suspension by a sediment-laden (**turbidity**) current. A **proximal** turbidite was deposited near its source; a **distal** turbidite further away from its source.
Unconformity: A break in a sedimentary succession representing a major time gap. There is often an angular difference between beds above and below the unconformity.
Valley bulge: Bulging of valley sides and bottoms caused by the loading of incompetent beds in the valley floor.
Variscan Orogeny: An episode of mountain building that started in the Devonian and reached a climax during the late Carboniferous. In the UK, the rocks of SW England were most strongly affected, but also caused folding and faulting of Palaeozoic rocks in the Midlands.
Vesicular/vesicles: Rounded holes formed by de-gassing of lavas during extrusion.
Volcaniclastic: Sediment composed mainly of volcanic-derived fragments.

Vugs: Irregular cavities in a rock sometimes lined with crystals.
Wadi: A narrow desert valley, prone to **flash floods**.
Weathering: Chemical, physical and biological alteration of rocks at the earth's surface.
Westphalian: The youngest division of the Carboniferous system preserved in the East Midlands. This was the time of Coal Measures sedimentation.
Wolstonian: The British name for the last but one period of glaciation during the **Pleistocene**. Ice sheets were more extensive than the more recent **Devensian** glaciation.
Wrench fault: A **fault** that shows horizontal displacement.
Younging direction: Direction in which a rock succession becomes younger.
Zechstein: Late Permian limestones, **dolomites** and **evaporites** deposited in the Zechstein Basin that occupied the present North Sea Basin. The basin was alternately flooded by seawater and dried out in an arid climate forming thick **evaporite** deposits.

FURTHER READING

Aitkenhead, N. 1977. Institute of Geological Sciences borehole at Duffield, Derbyshire. *Bulletin of the Geological Survey of Great Britain No.59*.

Aitkenhead, N. & Chisholm, J.I. 1982. *A standard nomenclature for the Dinantian formations of the Peak District of Derbyshire and Staffordshire*. Institute of Geological Sciences Report 82/8.

Aitkenhead, N, Chisholm, J.I. & Stevenson I.P. 1985. *Geology of the country around Buxton, Leek and Bakewell*. Memoir Geological Survey of G.B., Sheet 111.

Anderton, R,. Bridges, P.H., Leeder, M.R. & Selwood, B.H. 1979. *A dynamic stratigraphy of the British Isles*. George Allen & Unwin, London. 301pp.

Boynton, H.E. & Ford, T.D. 1994. Ediacaran fossils from the Precambrian (Charnian Supergroup) of Charnwood Forest, Leicestershire. *Mercian Geologist*, **13**, 165-182.

British Museum of Natural History 1975. *British Mesozoic Fossils*, Publication No. 703.

British Museum of Natural History 1975. *British Palaeozoic Fossils*, Publication No 704.

Carney, J.N. 1994. *Geology of the Thringstone, Shepshed and Loughborough districts* (SK41NW, SK41NE & SK51NW). British Geological Survey Technical Report WA/94/08.

Charsley, T.J., Rathbone, P.A. and Lowe, D.J. 1990. *Nottingham: a geological background for planning and development*. BGS Technical Report WA/90/1.

Chisholm, J.I. 1981, Growth faulting and sandstone deposition in the Namurian of the Stanton Syncline. *Proceedings of the Yorkshire Geological Society*, **41**, 305-323.

Compston,W., Wright, A.E., & Toghill, P. 2002. Dating the late Precambrian Vulcanicity of England and Wales. *Journal of the Geological Society,* **159**, 323-339.

Cope F. W. 1999. *Geology explained in the Peak District*. David and Charles 192pp.

Cope, J.C.W., Ingham, J.K. & Rawson, P.F. (editors) 1992. *Atlas of Palaeography and lithofacies*. Geological Society Memoir No.13.

Elliott, R.E. 1961. The stratigraphy of the Keuper Series in southern Nottinghamshire. *Proceedings of the Yorkshire Geological Society*, **33**, 197-331.

Ford, T.D. 1999. The growth of geological Knowledge in the Peak District. *Mercian Geologist,* **14**, 161-190.

Ford, T.D. 2002. Dolomitization of the Carboniferous Limestone of the Peak District: a review. *Mercian Geologist*, **15**, 163-170.

Ford, T.D. & Rieuwerts, J.H. 1983. *Lead mining in the Peak District*. Peak Park Publication, Bakewell. 3rd edition. 160pp. (new edition in preparation)

Frost, D.V. & Smart, J.G.O., 1979. *The geology of the country around Derby*. Memoir Geological Survey of GB, Sheet 125.

Harrison, D.J. & Adlam, K.A.McL. 1985. *Limestones of the Peak*. British Geological Survey Mineral Assessment Report 144, 40pp.

Howard, A.S., Warrington, G., Carney, J. n., Ambrose, K., Young, S.R. and Pharaoh, T.C. in press. *The geology of the Nottingham District*. Memoir of the British Geological Survey, Sheet 126.

Jones, C.M. & Chisholm, J.I. 1997. The Roaches and Ashover Grits: sequence stratigraphic interpretation of a turbidite-fronted delta system. *Geological Journal,* **32**, 45-68.

Le Bas, M.J. 1996. Mount Bardon volcanism. *Transactions of the Leicester Literary & Philosophical Society*, **90**, 26-34.

McIlroy, D., Brasier, M.D. & Moseley, J.B. 1998. The Proterozoic-Cambrian transition within the 'Charnian Supergroup' of Central England and the antiquity of the Ediacaran fauna. *Journal of the Geological Society*, **155**, 401- 411.

Moseley, J. & Ford, T.D. 1985. A stratigraphic revision of the late Precambrian rocks of Charnwood Forest, Leicestershire. *Mercian Geologist*, **10**, 1-18.

Moseley, J. & Ford, T.D. 1989. The sedimentology of the Charnian Supergroup. *Mercian Geologist*, **11**, 251-274.

Neves, R. & Downie, C. 1967. *Geological Excursions in the Sheffield Region and Peak District National Park*, University of Sheffield.

Pharaoh, T.C. & Gibbons, W. 1994. Precambrian rocks in England and Wales south of the Menai Strait fault system. pp. 85-97 in *A revised correlation of Precambrian rocks in the British Isles*. (edited by W.Gibbons & A.L.Harris) Geological Society Special Report no. 22.

Sarjeant, W.A.S. 1967. Fossil footprints from the Middle Triassic of Nottinghamshire and Derbyshire. *Mercian Geologist*, **2**, 327-341.

Sarjeant, W.A.S. 1996. Re-appraisal of some supposed dinosaur footprints from the Triassic of the English Midlands. *Mercian Geologist*, **14**, 22-30.

Shirley, J. 1958. The Carboniferous Limestone of the Monyash-Wirksworth area. *Quarterly Journal of the Geological Society, London,* **114**, 411-429.

Smith E.G. Rhys G.H. & Eden R.A. 1967. *Geology of the country around Chesterfield, Matlock and Mansfield*. Memoir Geological Survey of G.B., Sheet 112.

Sumbler, M.G. 1993. The Lias succession between Fulbeck and the Vale of Belvoir. *Mercian Geologist*, **13**, 87-94.

Sweeting G.S. 1946. An outline of the geology of Ashover and Derbyshire. *Proceedings of the Geologists' Association,* **57**, 117-136.

Sylvester-Bradley, P.C. and Ford, T.D. (Editors), 1968. *The Geology of the East Midlands*. Leicester University Press. 400pp.

Waltham, A. 1996. *Sandstone Caves of Nottingham*. East Midlands Geological Society, Nottingham.

Watts, W.W. 1947. *The Geology of the Ancient Rocks of Charnwood Forest Leicestershire*. Leicester Literary & Philosophical Society Publication. 160pp.

Woodcock, N.H. and Strachan, R. 2000. *Geological History of the British Isles*. Blackwell Science. 423pp.